Human and Economic Geography

for certificate students

Human and Economic Geography

Third edition

H. R. Cain, M.A.
Formerly Head of the Geography Department
Alderman Newton's School, Leicester

Longman

Longman Group Limited
London
*Associated companies, branches and representatives
throughout the world*

© H. R. Cain 1963
This edition © Longman Group Limited 1975

*First published 1963
Third edition 1975
Second impression 1977*

ISBN 0 582 34145 0

*Printed in Hong Kong by
Dai Nippon Printing Co. (HK) Ltd*

Preface

The present volume covers the material required in answering the questions on General Human and Economic Geography in the 'O' Level papers of the General Certificate of Education of the chief examining bodies.

Production figures for the various commodities are for the most part taken from the Statistical Yearbook of the United Nations. They refer, in general, to the year 1958, but where the figures for that year seem exceptional I have substituted figures based on the average of recent years. Any subsequent deviations of significance are noted in the text.

My sincere thanks are due to: Professor F. J. Monkhouse, for many wise counsels and much practical assistance; Mr A. Carson Clark and his team of draughtsmen, who have drawn for me most of the maps and diagrams; Mr A. Campbell, Technical Press Officer of the United Kingdom Atomic Energy Authority, who read for me the chapter on Atomic Power; Mr Philip M. Rose, Press Officer of the British Man-made Fibres Federation, who read for me the chapter on Silk and other fibres; the General Editor of Unilever Booklets, for permission to make line drawings of pictures appearing in the firm's series of booklets; Dr H. Ian Moore, Principal of the Seale Hayne Agricultural College, Newton Abbot; Mr T. A. Kestell; the Examining Boards, for permission to reproduce examination questions; numerous organisations, for permission to reproduce photographs from their libraries (their names are given against each photograph); Mr A. H. Brown, Douglas Harwood and Malcolm and Joyce Liddle; my colleagues, who have always been ready to help on points connected with their own subjects; and lastly my wife, on whom has fallen so much of the burden of typing and sundry other incidentals of composition and preparation.

Leicester, 1962   H. R. C.

Preface to Third Edition

In this Third (1975) Edition production figures have been thoroughly revised in accordance with the latest information available at the time of going to press. Much of the book has been rewritten, most of the maps and diagrams have been redrawn, and many of the original photographs have been replaced. The book is now fully metricated, although imperial equivalents are also given, in brackets. The set of examination questions has again been revised and now forms a representative selection from the papers set by ten separate Boards during the last three years. I am, as always, sincerely grateful to the numerous organisations, authorities and experts who have devoted so much of their time to providing me with up-to-date information and checking the text.

Leicester, 1975   H. R. C.

Contents

Acknowledgements

We are grateful to the following for permission to reproduce photographs:–
Aerofilms: figs 147, 168, 169; Australian News and Information Bureau: fig. 70; Peter Baker: fig. 30; BEA fig. 154; Birds Eye Foods Ltd: fig. 17; The Bowater Organisation: figs 59, 60, 113; British Aluminium: fig. 110; British Railways: fig. 149; British Steel Corporation: figs 97, 101; British Sugar Corporation: fig. 16; Camera Press: figs 1, 2; Information Services, Canada House: figs 6, 43; J. Allan Cash: figs 13, 32, 56; H.R. Cain: fig. 69; Bruce Coleman: fig. 84; Courtaulds Ltd: fig. 78; The Dunlop Company: figs 62, 63; Elders & Fyffes Ltd: fig. 45; *Farmer & Stockbreeder*: figs. 19, 22; Fox Photos: fig. 151; The Harris Tweed Association: fig. 67; ICI Fibres: fig. 82; Eric Kay: fig. 114; F. J. Monkhouse: fig. 134; National Coal Board: figs 115, 117; North of Scotland Hydro-electric Board: fig. 139; Popperfoto: fig. 37; The Royal Netherlands Embassy: fig. 90; The Principal, Seale Hayne Agricultural College: fig. 20; N.R. Shave: fig. 106; Sté Française des Petroles BP, photo B. Beaujard: fig. 124 Tate & Lyle Ltd: fig. 40; Textile Council: fig. 73; John Topham: fig. 9; Trinidad Lake Asphalt: fig. 129; UKAEA: fig. 145; Unilever Ltd: figs 51, 53; United Press International (UK) Ltd: fig. 88; US Department of Agriculture: fig. 94; USIS: fig. 58; WHO, photo by J. Abcede: fig. 83.

Introduction

About 2½ million years ago one of the ape-like creatures who lived at that time made the first tool or weapon, probably by striking one piece of stone upon another. He was now no longer forced to rely on his teeth or his hands in the struggle for survival. He had, by his own ingenuity, added to the equipment with which Nature had endowed him; he had fashioned part of his natural surroundings or *environment* for his own purposes. It was this achievement which distinguished him, as a toolmaker, from his fellows, and which enables us to describe him as the first MAN.

The story of Human Geography begins with this apparently trivial incident; it goes on to depict men and women throughout the ages gradually acquiring, despite rebuffs and delays in their efforts to make for themselves a home on the surface of the earth, a more complete control over their environment. It shows them learning new skills, discovering new materials and new processes, devising with the resources placed at their disposal ever more complicated pieces of equipment.

Broadly speaking, the one word 'Geography' is sufficient to describe the constant interplay between man and his environment. When, however, the environment itself is under discussion, we speak of *Physical Geography*, but when attention is particularly directed to the activities of man against the background of the physical environment, the term *Human Geography* is used.

'Economic' comes from two Greek words, which mean, roughly, 'keeping house'; hence *Economic Geography* is the study of the resources which man uses in running his home on the earth and providing for his needs—in fact, his 'housekeeping'.

The physical environment has already been described in a companion volume in this series. Fascinating though it would be, it would take far too long to trace chronologically the full story of Human Geography from the first man splitting a stone to modern man splitting the atom. We shall, therefore, in the present volume first decribe certain selected communities whose present way of life provides us with glimpses of what existence may have been like for our remote forefathers, and then survey the main modern types of resources and activities, with now and again a brief look back into the past.

1

TYPES OF COMMUNITIES

Man's early progress

At the beginning of the story of Human and Economic Geography, man, in providing for his basic needs of food, clothing and shelter, could do little more than use, in the form in which it was presented to him, anything which came to hand. His food consisted of the fruits and berries he found growing on the plants around him or of the flesh of such animals as he could kill. For clothes he used the hide discarded when the flesh had been eaten, and for shelter from wind and rain he sought the cover of an overhanging rock or a hollow in a cliff-face.

His progress at first was slow, but gradually his capacity for reasoning about what he observed, for anticipating his wants and for adapting the available resources, increased. He learnt how to make more efficient tools and weapons; he learnt how to produce fire, how to make pottery, how to spin and weave; he hit on the ideas of the sail and the wheel, and he discovered that the earth could be made to yield metals. He learnt, too, that some animals were of much more use to him if they were tended and reared than if they were hunted and killed. And, probably most important of all, he discovered that, within limits, he could grow the particular kinds of plants he wanted.

How these discoveries were made is largely a matter of intelligent guesswork. The first pottery may, for instance, have been the result of observing that the clay beneath a fire had hardened, and metals may have been discovered accidentally in much the same way. Agriculture probably began when it was noticed that a few stray seeds left lying on the ground sprouted when they got wet and grew into the same sort of plant as the one from which they had come. Such discoveries may well have been made by different groups of people at different times, although to a certain extent the news would be passed on from one group to another. Moreover, to early man some environments were more favourable than others, and we may therefore suppose that progress in these was more rapid. But the possibility always existed that some groups—or some individuals within groups—would be more observant and more fertile in invention than others, and so much less at the mercy of an unfavourable environment.

Types of economy

The manner in which groups of people supply themselves with the most essential of their basic requirements enables us to recognise four main types of *economy* or ways of making a living:
1. The *food-gathering, hunting* and *fishing* (or *collecting*) economy.
2. The *pastoral* economy, in which the food supply is very largely derived from 'domesticated' animals, which are reared and protected.

People who live by these two types of economy are often *nomads*, who wander from place to place.
3. The *agricultural* economy, in which the chief items of food come from cultivated crops. This usually necessitates the people remaining in one place, practising *sedentary agriculture*. In some parts of the world, however, the soil after a few years becomes exhausted, and the people are forced to move to another patch of ground. This is called *shifting agriculture*.
4. To the above list of three types of economy we may add a fourth, the *industrial* economy. Machines of one sort or another have, since the beginning of the Industrial Revolution in the eighteenth century, played such a large part in our modern economy that Man the Mechanic is as necessary as Man the Farmer.

It was at one time thought that mankind in all parts of the world must have risen steadily up a scale of progress from food-gatherer and hunter to pastoralist, and from pastoralist to cultivator, and that one type of economy was abandoned as the next highest was adopted. This seemed at the time a fairly reasonable supposition, and in a very general way may well be true, since it accords with the idea of a gradual increase in man's powers and resource. It is obviously far more intelligent to cultivate the crops you require than merely to collect food off the plants provided by Nature; and to use animals and rear them than to destroy them. When, however, we examine the economies of the primitive peoples who still inhabit certain parts of the world, we find that, although these peoples may depend chiefly on one particular method of obtaining their food, they do not do so to the exclusion of any other, nor, indeed, do the types of economy follow one another in a set order. The more remote parts of the world even today contain groups of people still essentially in the food-gathering and hunting or pastoral stages.

The scale of progress

It is important that we should get in the right perspective the broad outlines of man's progress in his constant battle with his environment. Man the 'tool-maker' first made his appearance about 2½ million years ago, and it was not until about 5000 BC that he reached the agricultural stage. If we scale down these figures and imagine the whole of prehistory and history to be represented by the space of the last 24 hours, Man the Farmer did not appear until 3 minutes ago, and Man the Mechanic appeared within the last 8 seconds.

The evidence

Of course, no written records exist of the life of early man. There are, it is true, some quite remarkable drawings of animals scratched by primitive men on the walls of caves in southern France, the Pyrenees and the Sahara Desert. But apart from these drawings our knowledge is almost entirely derived from the findings of archaeologists all over the world. 'Remains', such as crude weapons of shaped stone and fragments of pottery and metal, together with skulls and bones, are continually being unearthed. By studying these finds and plotting their distribution on maps, trained investigators have learnt a great deal about the mode of life and the capabilities of our remote ancestors. There are, however, many gaps in our knowledge, which have to be bridged by intelligent surmise based on observations of backward peoples in the world today. Brief descriptions of the way of life of some typical communities occupy the rest of this chapter.

Food-gatherers, hunters and fishers (fig. 1)

The Bushmen of the Kalahari Desert
The Bushmen are among the most primitive people alive today. They lived formerly in the temperate grasslands (or *veld*) to the east of their present habitat, but were driven into the Kalahari by stronger and better equipped Negro tribes. They have yellow-brown complexions and tufted hair; they are only about 150 cm (5 ft) tall, and wander over the semi-desert regions in search of food. Their diet consists mainly of edible roots, lizards and small rodents. They are, however, expert trackers, and hunt a species of antelope with bows and arrows tipped with a vegetable poison. When they have made a kill or if they come across a

Fig. 1 A survivor from the Stone Age. The Camayurá, a group of primitive Indian fishermen, live in the Mato Grosso area of Brazil and were discovered only recently, when the Brazilian government sent out an expedition to explore the possibility of laying a series of airstrips. Although hitherto untouched by modern civilisation, the Camayurá display remarkable ingenuity. The man in the picture is splashing a bundle of timbó on the water, so releasing a poison which acts on the respiratory organs of the fish and drives them gasping to the surface.

rotting carcass, they eat enormous quantities. In such circumstances they probably remain in one place for a day or two, in a rough shelter of leaves and branches, until hunger compels them to move on. The man carries nothing but his bow and arrows, so as to be free to hunt, but the wife is laden by her infants and certain pieces of portable equipment such as shells of ostrich eggs containing the family's supply of water. This they obtain by means of reeds through which they suck up or siphon the water that—after a time—collects in the soil.

Only a few thousand Bushmen now remain. That they have survived at all is due to the remoteness of their habitat and the lack of competition for possession of so harsh a stretch of country.

The Pygmies
The Pygmies are related to the Bushmen and live in the remote parts of the dense equatorial forests of the Congo (Zaïre) Basin. When fully grown they are little more than 120 cm (4 ft) tall. They are hunters who roam through the forests clad in a loincloth made from animal skin, carrying only a bow and a supply of poisoned arrows and perhaps a spear or knife. They eat grubs, beetles, caterpillars and edible roots, and occasionally the raw flesh of monkeys, wild pigs and any small animals they have been able to shoot or snare. When they stay for a short time in any one place, they build shelters of boughs and leaves, but, apart from their hunting weapons, they own no tools or utensils.

The Pygmies do not live completely out of touch with the Negro inhabitants of the more accessible parts of the Congo forests, who outnumber them by about ten to one. They sometimes perform small services for the taller and more advanced Negroes and are rewarded with sugar cane, bananas and salt, for which they have a great craving. Although quite savage, the Pygmies are in some ways surprisingly timid, and their contact with the Negroes is frequently by 'silent barter'. One night they stealthily place a lump of meat outside the door of a Negro hut, and the next night, equally stealthily, collect the fruit or salt put there in its place by the occupants. Incidentally, it is said that the Pygmy has a very good sense of comparative values, and seeks a rough revenge if he fails to secure a good bargain! It is by such transactions as this that many of the weapons now used by the Pygmies have reached them.

The Australian Aborigines

Until 1788 the Aborigines[1] were the only inhabitants of Australia. They are a dark-skinned, hairy people, who are thought to have wandered or been driven into the continent from the north. When the level of the sea rose after the end of the Ice Age, they found themselves marooned on a large island, over half of which is desert. It is, of course, extremely difficult to count people who wander in isolated groups over so vast an area as Australia, but it is quite certain that the Aborigines are far less numerous today than they were at the coming of the white man. This is largely due to the fact that they have become infected with diseases like measles, mumps and even the common cold, which, although comparatively harmless in civilised communities, often prove fatal to primitive races.

The Aborigines rank somewhat higher than the Bushmen and the Pygmies, as can be seen from their crafts and weapons, among which is the boomerang. They know nothing of agriculture (although they refrain from pulling up plants which bear fruits they are accustomed to eat) or of the domestication of animals, for which, it is true, they have had no opportunity. Their food consists of a variety of small creatures from birds and rodents to grasshoppers and chrysalises, and it has been calculated that they eat over three hundred different kinds of plants. Their clothes are of the scantiest and their temporary 'houses' consist of interlaced branches and leaves. Pottery is unknown to them, but the Aborigine tribes in the coastlands of northern Australia are capable of making nets and baskets in which they catch fish, and they use a primitive kind of boat with sails.

[1] From Latin *ab origine,* meaning 'from the beginning.'

The 'blackfellows' in some respects present a puzzle to the anthropologists. Their complicated dances, the elaborate ritual of their magic, and their strangely high standards of morality have led some investigators to think that they were at one time less primitive than they are today. This appears to be further borne out by the capabilities of those Aborigines who come into contact with the white Australians. Some are employed in labouring jobs in small settlements in the 'outback', where they prove to be more intelligent and quick to learn than one might suppose. An Aborigine labourer is always addressed as 'Jacky', and is quite incapable of remaining in one place or one job for very long. His nomadic instinct periodically asserts itself, and he disappears for a time. He will, however, quite probably return after a spell of roving in the 'bush', and will explain his temporary absence by saying 'I felt I just had to go walk-about!' It should be remembered that only about half of those normally referred to as 'Aborigines' are full-bloods, living in remote situations and in the manner described above. The remainder are the product of mixed marriages and may have only a little aboriginal blood in their veins. Many such 'Aborigines' have become part of the general rural and urban life of Australia. Some exist in conditions of appalling squalor in makeshift housing on the edge of towns, but others have won fame and popularity, as, for instance, the painter Albert Namatjira and Evonne Goolagong, the Ladies Singles champion at Wimbledon in 1971.

The Eskimos
The Eskimos of northern Canada are essentially nomadic hunters and fishermen, of a more advanced type than any so far discussed. Their economy has undergone rapid changes in the last few decades, as modern communities extend their influence into the tundra regions which form the Eskimos' home.

Agriculture is obviously impossible in such areas, but the Eskimo is highly skilled in reaping the harvest of the sea. His way of life is an excellent example of adaptation to environment. His food is derived from fishes, seals and walruses; his clothes are made from the skins of these creatures; his implements are fashioned from their bones, and the huts or *igloos*, in which some of the Eskimos live during the long winter period of perpetual darkness, are built of snow-blocks. When he encamps in the summer, he uses a tent made of hides. He is to some extent a pastoralist, and follows herds of caribou to the summer pastures; and he has domesticated the dog (or 'husky') to draw his sledge and act as a beast of burden.

Fig. 2 An Eskimo woman being taught to operate a sewing machine by the wife of a Hudson's Bay Company's post manager.

The *kayak* or canoe displays his craftsmanship. This is skilfully fashioned from seal skins so as to form a vessel which fits the Eskimo very closely, but which is so light that it can be carried overland very easily on his shoulders. His harpoon is equally well made, and he is ingenious in his use of inflated bladders to assist him in towing home his catch. The drilling-stick with which he starts a fire is elaborated with a piece of string so that he can twirl it more rapidly. His womenfolk are particularly adept at sewing together skins with a bone needle and a thread made from sinews. The fashioning of soapstone carvings, a craft industry now carried out on an enormous scale, has become a major source of income. The products are sold by the Hudson's Bay Company.

In many parts of Canada the Eskimo is becoming quite up-to-date. The motor-boat is replacing the *kayak*, rifles are being used in place of harpoons, and there is considerable activity in supplying hides and furs on a commercial scale to white traders. Moreover, increasing numbers of Eskimos are attending schools set up by the government, and some of the more highly gifted are sent on to universities. In recent years Eskimos have been employed on airfields, mining camps, meteorological bases and 'Dewline' (Distant Early Warning) stations.

Pastoralists

The Lapps
The Lapps have been described as 'the last nomads in Europe'. Their flat faces and slanting eyes suggest kinship with the Mongols of eastern Asia, yet they wander, regardless of national boundaries, over the northern territories of Norway, Sweden and Finland. They have until quite recently led a comparatively primitive life, following their herds of reindeer from pasture to pasture. In the snow-covered wastes which form their environment, they depend upon these animals for their essential requirements to a remarkable degree. They eat reindeer meat, they drink reindeer milk, they make clothes and tents from the hides and implements from the horns, and they harness reindeer to pull their sledges. The Lapps are skilful with a lasso, and are accustomed to travel over the snow on wooden skis, reaching, so it is said, a speed of 25 kph (15 mph).

Of late many changes have come over their traditional way of life. Iron saucepans are now in common use, and even such incongruous pieces of equipment as sewing machines have been observed in their tents. Tourists who come by ship to the Arctic ports of Norway to see the midnight sun are sometimes greeted by Lapps selling spoons and similar small articles made of reindeer horn. The Swedish government takes a great interest in the welfare of these people, and is in general helping them to become adjusted to a new way of life. Doctors and teachers are provided for them, and many Lapp children now go to school at the age of seven, and learn, amongst other things, Swedish and English.

The Masai
The Masai live in Kenya and at one time they roamed freely over the savanna lands of East Africa, tending their herds of cattle, sheep and goats, marauding and fighting as they went. Settlement by Europeans in the Kenya Highlands and the increasing power of other tribes deprived them of much of their best grazing land, and they were eventually confined to two large 'reserves', set aside for their exclusive use. Although their territory is nearly 400 000 sq km (150 000 sq miles) in area, it is no longer possible for the 10 000 Masai who remain to carry on their traditional, nomadic way of life. They now live for the most part in *kraals*, groups of flat-roofed huts made of a framework of branches covered with leaves and plastered with mud, and surrounded by thick fences constructed with stakes and thorns as a protection from wild animals.

Cattle play as large a part in the Masai economy as do reindeer in that of the Lapps. They are not, however, employed as draught animals, nor are they ridden; for this purpose donkeys are occasionally used. Nor are they reared and slaughtered for meat; the flesh is eaten only when a beast dies of disease or old age. These cattle – scraggy, hump-backed animals of the Zebu type (pp. 35–7) – are valued by the Masai as a source of blood and milk, and the number he owns is a measure of his wealth and import-ance. Cattle are in fact used as a form of currency.[1] The women and children do most of the work, building and repairing the huts, milking the cows and other such chores. The young men are given a long training in which they are initiated into the mysteries of the tribe; eventually their heads are shaved and they graduate as 'warriors', armed with a long spear and wearing a 'uniform' consisting of one garment only, a kind of double apron made of leather – although there is now no fighting for them to do. A little maize or millet, acquired by barter with neighbouring agricultural tribes, is eaten, but chiefly by the women and children and never by the warriors, who live almost entirely on milk and on blood drawn from the animal's neck by piercing a vein with a spear or an arrow.

The Kirghiz

A race of nomadic pastoralists, the Kirghiz live in Turkestan, in the extreme south of the USSR. They have a fanatical zeal for their own independence. From as far back as 1734 successive Russian governments tried in vain to subjugate them, but they have now settled down under the Communist regime.

Their environment consists largely of dry steppes and mountains, and until lately they were occupied almost entirely in tending their flocks and herds. They spend the summers on the slopes of the mountains where pasture can be found for their sheep, cows and goats, and in winter descend to the valleys and plains, where they live in tent-villages or *auls*. They had a reputation for interspersing their pastoral activities with frequent raids on their agricultural neighbours, who, in fact, gave to them the name of Kirghiz or 'robbers'. They are fearless horsemen, and are lavish in their affection for their steeds. As beasts of burden, yaks are commonly used.

The Kirghiz are very fond of mutton, but at their great feasts they eat large amounts of horse-flesh. They have no bread, but occasionally make a kind of porridge with millet. Tea is a favourite beverage, but *koumiss* made from fermented mare's milk might be called their 'national drink'. It is reputed to be

[1] See footnote p. 37.

very wholesome, and in the last century it was recommended by many English doctors as being very good for patients suffering from tuberculosis. They are a very hardy people, who can go without food for days on end. The men, however, are lazy, and leave such routine work as milking to the women. They are short in stature and swarthy, and they shave their heads, but allow small beards to grow.

The Kirghiz have for long been skilled in spinning and weaving, and make magnificent velvet robes embroidered with gold and silver. They wear oddly-shaped hoods made of sheepskin, coarse shirts, immensely baggy trousers and leather boots, with an outer garment resembling a long dressing-gown—often two or three, if the weather is cold. Leather is widely used for their utensils, belts, saddles and bridles. They are, moreover, capable of making very beautiful rugs and carpets.

Cultivators

The Boro

The Boro of the south-western parts of the Amazon Basin are interesting in that they are a primitive people who live chiefly by agriculture. In an environment very much like that of the Congo Pygmies, they grow roots like large potatoes, called yams, and manioc, a poisonous plant which, after washing and straining to remove the poison, is finally made into flour. Besides these crops they grow beans and pineapples, and also cacao, from which they make an intoxicating drink.

Before they can cultivate the ground in these hot and steamy equatorial forests, the Boro have to burn down parts of the existing vegetation in order to make a clearing. The soil is then stirred up with wedge-shaped digging-sticks, but it becomes exhausted after two or three years and the Boro are forced to move to another patch of ground, where the process begins all over again. They have no domestic animals, but do a certain amount of hunting, armed with blowpipes 2·5 m (8 ft) long, through which they are able to direct darts to hit a monkey, reptile or bird as far away as fifteen metres. *Curare*, the poison with which the darts are tipped, is prepared from the sap of a tree according to a recipe handed down from generation to generation. It paralyses the target within a few seconds.

The Boro are acquainted with the craft of pottery, make nets and baskets and use canoes fashioned by hollowing out tree trunks. Within an area of 13 000 sq km (5 000 sq miles) there are about fifty settlements of these dark-skinned Boro people, each with about

200 inhabitants. Their villages are situated some distance away from the rivers as a precaution against floods, enemies and insects. Their large communal houses, shaped like great marquees, are divided into compartments, each accommodating one family and containing a fireplace, hammocks for sleeping and an assortment of bone, pot and wooden instruments and utensils. There are no windows, a single hole in the roof serves as a common chimney, and a space is left in the centre of the building for dancing. The Boro wear only a loincloth or apron made by beating tree-bark until it is soft and pliable. The men allow their hair to grow very long, but the women have theirs 'bobbed'.

The Hausa
The Hausa, of whom nearly six million live in the savanna lands of northern Nigeria, may be taken as typical of a number of Negro peoples who have adopted an agricultural economy. They provide a striking contrast with the Boro.

The Hausa live a settled life cultivating a wide variety of crops ranging from maize and millets to tobacco and cotton, but they also own many flocks and herds. They are skilful potters and leather-workers, they spin and weave, and colour their fabrics with a beautiful indigo dye of their own manufacture, and for many centuries they have been able to make castings not only of iron, but also of what they call 'red iron' or bronze. Although the Hausa have never exerted political or military control over their neighbours in West Africa, their cultural influence has been considerable. They are the only West African people who have expressed their language in writing, and they are particularly famous as traders.

The ancient Hausa city of Kano is a remarkable place. It grew up on a great trade route, and has for over 800 years been a centre for the exchange of goods such as hides, salt and cotton. Its 295 000 inhabitants now spread beyond the crumbling walls, which once served to defend the city, and it is surrounded by 'satellite towns'. Most of the buildings are flat-roofed and made of mud bricks, yet the city is lit by electricity and has a piped water supply. It is the southern terminus of camel caravans from across the Sahara Desert and the northern terminus of the railway line to the Gulf of Guinea ports. It also has an international airport.

In the foregoing pages we have taken brief glimpses at the traditional economies of a number of peoples who live in environments very different from our own. Hardly any of these peoples are now so completely cut off from the rest of the world that their lives are unaffected by developments elsewhere. It is now some time since a traveller in the remoter parts of Africa remarked that somehow or other the matchbox always seemed to get there before him, and you may find Eskimos in Greenland eating tinned foods and living in prefabricated wooden huts supplied by the Danish government, or perhaps a Pygmy using a penknife which came originally from a department store in Kinshasa.

It might perhaps have been more appropriate if the above descriptions had been written in the past tense. Changes in the economies of all but the most primitive peoples are now taking place so rapidly (particularly in Africa) that much of what has been recorded may be out of date even before this edition is printed. Nevertheless, a glance at the lives of people in less advanced communities will help us to understand the lives of our ancestors in bygone ages, and will enable us to appreciate the extent of our own control over our environment in the modern world.

2

FOODS FROM GRASSES

The chief kind of food eaten by mankind is that which comes from the seeds of certain cultivated grasses. The flesh of animals has a much longer history as a food, and still forms a very important item in the diet of nearly all peoples, but bread is, nevertheless, well called 'the staff of life'.

If grass is allowed to grow long enough, seed-heads may be found on the tops of tough cylindrical stalks growing among the flat blades. These are similar to, but much smaller than, those which grow at the tops of stalks of wheat. By sowing the seeds from those stalks which grew tallest and whose heads grew largest, our early ancestors gradually developed from the different kinds of grasses what are collectively known as *cereals*.[1] The seeds were separated from their husks (or cases) by threshing and winnowing, and then milled (that is, ground to a powder) between two heavy stones. Flour can be formed in this way by grinding other cereals besides wheat, and is the basis of various kinds of bread and similar foods, such as cake, biscuits and pastry.

The appearance of the heads of the main cereals is shown in fig. 3.

Wheat

Wheat is the most important of the cereal crops which have been developed as a result of this process of selection. It is the staple foodstuff of the white races, and in recent years increasing amounts of wheat have been eaten by the Japanese and Chinese, who are popularly thought to live almost entirely on rice. Throughout the world, over 160 million hectares (400 million acres) are estimated to be devoted to wheat cultivation—a greater area than that of any other grain crop—and more wheat enters international trade than any other cereal.

It has been cultivated in the western world for over five thousand years, and was introduced to America by Columbus. Since early

[1] From *Ceres*, the Roman goddess of corn.

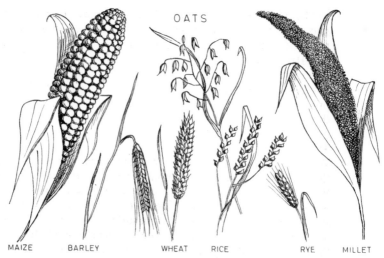

OATS

MAIZE   BARLEY   WHEAT   RICE   RYE   MILLET

Fig. 3 The heads of the main cereals (about quarter-size).

times, many varieties of wheat have been developed, adapted by cross-breeding for use in different soils and different climates, and giving very much greater yields than the original types.

Conditions of growth

Since wheat is really a cultivated grass, it is not surprising that it grows best in the mid-latitude grasslands. It can be grown outside these areas in countries as far apart as Finland and India, but not so successfully as in the prairies, the pampas and the steppes, where the climate is best suited to its growth and where the climatic conditions over thousands of years have led to the formation of the rich, deep chernozem soils which wheat prefers.

During the period of germination and early growth the weather should be cool and moist; such conditions produce a dense crop of stalks and hence a good yield of grain. Later on, a warm, sunny period is necessary, to ripen the ears and enable the farmer to gather his crop safely, but a few showers just before the harvest are an advantage, since they help to 'swell the grain'.

Wheat requires an annual rainfall of between 375 and 900 mm (15 and 35 in). In places where the rainfall is less than 375 mm (15 in), as, for instance, in parts of the Californian Valley, irrigation is necessary, or possibly the system of 'dry farming' may be used (see p. 163). The exact amount of rainfall required within the above limits is also dependent on the rate of evaporation. In warm climates, much of the moisture is evaporated into the atmosphere before it can sink into the soil.

The average temperature of the warmest month must be above 16° C (60° F) if the ears are to fill and ripen properly, but the young wheat crop is hardy enough to survive where the average temperature of the coldest month is about –7° C (20° F). Although a prolonged hard frost would damage the crop, a covering of snow does no harm. It is, in fact, beneficial, since it protects the seedlings from the effects of alternate freezing and thawing.

Types of wheat

Wheat is commonly sown in the autumn and harvested towards the end of the following summer; this is called *winter wheat*. But where the winter temperature falls below –7° C (20° F), it is necessary to grow *spring wheat* (that is, wheat sown in the spring), but this is possible only if a sufficiently long period occurs between the end of one winter and the beginning of the next for the crop to reach maturity (fig. 4). The importance of the prairies

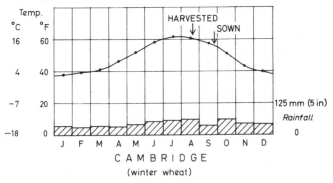

CAMBRIDGE
(winter wheat)

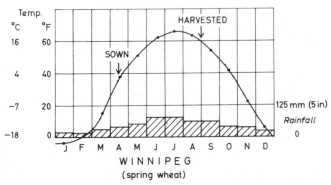

WINNIPEG
(spring wheat)

Fig. 4 Climatic graphs for Cambridge, England, and Winnipeg, Canada, illustrating the conditions in which winter wheat and spring wheat respectively are grown.

of Canada as a great wheat-growing area is due to the fact that in the last quarter of the nineteenth century a type of grain was evolved which would ripen quickly enough to avoid the frosts of early autumn. Experiments in cross-breeding are continually being carried out, but at present a growing period of at least ninety days is still required for successful cultivation.

The warm, sunny summers of the continental type of climate produce *hard* wheat, with a low moisture content, whereas the moist summers of the British Isles, for example, produce *soft* wheat, containing a comparatively large amount of moisture.[1] Bread made solely from soft wheat has a coarse, uneven texture, and is sometimes known as 'farmhouse' bread. Soft wheat is, however, much more satisfactory for making biscuits. The drought conditions of summer in the 'Mediterranean' type of climate produce an extremely hard grain, from which macaroni, spaghetti and vermicelli are made.

Soil and other considerations

Wheat needs a fertile soil, but this soon becomes exhausted unless steps are taken to replace the minerals on which the crop feeds by means of fertilisers or some system of crop rotation (see pp. 169–70). The soil should also be moderately heavy, in order to support the heavily laden stalks, and it is clearly a great advantage if the land is flat enough to be ploughed easily. Quite apart from the climate, these last two considerations make the boulder-clay lands of eastern England very suitable for wheat-growing.

The *yield*—that is, the quantity of wheat produced from a given area of land—is very important. It is traditionally measured in bushels per acre (but see caption fig. 5). A bushel is a measure of *volume* (8 gallons, or 52 litres), and the *weight* of threshed wheat required to fill a bushel measure is normally about 60 lb (27 kg), but it varies slightly with the type of wheat and the tightness with which it is packed.[2] In the United Kingdom the average yield is 50 bushels per acre and in the Netherlands 58. It comes as a surprise to many people that the prairies of Canada, which used at one time to be called 'the bread-basket of the Empire', have a yield of only 23 bushels per acre, and that in Australia and Argentina the yield is about the same (fig. 5).

[1] Soft wheat is sometimes described as 'weak', since it contains a low proportion of protein, and hard wheat, containing a higher proportion of protein, as 'strong'.

[2] A bushel of oats weighs about 32 lb (15 kg), of barley about 48 lb (22 kg) and of maize about 56 lb (25 kg).

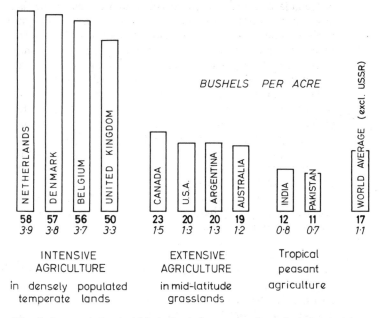

BUSHELS PER ACRE

NETHERLANDS	DENMARK	BELGIUM	UNITED KINGDOM	CANADA	U.S.A.	ARGENTINA	AUSTRALIA	INDIA	PAKISTAN	WORLD AVERAGE (excl. USSR)
58	57	56	50	23	20	20	19	12	11	17
3·9	*3·8*	*3·7*	*3·3*	*1·5*	*1·3*	*1·3*	*1·2*	*0·8*	*0·7*	*1·1*

INTENSIVE
AGRICULTURE

in densely populated
temperate lands

EXTENSIVE
AGRICULTURE

in mid-latitude
grasslands

Tropical
peasant
agriculture

Fig. 5 Average wheat yields in bushels per acre for selected countries. Nowadays yields are sometimes quoted in *tons per hectare*. In the above diagram yields calculated in this way are shown in italics.

Intensive and extensive farming

The low yields in Canada, Australia and Argentina are no reflection on the efficiency of the farmers, who are quite satisfied to produce a large quantity of wheat by cultivating a large area of land. This method of farming is described as *extensive* agriculture, in contrast to *intensive* agriculture, in which no effort is spared to obtain the maximum yield from a small amount of land. If the same kind of crop is grown year after year on the same piece of ground (*monoculture*), the soil loses its fertility, and yields become so low that it is no longer economic (in other words, it no longer pays) to go on growing that particular type of crop. When this point is reached, the plant foods have to be replaced by means of fertilisers or by practising crop rotation.

In densely populated countries like England, where so much space is taken up by buildings, roads, railways and so on, it is essential to make the best possible use of all the available agricultural land. Fewer farm-workers are needed to grow wheat on the extensive system, and great use is made of such time- and labour-saving machinery as the combine harvester, which cuts and threshes in one operation. Although, therefore, the yield *per unit of area* under extensive farming is comparatively low, the yield *per man* is high. In countries where agriculture is intensive, the farms are comparatively small. Often the land is divided by hedges into fields, and it is not always practicable or economic to make use of the huge machines which are to be found in the wide open spaces of the mid-latitude grasslands (fig. 6).

Wheat-producing areas

In the following pages no attempt will be made to describe at length the great wheat-producing areas of the world; full details will be found in the appropriate regional textbooks. Certain topics which illustrate some of the foregoing considerations must, however, be mentioned.

The *Canadian Prairies* (fig. 6) produce in an average year 19 million tons[1] of wheat out of a world total of 315 million. Since Canada has a population of only 22 million, two-thirds of the crop is available for export, most of it being absorbed by the United Kingdom. Winters in the prairies are severe, and the seed has of necessity to be sown in spring. Fortunately, the area is subject at this time of year to the warm Chinook wind, which can effect overnight such remarkable and sudden increases in the temperature that the snows of winter are quickly cleared away, and a period of about 110 days follows, in which the wheat is able to ripen fully. Declining yields and the onset of soil erosion (see pp. 170–3) have in recent years led to the introduction of mixed farming, in which animals help to restore fertility of the soil by supplying manure.

The *United States* is the world's second largest wheat-producing country, but having such a large population (estimated in 1971 to be 207 million) it was not normally, until after the Second World War, an exporter of wheat. In the colder northern parts around Minneapolis the crop is spring-sown, but farther south, in Kansas and Oklahoma, it is possible to grow winter wheat. As in Canada, the wheat is grown on the extensive system and the yield per unit area is less than half that of the United Kingdom.

The *USSR* is now the world's largest wheat producer, but although thirty years ago the country was a major exporter, in recent years it has been forced to import considerable quantities from Canada and the USA. Most of the wheat is grown (on the extensive system) in the 'black earth' steppelands north of the Black Sea, and the yield is slightly lower than in any of the other

---

[1] There is little point in distinguishing between the imperial ton (2 204·62 lb) and the metric ton (or tonne) of 1 000 kg. For general purposes the difference is negligible, since a metric ton is 0·9842 of an imperial ton. The 'short' ton used in America is of 2 000 lb.

Fig. 6 The town of Lewvan, Saskatchewan, showing the railway and the grain elevators in the foreground and the wide farmlands stretching into the distance. After harvest the grain will be graded by inspectors of the Board of Grain Commissioners for Canada and stored in the elevators while awaiting transport to the ports.

mid-latitude grasslands. With improved transport facilities and the discovery of varieties which will resist drought and ripen more quickly, the producing area has expanded some 3 200 km (2 000 miles) eastward into Siberia.

Europe (excluding the USSR) ranks high among the wheat-growing regions of the world. In fact, France alone produces 4 million tons more than Australia. But insufficient grain is grown in Europe to feed the dense industrial populations, and considerable quantities are imported from the mid-latitude grasslands. Since land is valuable and the winters are not severe, the wheat is sown in the autumn and grown on the intensive system.

The pampas of *Argentina* and the downs of *Australia* provide immense tracts of land suitable for extensive wheat-growing, and both countries have small populations. They are, therefore, notable exporters. Moreover, since they are situated in the southern hemisphere, their crops become available when stocks in the northern hemisphere are running low. But they suffer from the

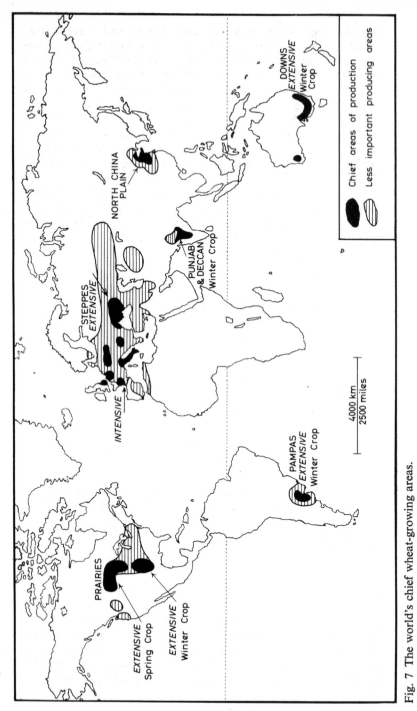

Fig. 7 The world's chief wheat-growing areas.

DOWNS
EXTENSIVE
Winter
Crop

NORTH CHINA
PLAIN

STEPPES
EXTENSIVE

PUNJAB
& DECCAN
Winter Crop

INTENSIVE

PAMPAS
EXTENSIVE
Winter Crop

PRAIRIES

EXTENSIVE
Spring Crop

EXTENSIVE
Winter Crop

Chief areas of production

Less important producing areas

4000 km
2500 miles

20   Foods from grasses

disadvantage of being at a great distance from their markets (that is, countries which are willing to buy their products). In Argentina wheat is now grown in areas where not so long ago *gauchos* (half-Indian cowboys) reared horses and cattle. The industry is not very highly organised, and since there are few facilities for milling, the crop is exported as wheat and not as flour.

Northern China produces nearly twice as much wheat as Canada, but all of it is consumed within the country. The Chinese have of recent years displayed an increasing taste for wheat, which can easily be satisfied by exploiting the vast resources of Manchuria.

Wheat production in *India* and *Pakistan* totals 25 million tons a year, but both countries need to import additional supplies. The crop is grown in the cool season, with the help of irrigation, in the drier regions of the northwest and the Deccan.

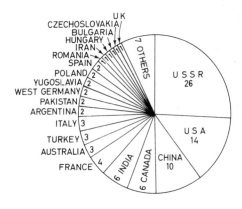

Fig. 8 World production of wheat. The figures indicate percentages of the world's total production of 315 million tons per year.

The chief producing areas of the world are shown in fig. 7, and their annual production in fig. 8.

Maize

Maize is the only cereal crop to have originated in America, where it was cultivated in prehistoric times and was the staple food crop of the Aztecs and the Incas. It was unknown in Europe till the end of the fifteenth century. World output today (265 million tons per year) is only a little less than that of wheat or rice.

Fig. 9 Maize being cut green for fodder on a farm in Kent. The grain will be stored in a silo until it is required for stall-feeding cattle in winter.

The crop grows to a height of anything between 2 and 5 m (6 and 16 ft), and the head (or 'cob') is much larger than that of any other cereal. As the plant ripens, a long bud-like growth bursts open, revealing a mass of grains arranged on a central pithy stem.

Conditions of growth
Maize is a subtropical rather than a temperate crop, which requires abundant rainfall—between 625 and 1 025 mm (25 and 40 in) per year—and long, sunny summers with a mean temperature of 24° C (75° F). It is injured by frost, and prefers a well-drained medium soil. Maize can sometimes be seen growing in southern England, but the summers are not really warm enough to ripen the crop fully, and it is cut green for fodder (fig. 9). In tropical lowlands, on the other hand, it grows very quickly and the yield is therefore unsatisfactory.

Uses, types and producers
The fact that maize is the richest cereal in oil makes it particularly suitable for fattening animals, and most of the world's production is devoted to this purpose. But since the oil has a disagreeable odour, maize is not widely used as a human food. It is, however, grown as a subsistence crop (see p. 153) by Bantu farmers in subtropical Africa, where it is roughly ground and made into a kind of porridge known locally as 'mealie meal'; in Italy, maize

meal is made into *polenta,* and in Mexico into cakes called *tortillas,* which are eaten while still warm.

There are two main commercial types of maize—*dent* (or 'soft' maize), which crops more heavily and has soft, flat grains, and *flint* (or 'hard' maize), which ripens quickly and has hard, round grains. In recent years numerous hybrids have been produced in the USA and in south western France.

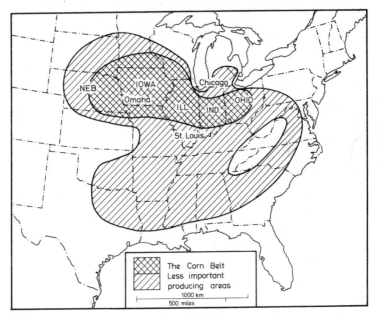

Fig. 10 Maize-growing areas of the U.S.A.

Over two-fifths of the world's maize is grown in the United States, chiefly in the Corn[1] Belt of Ohio, Indiana, Illinois, Iowa and Nebraska (figs. 10 and 11), where it is said to be marketed 'on the hoof' (i.e. fed to animals). Chicago is the centre of a great meat-packing industry, based on vast numbers of pigs and beef cattle, which are fattened on 'corn' grown in the vicinity. In the last fifty years tinned pork and 'corned' beef have replaced frozen meat as an important export of the region. Although the bulk of America's maize is fed to animals, smaller quantities are used for other purposes. Some is eaten as *hominy,* or 'grits', which is similar to the African's mealie meal, some is roasted to

[1] It should be noted that while in Britain the word 'corn' is applied to the chief kind of grain grown locally, in the USA it refers only to maize. Maize is also called 'Indian Corn'.

make popcorn, and a special variety of 'sweet corn' provides corn-on-the-cob (the head boiled whole). The ears ground without their skins form cornflour, for making invalid foods, blancmange, custard powder, etc., and maize is a common constituent of breakfast cereals (e.g. cornflakes). It is also used in the manufacture of industrial alcohol, starch and certain kinds of beer and spirits. Only 3 per cent of America's maize is exported as grain, but, nevertheless, the USA is the world's chief exporter. At one time Argentina led the world in the export of maize, but she is now using most of her crop to improve the quality of her beef.

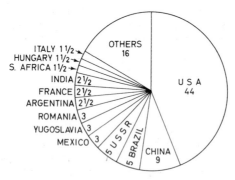

Fig. 11 World production of maize. The figures indicate percentages of the world's total production of 265 million tons per year.

Barley

Barley is a cereal of great antiquity, and was the bread plant of the ancient Mediterranean civilisations. The loaves referred to in the biblical story of the loaves and fishes were almost certainly made from barley, but it is now used only for bread where conditions are unsuitable for the growth of wheat.

The crop is fairly easily recognised in the field. It has a drooping head, and the ears are interspersed with hairs in such a way as to suggest the description used by Tennyson, 'bearded barley' (fig. 3). Although the barley lands, generally speaking, coincide with the wheat lands of the world, barley is much more adaptable than wheat as far as temperature, rainfall and soil are concerned, and production responds more to local needs than to climate. Barley can be grown on high lands in the tropics, and it is the grain best suited to 'Mediterranean' conditions, in which summers are too dry for wheat, maize or oats. Some varieties need only eight weeks between seed-time and harvest, and barley can therefore be grown farther north than any other cereal—in Norway well beyond the Arctic Circle. In England it occupies the drier, sandy soils of East Anglia.

World production of barley has increased considerably over the last decade and now stands at 137 million tons per year. Only about 5 per cent of this enters into international trade, and apart from the USSR, which grows one-quarter of the world's barley, there are no outstandingly large producers. Considerable quantities are used as animal feed, but the chief use of barley is in the brewing and distilling industries. Malt is made from grain with a low nitrogen content which has been allowed to germinate and has then been 'killed' and fermented. It is not surprising that the heaviest consumers of barley are the chief beer-drinking countries of the world — the United Kingdom and West Germany.

Oats

Oats in appearance are quite distinct from the other cereals. The ears, instead of being packed on a central stem, are spread out, and hang loosely in twos and threes from tiny off-shoots (fig. 3). Very little mention is made of the grain in the history of countries around the Mediterranean Sea, although there are indications that it was grown in quite early times in central Europe. Since oats prefer a cool, damp climate, it may well be that they were little cultivated until the practice of agriculture had spread northwards from the ancient home of civilisation. They are less resistant to cold than either wheat or barley, though they can be grown successfully in a variety of soils.

Oats take rather longer to grow than barley, but since a crop of oats alone is very liable to be blown flat in a strong wind, barley is sometimes sown together with the oats in windy areas, such as the more exposed parts of south-western England. The combined grain so produced is known as 'dredge-corn' and is fed to animals.

The use of oats as a human food is confined to Ireland, Scandinavia and, in particular, Scotland, where the grain is ground into oatmeal for making oatcakes and porridge. It is remarkable that so few nations have realised how nutritious oats are. Most of the world's crop is used as fodder for horses and cattle—chiefly, nowadays, for cattle, since the number of horses has declined. Oats are for their weight a bulky grain, and the tendency, therefore, is for them to be grown in the areas where they are required—often on the actual farms. The inconvenience involved in transporting oats is reflected in the fact that only 2 per cent of world production enters international trade. Cultivation is heavily concentrated in the Northern Hemisphere, the largest producers being the USA and the USSR; world output, which now amounts to about 55 million tons, is slowly increasing.

In the British Isles the growing of oats corresponds very closely to the dairy cattle regions.

Rye

Rye was first cultivated in eastern Europe, and today four-fifths of the world's output of about 30 million tons is grown in the USSR, Poland and East and West Germany. It is the hardiest of all cereals, and the one most capable of resisting intense cold, pests and diseases. Unlike other grains, it will grow in poor soils and can, therefore, be raised in the great band of infertility which stretches across northern Europe from the eastern Netherlands to Russia.

Where living standards are low, peasant farmers make from it a soggy, unpalatable, but nevertheless nourishing form of bread, which, although it is actually dark brown in colour, is referred to as 'black bread'. With the improvement of living conditions in central and eastern European countries, rye has been largely replaced by wheat for bread-making. The crop does, however, provide fodder for cattle and pigs, and long, fine straw for thatching. The straw is also used in the manufacture of the coarser forms of cardboard ('strawboard'). In the USA rye whisky is made from the grain.

The only export of rye is from one country of eastern Europe to another.

Rice

Rice is the cereal crop of the monsoon and equatorial regions. It grows to a height of about 1·5 m (4 ft 6 in), and several seedheads are found attached to each of the stalks (fig. 3). Rice not only produces on any given area more food than any other grain, but also grows so quickly—7 or 8 cm in twenty-four hours—that under favourable conditions the same piece of ground will yield two crops in the same season. The chief rice-growing areas in South-east Asia are, not surprisingly, among the most densely populated regions of the world, and rice feeds more of the human race than does any other grain.

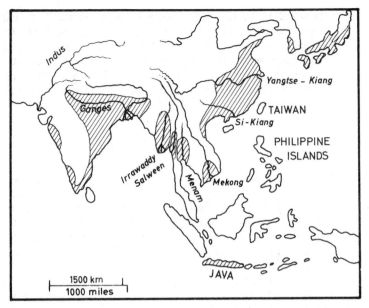

Fig. 12. The chief rice-growing areas of South-east Asia. Notice that rice is grown chiefly in the flood plains and deltas of the great rivers.

While still in the husk or outer skin, the crop is known as *paddy;* the term 'rice' is not used until the husk has been removed. Since the grain contains only a negligible proportion of a sticky substance called gluten, it does not make a satisfactory bread; the ears are, therefore, not ground into flour, but boiled in water and eaten whole. Sometimes the dish is flavoured with spices, and sometimes a little fish or meat is added, but rice alone still forms the only really substantial article of diet of a vast number of Asiatic peasant farmers. The rice which is familiar in European countries as the chief constituent of rice pudding has been specially polished to give it a more attractive appearance, but it is less nutritious than the unpolished rice eaten in the Far East.

For the growth of rice there are three main essentials—a summer temperature of over 24° C (75° F), abundant rainfall amounting to at least 1 025 mm (40 in) a year (or its equivalent in irrigation) and flat land on which the water can lie. The valleys and deltas of such rivers as the Yangtse-Kiang, the Mekong, the Irrawaddy and the Ganges, together with coastal lowlands in the East Indies and similar areas, provide ideal conditions for rice cultivation, and some are crowded beyond belief with poverty-stricken peasants, each endeavouring to snatch a precarious

Fig. 13 Paddy fields at Akamizu in Kyushu Island, Japan.

living from his own meagre portion of fertile ground. In some cases—as, for instance, in Java and Sri Lanka (Ceylon)—farmers have been forced to cultivate the hillsides, and, at an immense cost in human labour, the slopes have been built into terraces or steps flanked by low earth walls so that water can be retained and regulated (fig. 85).

In preparation for the young crop, the flooded fields are ploughed into mud with the aid of primitive ploughs drawn by water-buffaloes or oxen, and the seedlings, only a few centimetres high, are planted under water. They remain covered for a few weeks, but soon grow at a remarkable rate and are eventually harvested by hand. By this time in some monsoon lands the ground has so completely dried out that it presents the appearance of crazy paving.

It has been said that nowhere is there so little reward for so much labour as in rice cultivation. The expenditure of human energy is enormous, the instruments used are hopelessly out of date, and rheumatism of the wrists and ankles is a serious occupational hazard. The peasant is tied very closely to the soil and his only guarantee against starvation is the reliability of the rainfall. Yields and efficiency, of course, vary; the average yield in India, for example, is only one-third of that of Japan, where high-yielding 'Japonica' hybrid types of rice have been produced. But the yields in India and many other areas where the farming is inefficient could be vastly improved by the introduction of better varieties of seed.

Since so much rice is grown on small individual holdings for family consumption, it is difficult to assess world production. It is, however, estimated to be in the region of 295 million tons a year. Nearly two-thirds of this is grown in China, India and Pakistan, which even so have to import from other countries to satisfy their needs. The only rice-producing areas of any significance outside Southeast Asia are in Brazil and in the lower Mississippi valley in the USA, both of which have small surpluses available for export (figs. 12 and 14).

Over a thousand varieties of rice exist—most of them being 'swamp' rice, as described above. 'Upland' rice can, however, be grown in some regions without flooding. It relies on continuous heavy rainfall, provides only a low yield and is of minor importance.

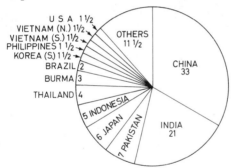

Fig. 14 World production of rice. The figures indicate percentages of the world's total production of about 295 million tons per year. Notice that only about one-seventh of the world's rice is grown outside South-east Asia.

Millets

Millets are the humblest members of the family of cultivated grasses. Each stalk produces a head, 25 cm (10 in) or more in length, consisting of small, tightly-packed seeds, which have only limited value as human food. The grain is grown as a subsistence crop in various parts of the tropical and subtropical lands where the climate is too dry for rice or the soil too poor for wheat, but, broadly speaking, the cultivation of millets for food is indicative of a very low standard of living. The gritty kind of meal produced by grinding millets is used in the preparation of a dish which resembles porridge. Outside the tropics they are grown as a fodder crop, notably in the USA and southern Europe.

Chief of the millets is the type of grain known as *sorghum* (Great Millet, Indian Millet or Guinea Corn), but there are many other varieties and many local names, as, for instance, in Africa, Kaffir Corn and *dhurra*.

In European countries 'cat-tail' millet, which has particularly small grains, is sometimes used as bird-seed.

Other food crops

A number of other food crops are described below, which, although not cereals, may be most conveniently dealt with in the present chapter.

Buckwheat

Buckwheat does not belong to the grass family. It is an annual plant, native to eastern Asia, and was introduced to Europe by the Arabs. It grows about 50 cm (2 ft) tall, has brown leaves and white flowers, and is a distant relative of several English weeds. Buckwheat is cultivated in cool temperate regions as animal fodder or chicken feed, but in Canada cakes are made from buckwheat flour and eaten with maple syrup.

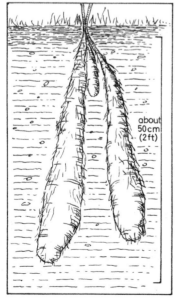

about 50 cm (2 ft)

Fig. 15 Yams.

Yams

Yams (fig. 15) are the tubers (i.e. the swellings formed on the roots) of a small tropical bush. Their size varies between that of a potato and that of a large marrow, but some weigh as much as 50 kg (110 lb). They grow in wet, tropical regions, and form the chief starch food of many people in West Africa.

Manioc

Manioc is also a small tropical shrub. From its tubers, which somewhat resemble parsnips, *cassava* (or tapioca) is made. The tubers are not suitable for use as food until the deadly poison which they contain has been extracted by heating and compression. Manioc is a native of the Amazon Basin, but it is now common in other tropical regions.

Sweet potatoes

These are grown in tropical and warm temperate lands. They are similar in appearance to and are used in much the same way as the more familiar potatoes of the cooler parts of the world. In the rice-growing areas of China and Japan they form one of the crops cultivated with the help of irrigation in the dry season.

Sago

Sago is prepared from the pith of a palm grown in the East Indies. It is exported in sacks made from the leaves of the tree.

Pulses

These include a wide range of leguminous plants—that is, plants whose seeds, like those of peas and broad beans, are enclosed in pods. In cool climates pulses are used as what are loosely called 'vegetables', merely to add variety to the diet, but in lands where butcher's meat is not available they are particularly useful, since they supply the same vitamins as the flesh of animals. They are also used as fodder. Some of the less familiar pulses are lentils, vetch and chick-peas (known in India as *gram*). Soya beans and groundnuts are also classed as pulses, but as they are valued chiefly for their oils, they will be considered in Chapter 7.

Potatoes

Potatoes came originally from the Andean regions of South America, and are thought to have been introduced into Ireland from Virginia by Sir Walter Raleigh in 1586. Over a hundred years passed before they became popular in England, but gradually their cultivation spread to central and eastern Europe, where about half the world's potatoes are now grown.

Fig. 16 Harvesting sugar beet in Suffolk.

Although less nutritious than grain, potatoes produce a greater weight of food per unit area than any of the cereals. In the United Kingdom 30 tons per hectare (12 tons per acre) is not uncommon. They are an extremely useful and important food-stuff, particularly in mid-latitudes, but can also be cultivated throughout a wide range of climatic conditions, from the tropics to the Arctic Circle. In Ireland in the first half of the nineteenth century potatoes were the staple food of the poorer classes, and even today they form the main item in the diet of many European peasants.

Apart from the trade in 'early' potatoes and potatoes grown specially for seed, crops are rarely exported. Potatoes are a bulky commodity, and their value is not sufficient to offset the comparatively high cost of transport.

Potatoes are also used as fodder, and for the manufacture of certain industrial products, such as alcohol and starch.

Root crops
Crops such as carrots, turnips, swedes,[1] mangolds[2] and parsnips, which are grown primarily for their roots, are essentially products of the cool temperate lands. They often form part of a four-year rotation, and, while their main use is for fodder, some are used as human food. Like potatoes, they are in general far too bulky in proportion to their value to stand the cost of transport over

[1] i.e. Swedish turnips.
[2] Or mangel-wurzels. *Mangel-wurzel* is German for 'beetroot'.

long distances. During the last seventy years or so sugar beet has assumed considerable importance as a source of sugar (see p. 83).

Market garden produce

A group of miscellaneous crops ranging from onions and tomatoes to lettuces and cauliflowers is collectively known as market garden produce. These are mostly perishable commodities with a comparatively low value, and have a general tendency, therefore, to be cultivated close to the areas in which they are needed. But proximity is now of less significance than formerly, due to the growth of vegetables on a large scale under contract, using such modern machinery as mobile viners (e.g. for peas in Norfolk and Suffolk). Much is grown in this way for canning and drying and for sale from the deep-freeze cabinets of supermarkets. Some market garden produce enters international trade. Countries where climatic conditions are sufficiently favourable to permit the production of 'early' crops before supplies are available in the consuming areas hasten to export their produce while, on account of its scarcity, it still commands a fairly high price. Tomatoes from the Canary Islands and the Channel Islands, and early vegetables from Brittany and the south of France, reach England in these circumstances.

In the United States market gardening is referred to as 'truck-farming' and there is a similar 'export' of early lettuces, etc., from the Atlantic coastal plain as well as from Florida and California to the region of New York.

Fig. 17 Harvesting peas for the deep-freeze factories. Mobile viners move into the fields behind the cutters. Within less than an hour and a half of cutting, the peas will have been washed, graded and deep-frozen.

3

FOOD FROM ANIMALS

Domestic animals

At some stage in history certain of the animals ceased to be regarded by man as creatures to be hunted as his natural prey and came to be closely associated with him in his home surroundings and his work. The circumstances which led to this 'domestication' of animals have for many years been the subject of much varied speculation. It has been suggested that dogs, for instance, originally hung about the settlements of early man as scavengers seeking discarded bones, and so became his companions in the hunt; and that the domestication of sheep and cattle was the result of men and beasts being thrown closely together in the oases of fertility that remained when drier conditions overtook the once productive regions of Arabia and the Sahara. But whatever may have been the circumstances leading to domestication, it seems reasonably certain that it was a comparatively sudden event which took place between 5000 and 3000 BC, and that the domestication of nearly all the animals which are fitted for it occurred about that time. A surprisingly large number of animals are capable of being tamed, as any visitor to a modern circus can testify, but few species seem capable of being domesticated in the full sense of the word. An attempt made about a hundred years ago to domesticate zebras ended in failure.

The uses found for the domesticated animals of early times were not necessarily the same as they are today; and we must remember, too, that just as man has throughout the centuries improved upon the original grasses by selective breeding, so he has by a similar process deliberately adapted those members of the animal kingdom for which he could foresee useful purposes. Although in the present chapter we are primarily concerned with animals as producers of meat and milk, we may note in passing several other uses. Reindeer, camels, yaks, llamas, elephants and donkeys, for instance, are used in various parts of the world as beasts of burden. Oxen and water-buffaloes in backward areas serve as draught animals pulling carts and ploughs, but the number of horses used for this purpose is, of course, decreasing, as in more highly organised communities they are replaced by cars, lorries and tractors. Various industrial raw materials are derived from animals. Bones and horns, for example, yield buttons, handles and fertiliser; glue is made from hoofs, and, quite apart from sheep's wool (which is probably the most important of all such raw materials), hair is used for making brushes and padding. It would, moreover, be impossible to ignore the part played by animals as domestic pets and in connection with sport.

Cattle

Although sometimes used in a looser sense to include a much wider range of animals, the word 'cattle' properly applies to certain members of the ox family, which are known to have been domesticated in Europe and Asia from prehistoric times. Today in many parts of the tropics they remain little more than draught animals, but in mid-latitudes, as producers of meat and milk, they make an indispensable contribution to the world's food supply.

World distribution of cattle

Cattle are essentially animals of the grassland areas. They have long tongues, and feed by twisting them round the grass and tearing it up. They thrive best, therefore, in wet lowlands, where the ground underfoot is damp and clayey, and where the grass is long and rich. Cattle are found in almost all of the mid-latitude and tropical lands, the only exceptions being regions which are heavily forested or rugged, but their distribution and density are really a reflection of man's needs and capacity for adaptation and organisation rather than conditions of climate and vegetation (fig. 18).

Types and uses of cattle

The world's cattle number over 1 100 million and consist of two main types of animal.

1. *Zebu or humped cattle* are found mainly in the tropics. Unlike the cattle which have evolved in mid-latitude lands, they possess sweat glands which enable them to endure high temperatures. Zebu cattle are generally small, strong and bony, and are used chiefly as draught animals. They yield comparatively little milk and the meat is scraggy and tough; very little interest is, in fact, taken in them as beef-producers. This is not entirely due to inefficiency on the part of their owners; it is largely the result of

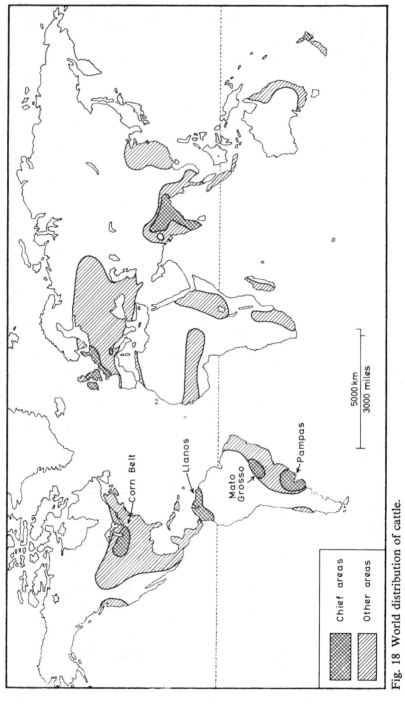

Fig. 18 World distribution of cattle.

Corn Belt

Llanos

Mato Grosso

Pampas

5000 km
3000 miles

Chief areas

Other areas

social and religious customs. India and Pakistan together contain one-fifth of the world's cattle, nearly all of them being of the Zebu type, but the Hindu is taught by his religion to regard cattle as sacred and is forbidden to touch beef, while the Muslim eats very little. It is more than likely that originally the prohibition was due to the problem of keeping meat in good condition in a hot climate. The Negroes of East Africa, on the other hand, regard cattle as a measure of wealth[1] and only rarely slaughter their animals.

2. *European cattle* are bigger and heavier than Zebu cattle, and are reared almost exclusively for meat and milk. The wide variety of types which they display is to some extent the result of different conditions of climate and pasture. A severe climate, for instance, produces a greater development of both hair and horns, and wet regions of island or mountain tend to be inhabited by somewhat smaller types, such as the Jersey breed.

Early attempts at cross-breeding also played their part, but the differentiation of European types of cattle is principally due to the more scientific efforts of English agriculturalists in the eighteenth and nineteenth centuries. Such pioneers of modern farming methods as Robert Bakewell, by carefully selecting animals for breeding and by paying great attention to the pastures on which they fed, succeeded in producing improved types of British cattle which gave increased yields of meat and milk, and in some cases both. These improvements led to the ascendancy of Britain as a producer of pedigree stock, which did much to build up the quality of herds in other parts of the world. Typical examples of breeds of cattle are illustrated in fig. 19.

Beef cattle

Although the finest and most productive types of cattle are reared in the cool temperate lands of Europe, where the natural cover of deciduous forest has been largely replaced by grassland, these areas do not under present-day conditions provide sufficient beef for their needs. Since they are densely populated and consumption of beef is high—in the United Kingdom, for instance, the average annual consumption is 19 kg (40 lb) per head—a very large number of animals would be required. Although it would be possible, by concentrating on beef production to the exclusion of all other branches of farming, to achieve self-sufficiency, it would certainly be unprofitable. As it is essential that the best use should be made

[1]It is interesting to note that *pecunia*, the Latin word for 'money', is derived from *pecus* meaning 'a herd'. Early peoples often used cattle as money.

Fig. 19 Typical breeds of cattle. 1. Aberdeen Angus. 2. Guernsey. 3. Ayrshire. 4. Beef Shorthorn. 5. British Friesian. 6. Hereford. Nos. 2, 3 and 5 are dairy breeds, the others are reared for beef. Crossbreds (notably Charolais) are becoming increasingly popular.

of the available agricultural land, *mixed farming*, in which animals and crops succeed one another in various forms of rotation, is the general rule. Thus only a proportion of the beef required is, in fact, produced. In Britain 'home-killed' beef accounts for about 40 per cent of the total consumption. The deficiency is not of any great consequence, because developments over the last hundred years have made it possible for Europe to import beef at a favourable price from distant countries where land is cheap and population scanty.

Refrigeration

Throughout history the problem of keeping meat fresh and in good condition over any appreciable length of time has been a very real one. Up to a hundred years or so ago, the only solution lay in salting or 'jerking' it. This was not very satisfactory, although the extensive use of spices helped to mitigate the salty flavour which could never be completely removed. The invention and development of the refrigerator ship between 1860 and 1880 afforded to the mid–latitude grasslands of the New World the opportunity to develop as beef-producing regions which could supply the industrial countries on the other side of the Atlantic. The carcasses were at first 'frozen' (that is, kept in specially constructed chambers at a temperature of –12° to –9° C (10° to 15° F), and still are at the present time if they have to travel over a particularly long distance,[1] or if they have to be kept in store for a very long period. But over shorter distances and shorter periods 'chilling' (at a temperature just below freezing point) has been found to halt the action of harmful bacteria, and has the advantage of retaining the natural juices—and hence the flavour—which are lost when 'frozen' beef thaws out.[2]

Beef production in the Americas

The mid-latitude grasslands of North and South America had originally been devoted by the early pioneers to cattle brought over with them from Europe. But as grain crops came to occupy more of the better, well-watered areas, the cattle were forced westwards to the drier, unwanted regions in the 'rain shadow' of the Rockies and the Andes. Here they were commercially valuable only for their hides, which were sold for making saddles, belts and other kinds of leather goods; the meat was regarded as an inconvenient byproduct. Changes, however, began to take place as increasing population led to a demand for beef.

North America. 'Western' films and television programmes provide a picture—sometimes an inaccurate one—of the kind of conditions which prevailed at this stage. On the prairies suitable cattle were rounded up in the early autumn of each year and driven overland in herds by 'cow-punchers' to be slaughtered in the more populous regions to the east. The meat was usually of

[1] From Australia to Britain, for instance. With modern methods of refrigeration freezing is no longer necessary on the journey from Argentina to Britain.

[2] Frozen lamb does *not* suffer in this way.

poor quality, since, by the time the animals had completed the journey, there was very little flesh left on them. With the invention of refrigeration and the building of railways commercial grazing became a much more profitable occupation. The open 'ranges' on which the cattle roamed at will were enclosed, pure-bred stock (notably Herefords) were introduced from Britain, and fodder crops were grown to feed the herds in winter.

By the beginning of the twentieth century sufficient beef was being produced in the United States not only to satisfy home demands, but also to provide a considerable export to Britain. In fact, between 1900 and 1910 more frozen meat was sent to Britain from the USA than from Argentina. Although the average American eats 32 kg (70 lb) of beef per year, there is still a surplus for export, but nowadays it takes the form of 'corned' beef. Cattle from the prairies are sent by rail to the Corn Belt of the Middle West to be 'finished' (i.e. fattened) on the locally grown maize before being slaughtered for the great meat-packing industry at Omaha, Chicago, St Louis and Kansas City.

South America. Early developments in the pampas of Argentina and Uruguay followed much the same course as in the prairies of North America. Originally, half-wild herds of cattle were tended on the open plains by almost equally wild *gaucho*[1] cowboys, who were extraordinarily skilful in their use of the lasso and bolas, and who are said to have been capable of sleeping for hours in the saddle while their mounts made for the nearest watering-place! By 1880, however, the technique of refrigeration had been mastered, and Argentina had begun to take up the position she now occupies as the chief purveyor of beef to the rest of the world.

The *gauchos* are now fast disappearing, the enormous farms or *estancias* are being further broken up and enclosed, and the animals depend for their food not so much on the natural grassland as on specially sown crops of alfalfa, a plant similar to clover, which was introduced to the Americas by the Spaniards some two hundred years ago. The business of preparing the meat for export in the great *frigorificos* or freezing-factories of Buenos Aires and neighbouring towns is extremely efficient and highly organised. Refrigerating plant in Buenos Aires alone is reputed to be capable of handling 5 000 cattle a day—in addition to 10 000 sheep. Hides and tongues form valuable byproducts, and lower grades of beef are made into meat extracts. There is also a large canning industry carried on in Uruguay at Fray Bentos and Paysandu. The name of the former town is familiar to many British housewives, since it figures prominently on tins of imported corned beef.

[1] i.e. of mixed Spanish and American-Indian descent.

The tropical grasslands

Although present-day beef production in the mid-latitude grasslands is well organised and scientific, it is doubtful whether these regions will in the future continue to be the chief producing areas. Crop cultivation, since it is a more profitable means of livelihood, is tending to replace cattle-rearing, and it is likely that we may soon be forced to look to the tropical grasslands to make good the deficiency. Considerable progress has already been made in the savanna lands of northern Australia where, on enormous cattle stations or 'outfits', enough beef is produced to supply the home market[1] and at the same time provide an export amounting to one-quarter of all the beef that enters into world trade. The Australian government is anxious that the country should produce still more beef for export, but the enterprise suffers from two major disadvantages—lack of rail transport to the freezing-factories on the east coast, and unreliable rainfall. The latter is, however, to some extent compensated by supplies of drinking water from artesian wells.

In other areas of tropical grassland cattle-rearing is an important occupation, but only rarely on a commercial scale. In the *Mato Grosso* region of Brazil, beef cattle are reared and driven overland to the coast, to be exported as frozen meat, but in the *llanos* of Venezuela and Colombia, despite the recent establishment of modern, enclosed estates, as yet few of the cattle are of commercial value. In the savannas of Africa the tsetse fly, which can produce a disease known in man as 'sleeping sickness' and in animals as *nagana*,[2] has not yet been completely controlled. Communications within the tropical grasslands are, in general, lacking, and in many areas it would be necessary to produce, by crossing European with Zebu types of cattle, breeds which would be both suited to the climatic conditions and commercially profitable.

Dairy cattle

Milk. Almost all of the world's peoples are accustomed to drink milk from one kind of animal or another. The Lapp, for instance, drinks reindeer milk, the Kirghiz mare's milk, and the Indian peasant buffalo milk, but in the diet of those of us who live in

[1] Each Australian—and each New Zealander—consumes in an average year three times as much beef as an Englishman.

[2] The disease is actually caused by a parasite (*trypanosoma*) carried inside the fly. Preventive measures include the inoculation of cattle by the drug antricide and the use of aircraft for spraying vegetation with insecticides. Other stock diseases in Africa are rinderpest, anthrax, redwater, East Coast fever, and also a form of 'foot and mouth' disease.

more advanced communities one of the most essential items is cow's milk. The present consumption of fresh milk per head of population in the United Kingdom is very nearly half a litre (1 pint) per day. In Switzerland and New Zealand consumption is somewhat higher, and in France and Australia rather less than this, but in all countries with a modern 'European' way of life it is approximately the same.

In all such countries there has been, during the last thirty years or so, a noticeable increase in the amount of fresh milk consumed, and although no actual figures are available, other records indicate that our ancestors two hundred years ago drank far less milk than we do ourselves. The steady increase over the last two centuries is very largely due to the introduction to mid-latitude lands of tea and coffee, both of which normally require the addition of milk. Until tea and coffee became everyday drinks of the mass of the people, the commonest beverages were home-made wines and beers.

The sudden and more spectacular rise in the consumption of fresh milk, which began about forty years ago, is due to the increasing realisation of its food value. In the 1920s there was no such thing as 'school milk', and there were no nationwide campaigns (e.g. 'drinka pinta milka day') to encourage people to drink more milk. Nor was so much trouble taken to ensure that milk should be perfectly pure and free from any kind of contamination. Nowadays, most governments lay down stringent regulations controlling the conditions under which milk may be produced and sold. In Britain for instance, it is illegal to buy or sell milk 'loose'; it must first pass through certain sterilisation processes in an approved dairy and be delivered to the consumer in closed bottles. It is also possible to buy pasteurised[1] milk (which, in order to kill any harmful bacteria, has been kept at a temperature of 63° C (145° F) for at least half an hour), or TT (tuberculin tested) milk, which comes from special herds tested at frequent intervals by government inspectors to make sure that they are not suffering from bovine tuberculosis. Yet only a few decades ago milk was carried from door to door in a large can and ladled by the milkman into a jug left on the doorstep!

Milk-producing areas. Milk is a highly perishable commodity and the concentration of population in urban centres which took place as a result of the Industrial Revolution posed a serious problem, to which under the existing conditions there could be only one answer—the development of areas of intensive farming, with milk production as the primary object, close enough to the

[1] 'Pasteurisation' is so called after its inventor, the famous French chemist, Louis Pasteur (1822–95), who also invented vaccines.

Fig. 20 The butter-making room at Seale Hayne Agricultural College, Newton Abbot, Devon. Traditional hand-operated churns are shown side by side with modern butter-making equipment driven by electricity. Cream, which occupies about one-third of the churn, is agitated with each revolution, and, in due course, the fat particles in the cream combine to form butter, leaving a thin, watery substance, known as butter-milk.

centres of population for fresh milk to be delivered daily. But, as in the case of market garden produce, modern conditions have brought many changes. Milking is now very largely mechanised, and in some areas pipelines are used for the transport of milk. Ideally, dairy cattle require mild, wet climatic conditions which encourage the growth not only of lush natural pasture, but also of fodder crops for stall-feeding the animals in winter. Such conditions are not always attained, however, in view of the over-riding consideration of demand. Much of the land in south-eastern England, for instance, where rainfall is under 750 mm (30 in) a year, has been devoted to dairy farming in preference to the cultivation of grain on account of London's pressing need for daily supplies of fresh milk.

Butter, cheese and other dairy products. Not all of the dairy farming areas are situated near centres of population. Certain regions of the mid-latitude zones, where the climate is suitable, produce milk far in excess of their own local requirements. This cannot, in the circumstances, be sold as fresh milk, but, provided markets and adequate transport facilities exist, it becomes a worth-while 'export' in some less perishable form, such as butter or cheese (fig. 20). In England, Devon and Cornwall, which are situated too far from the densely populated areas to concentrate on the production of fresh milk, specialise in making butter, cheese and their own particular kinds of 'clotted cream'. The American states of Wisconsin, Iowa and Minnesota are similarly situated and produce butter and cheese for the industrial regions of the east coast. With the exception of the USA and Russia, the industrial nations have little milk to spare for the manufacture of other forms of dairy produce after their requirements of fresh milk have been met. But under modern conditions they can draw supplies from countries in which the manufacture of dairy products for export forms an integral part of the national economy.

Denmark provides the most remarkable example of organisation on this scale. Her attempts about one hundred years ago to make good the wheat deficiencies of the rising industrial countries of Europe were frustrated by the introduction of cheap grain from the prairies. A switch to beef production followed, but the competition provided by refrigerated meat from the New World proved too great, and by the early years of the present century the resourceful Danes had already begun—with determination and considerable ingenuity—to mould the pattern of their present national economy. Denmark's dairy farming technique, which includes the 'cooperative' system (see p. 157) for the purchase of feeding-stuffs and the preparation and marketing of the produce, has become a model for similar schemes in other parts of the world. Denmark contributes one-quarter of the world's exports of butter, and considerable quantities of bacon are produced from pigs fed on the skimmed milk left over from butter making.

In the *Netherlands* the rearing of dairy cattle depends more on the excellent pastures provided by grasses cultivated on the *polders* ('reclaimed' lands formerly under water) than on specially grown or imported fodder crops, as in Denmark. Large amounts of butter are manufactured, but the Netherlands specialises in cheeses, such as the famous Edam and Gouda.

In *Switzerland* nearly three-quarters of the available agricultural land is devoted to dairy cattle. Great enterprise is displayed by the Swiss, who take every advantage of the moist climate and utilise to the full the fertile mountain pastures in the practice of transhumance (see pp. 158–9). The milk is made into cheese, used in the manufacture of chocolate or turned into evaporated or condensed milk in such factories as those of the Nestlé Company. In this process much of the water which milk contains is driven off by heating, sugar is (sometimes) added and the product is sealed in tins. Nowadays world production of condensed milk is surprisingly large; much of it goes to tropical countries, which are deficient in butter. If all the water is driven off by evaporation, dried or powdered milk remains, for which there is a wide demand for the manufacture of patent foods for babies and invalids, confectionery and ice cream.

The warm, moist lowlands of North Island of *New Zealand* provide excellent conditions for the rearing of dairy cattle, and although situated so far away from consuming centres, New Zealand is able to compete successfully in the world's markets (chiefly Britain). This is primarily due to the efficiency of her methods and modern techniques of refrigeration. Although she no longer enjoys the advantages of 'Commonwealth preference', her produce has been guaranteed entry into Common Market countries until at least 1977.

Australia, too, has a considerable surplus of butter for export, from the dairy farming regions along the south-east coast. Some idea of the importance of butter in the national economy may be gained from the fact that, when, soon after the outbreak of war in 1939, shipping was no longer available, the Australian government appealed to its people to eat, if possible, 3 lb of butter each per week, to use up accumulated stocks. In Britain butter was rationed!

One further product of the dairy industry may be mentioned here—*casein*, which is a constituent of skimmed milk. It was one of the first raw materials to be used in the manufacture of plastics (see pp. 246–7), and is now used in a number of other industries, for making paper and patent medicines, for instance.

Sheep

World distribution of sheep (fig. 21)
Sheep eat grass, not like cattle by tearing it up with their tongues, but by nibbling at it with their teeth. They thrive best, therefore, where the grass is short and crisp, as in the mid-latitude or 'temperate' regions; tropical grass is too long and tough. Moreover, when conditions underfoot are permanently damp, their hoofs are liable to a disease known as foot-rot. The ideal climate for sheep is one in which the rainfall is moderate and evenly distributed throughout the year, but they also flourish in highland areas with a heavy rainfall where drainage is promoted by sloping ground. The mid-latitude grasslands of the northern hemisphere, although highly suitable in many respects, suffer from long, cold winters,

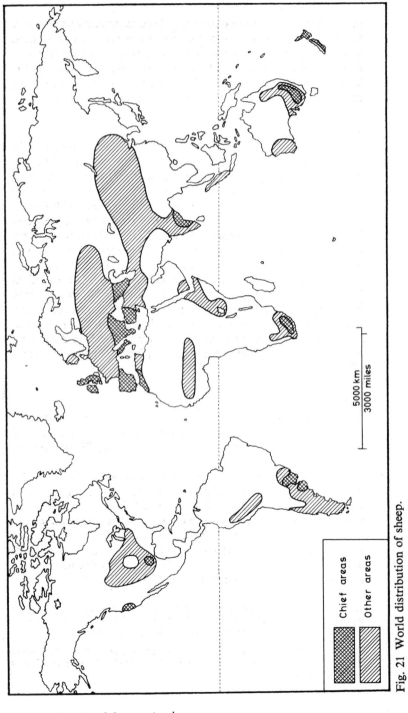

5000 km
3000 miles

Chief areas

Other areas

Fig. 21 World distribution of sheep.

in which it would be impossible for sheep to remain out of doors, but in the veld, pampas and downs of the Southern Hemisphere, which enjoy milder winter conditions, there is no such restriction. It is also of importance that sheep do well on land which is too high for the growth of cereals, too dry or too steep for the rearing of cattle or too inaccessible for the spread of population.

Types and uses of sheep
Sheep are the most numerous of all the domestic animals. The number fluctuates from year to year, but the world total usually exceeds 1 000 million. They are reared chiefly for their wool (which will be considered in more detail in Chapter 10) and for their meat. Their milk is of little commercial importance, although in some areas of southern Europe it is made into cheese (e.g. Roquefort cheese from the Central Plateau of France). Broadly speaking, types which yield the finest and heaviest fleeces are the product of warm dry environments, while the plump, mutton-producing varieties are found in cool, damp conditions. Many of the modern breeds of sheep are the result of 'improvements' which began in England in the nineteenth century, and in more recent years a great deal of very successful cross-breeding has taken place, as a result of which 'dual-purpose' animals yielding both wool and mutton have been produced. Typical examples of breeds of sheep are illustrated in fig. 22.

The world's mutton
Two countries have a particular interest in world trade—Britain, in that she takes 72 per cent of the world's exports of mutton and lamb,[1] and New Zealand, in that she produces 70 per cent of them.

In the *United Kingdom* consumption of mutton is 9 kg (20 lb) per head per year—higher than in any other country of the world except Australia and New Zealand.[2] The British taste for mutton is not surprising, since sheep have for centuries been important in the country's farming, and it was in Britain that breeds of sheep were produced which were later to form the basis of commercial flocks in other parts of the world. Today many sheep are reared especially for export as pedigree animals.

[1] Strictly speaking, 'lamb' is the meat produced by sheep up to eight months old, and 'mutton' by sheep over that age. The distinction is always made in butchers' shops, but only rarely in economic statistics.

[2] In the United States and Canada consumption per head of the population is only about one-seventh that in Britain. The Dutch, Belgians and Danes eat hardly any.

Fig. 22 Typical breeds of sheep. 1. Rough Fell. 2. Lincoln Longwool.
3. Merino. 4. Black Welsh. 5. Border Leicester. 6. Blackface.

Sheep occupy the wet highland regions of Scotland, the
Pennines, the Lake District and Wales, and the dry chalk-lands
of south-eastern England; and they also form an integral part
of rotation farming in lowland areas. There is some specialisation
in either wool or mutton in certain regions, but many well-known
breeds (such as Lincolns, Leicesters and Southdowns) are dual-
purpose animals.

Production of mutton and lamb is not large enough to satisfy
home demands, but this is of no great consequence, since further

supplies can be imported from Argentina, Australia and, in particular, New Zealand.

In the economy of *New Zealand*, where they outnumber the population by twenty-one to one, sheep are of very great importance. The natural vegetation over a wide extent of the Canterbury Plains behind Christchurch has during the last hundred years been cleared, and grasses have been specially sown on which graze 'Corriedale' sheep, obtained by crossing Merino[1] ewes with Leicester or Lincoln rams. Although wool forms a useful byproduct, the sheep are reared primarily to supply lamb to markets which, but for refrigeration, would be far out of New Zealand's reach. The inspection, grading and general preparation of the carcasses is as highly organised as in the beef industry of Argentina, and the fact that in Britain, for instance, what was until recently described as 'Canterbury lamb' can compete in price and quality with home-produced meat is a high tribute to the efficiency of the industry. After her overseas customers have been supplied, New Zealand has enough lamb remaining to enable each member of her population to eat 34 kg (75 lb) per year.

Sheep in the USA, Australia and the mid-latitude grasslands of South America are reared chiefly for wool, but mutton is also

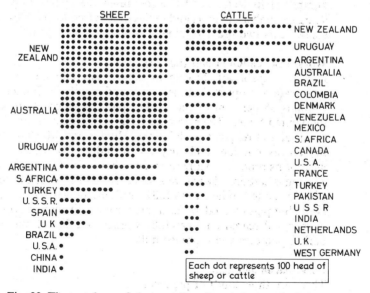

Fig. 23 The numbers of sheep and cattle per thousand of the population in selected countries.

[1] *Merino*—a breed of sheep which originated in the semi-desert areas of North Africa; more valuable for its wool than its meat (see p. 130).

produced in sufficient quantities to satisfy local requirements, and also, in the case of Australia and Argentina, to provide a valuable export.

Some indication of the comparative importance of cattle and sheep in the economy of certain selected countries may be gained from Fig. 23.

Pigs

The pig is a distant relation of the hippopotamus, and the wild pig or boar is a very ferocious animal. It was first domesticated in early times by the Chinese, who had always been very fond of pork, but in Britain the taste for pig-meat did not develop until after 1800, when pigs were introduced from China and the Mediterranean countries. As in the case of sheep and cattle, improvements have been carried out in the existing breeds, and modern types of pig which are important commercially are essentially the result of crossing imported animals with British wild boars. It is interesting that domestication has produced some quite remarkable changes in the pig; it has not only reduced the number of its teeth, but has also caused the female to produce a larger number of young and to litter more frequently. Nowadays a sow bears two litters of nine to twelve pigs each year.

World distribution of pigs (fig. 24)

Pigs are capable of thriving in almost any climate from cool temperate to tropical, but they are found mainly in China (which contains 35 per cent of the world's pigs), northern Europe and the United States. Their absence from many areas is largely due to social and religious prohibitions. Hindus and Muslims regard the pig as unclean, and they are forbidden to partake of its meat or its products in any form. Jews have a similar prohibition. The pig is certainly by nature a scavenger and a voracious feeder, and can be fed quite successfully on domestic garbage and 'pig-swill', but pigs on modern farms are far more likely to be confined in sties and reared on a carefully worked out diet of maize, rye, barley, potatoes and skimmed milk.

Pork, bacon and ham

There are three kinds of pig-meat:

1. *Fresh pork* undergoes no treatment except possibly refrigeration before it appears in the shops.
2. *Bacon* is meat from the body of the pig, which has been 'cured' (i.e. soaked in brine and then dried), and also, perhaps, 'smoked'.

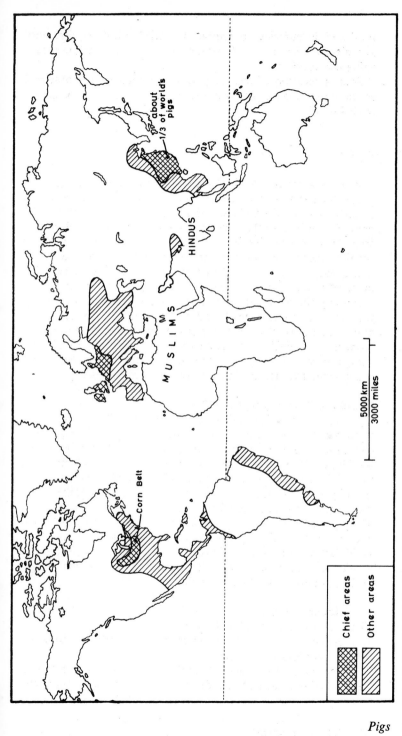

Fig. 24 World distribution of pigs.

Within the map:
- about 1/3 of world's pigs
- HINDUS
- MUSLIMS
- Corn Belt
- 5000 km / 3000 miles

Legend:
- Chief areas
- Other areas

3. *Ham* is meat from the upper part of the leg, which has been both cured and smoked.

Most of the pig-meat which enters into international trade is in the form of bacon and ham, although the export of refrigerated pork is increasing.

World production of pig-meat in all its forms is five times that of mutton and lamb. Consumption per head of the population is highest in the USA, Canada and Denmark, amounting to about 32 kg (70 lb) a year, while in the United Kingdom rather more bacon, ham and pork combined are eaten than mutton.

Producing areas

Since pigs can profitably use so many of the agricultural 'left-overs', they are found on most farms in Europe and North America, but in certain areas pig-keeping has become a specialised occupation. It is, for instance, a very important industry in the Corn Belt of the *USA*, where most of the meat needed to satisfy the American predilection for pork, bacon and ham is produced by fattening pigs on the local maize. Like the beef in this region, a great deal of the pig-meat is packed in tins as 'canned' or 'chopped pork'. At one time there was a large export of ham and bacon, chiefly to Britain, but today almost all of the American surplus leaves the country in the form of lard (the melted fat of the pig).

In northern Europe pig-raising on a large scale is closely allied to the dairying industry. In *Denmark*, for example, pigs are fed on the skimmed milk left after the cream has been removed for butter making or on the whey which remains when the curds (the raw material of cheese) have formed as a result of treating milk with a mild acid. Both of these give the fat of the bacon an attractive white colour. Here, as well as in other countries, such as the *Netherlands* and *New Zealand*, where dairying is a major occupation, ham and bacon are produced mainly for export.

Poultry

The term 'poultry' includes such domesticated 'farmyard' birds as ordinary fowls, geese, ducks and turkeys. The fowl is thought to have originated from the Indian jungle-fowl, and is found widespread throughout the world; the turkey, which exists in the wild state in North America from Canada to Mexico, is known to have been first domesticated in Europe in the early sixteenth century. The turkey is less hardy than the fowl the young being particularly susceptible to damp, and, for this reason, most of the turkeys which form part of the Christmas celebrations in Britain are reared in the drier counties of Norfolk and Suffolk.

Poultry meat was at one time less important than other forms of meat, largely on account of its price, but the modern method of mass-producing chickens in confinement (the so-called 'broiler-house' system) has led to a greatly increased consumption. At present each member of the British population eats 7 kg (16 lb) of poultry per annum, twice as much as in 1960. Even so, the American eats considerably more. Trade in poultry is limited in amount, and most of the birds are exported alive, chiefly from Eire, Denmark, the Netherlands, Hungary and Australia.

Perhaps the main reason for the presence of fowls on almost every farm is the fact that hens produce a large number of eggs. Hens which are kept on special poultry farms each lay over 300 eggs a year on the average. Improvements in transport and refrigeration have led to a great increase in world trade in eggs and also in consumption. Nowadays in Britain 250 eggs are eaten annually per head, and in the United States 400. The chief exporters are the Netherlands and Denmark. Eggs which are destined for household use are refrigerated in their shells, but the eggs used by confectioners reach the factories and bakeries in liquid form, shelled and packed in tins.

4

FOOD FROM THE SEA

Fishing

Fishing is really a form of hunting, and almost as soon as man learned to pursue his prey on land, he discovered, too, that the lakes and seas contained creatures which would serve to augment his food supply. We have seen in the two previous chapters, in considering the use which man has made of the grasses and the land animals, that there has been throughout the ages a continuous process of replacement and improvement. But fishing is a 'robber economy', in which man takes and uses without thought for the morrow. In later chapters, in dealing with the mining of coal, petroleum and other minerals, and the cutting down of timber, we shall come across other types of robber economy. Fishing differs from these in that, so far, Nature has been able to replenish supplies of fish as quickly as man has been able to remove them from the seas and oceans, but modern methods of fishing have become so efficient that thought is now being given to the possibility of exhaustion. This is a matter of considerable importance, since a very large proportion of the world's food[1] is derived from the sea, and fish, like meat, is a source of body-building protein.

Plankton

Oceans, seas and lakes make up 71 per cent of the earth's surface, but, as with the land, their fertility varies. From the fisherman's point of view, they range, as a recent writer has said, from 'sterile deserts to luxuriant pastures'. Most fish feed on plankton—minute particles of animal and plant life, which are particularly abundant in shallow water near to the land masses; where warm and cold currents meet; and where an upwelling of cold water occurs. Situations where the continental shelf is wide provide excellent conditions in which fish can live and breed. Since the water in such areas is no more than 180 m (600 ft) deep, sunlight can

[1] About 63 million tons of fish are caught every year. This is equivalent to 80 per cent of the world's production of meat of all kinds.

penetrate to the sea floor on which the fish spawn, and the movements of water with the rise and fall of the tide help to carry the plankton outwards from the land. Although fish of one sort or another are found in all parts of the seas and oceans, and at almost every depth, they are naturally most plentiful in areas such as these.

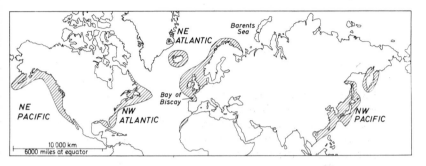

Fig. 25 The chief commercial fishing grounds of the Northern Hemisphere. The only considerable ground in the Southern Hemisphere as yet is off Peru, whose fishing industry, almost non-existent in 1940, has expanded so rapidly that in weight of catch she is now the world's leading producer. Most of Peru's catch is anchoveta, which is made into fishmeal and fertilisers. Deep-sea fishing off the Falkland Islands and off South-west Africa promises in the near future to be of considerable importance. Reference should be made to Fig. 167, p. 306, which shows the world's most densely populated areas.

The general distribution of fishing grounds

The most highly developed fishing grounds are found in the north-western and north-eastern Atlantic and the north-western and north-eastern Pacific (fig. 25). The fertility of these areas of sea is not by itself sufficient to explain the fact that they have become the centres of great commercial fisheries. In times past the inhabitants of certain of the bordering lands were driven by lack of good agricultural lowland to look to the sea for part of their food, while indented coasts provided sheltered anchorage for boats and calm waters on which they acquired a familiarity with the sea and its ways. Japan, Norway, Brittany and Newfoundland all provide examples of environments in which such conditions existed. The original necessity for augmenting the food supply with fish may well have become in time little more than a taste for fish, but, with the growth of dense industrial populations as potential markets, and with developments in lagd transport which made it possible for the catch to be distributed with speed and efficiency, the opportunity was provided for fishind to be carried on extensively and profitably.

Types of fish

The various parts of the hydrosphere differ also in the type of fish they contain. Tropical waters contain many different kinds, which in China and India, for example, supplement the normal diet of the people, but there are no large-scale fisheries such as we find in mid-latitude regions, where fewer species exist. Here the fish are of two main kinds:

1. *Pelagic*[1] fish, such as herrings, mackerels and pilchards, live near the surface and 'migrate' during the year along more or less well defined routes. Of the world's total catch, 25 per cent belongs to this type.

2. *Demersal*[1] fish, such as cod, haddock, whiting, halibut, plaice and sole, live near the bottom of the shallow seas, and do not as a rule move far from their usual feeding grounds. These make up 11 per cent of the world's catch.

Salmon are *anadromous* fish, which, although they live in the sea, swim into the fresh water of rivers every two or three years to spawn.

Methods of catching fish

Throughout the world many different ways of catching fish are used. They are caught by means of spears, bows and arrows, bags, nets and traps and even, near the mouth of the Danube, by draining away the water and leaving the fish stranded! But in the great commercial fisheries the devices in general use are:

1. *Drift nets*. These are used for catching pelagic fish. They are laid down by small ships appropriately called 'drifters', carrying a crew of nine or ten men, and the nets hang like vast curtains a few metres below the surface of the water (fig. 26). The gills of the fish become entangled in the meshes of the nets.

2. *Seine nets*. These are similar to drift nets except that each end of the seine net is attached to a ship specially built for the purpose. As the net fills up, the ships draw closer together, so as to enclose the fish in a kind of bag. The seine net is used principally near the shore, and is considered to be more efficient than the drift net.

3. *Trawls*. These consist of large cone-shaped bags made of netting, which are kept open by 'otter boards' and dragged by 'trawlers' along the bed of the sea at about 8 kph (5 mph) to catch the 'bottom' or demersal fish (fig. 27). Trawlers are bigger than drifters and hold upwards of twenty men.

4. *Lines*. Where rocks on the sea floor would be likely to damage the trawls, baited lines are used instead. At one time it was common practice to send out from a base ship a number of

[1] *Pelagic*—from the Greek word *pelagos*, meaning 'sea'.
[1] *Demersal*—from Latin *de*, meaning 'down', and *mare*, meaning 'sea'.

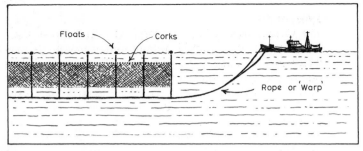

Fig. 26 Drift-net fishing. The size of the mesh is controlled by international agreement, so that young fish may pass through the net.

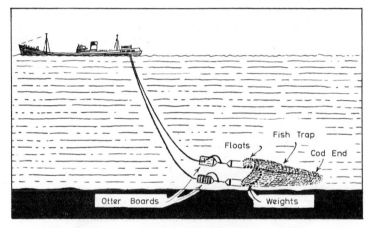

Fig. 27 Trawl fishing.

rowing boats, each trailing over a thousand lines, but the use of small subsidiary boats is now on the decline, since it is wasteful of manpower.

Much of the success of the above operations depends on the experience of the skipper of a craft in choosing the best places in which to let out his drift nets or trawls. In recent years, however, the invention of Asdic and echo-sounding apparatus has made it much easier for him to locate the shoals. Steam and diesel oil have in turn replaced sail, and many modern vessels, such as those belonging to the big fishing combines, are extremely well-equipped, and include crews' quarters which exceed in comfort and convenience the wildest dreams of fishermen half a century ago. Such vessels stay at sea for much longer periods than was at one time customary—often for two months at a time.

Nowadays many vessels are equipped with special machinery for gutting and filleting, for converting the offal into fish-meal and for keeping the fish fillets in cold storage. With the increasing popularity of domestic deep freezers, much of the fish is now sold in packaged form to frozen food suppliers.

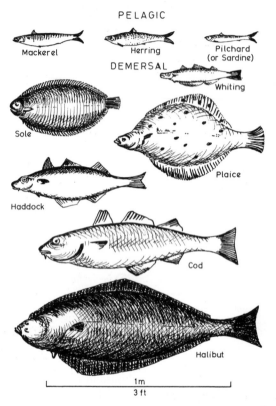

Fig. 28. Some of the main types of fish caught in the fishing grounds of the north-eastern Atlantic.

Salmon, which are the chief freshwater fish of commerce, are caught in the rivers, when they come to spawn, by means of traps of string- or wire-netting, and sometimes by trawls or seine nets. Dams, where the water is held up for the generation of hydro-electricity, can seriously affect salmon fishing, unless some means is provided, such as a fish-ladder, by which the salmon can surmount the walls of a dam. Considerable progress has, however, been made in artificially introducing spawn to river to form 'salmon-hatcheries'.

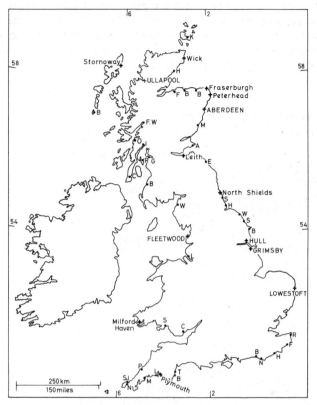

Fig. 29 The chief fishing ports of the British Isles. Major fishing ports are named in capitals, other important centres in small print. Some minor ports are indicated by dots and the initial letters of their names; their full names should be traced with the help of an atlas.

The world's chief fishing areas

North-eastern Atlantic. One of the most productive areas of sea in the world is that which covers the continental shelf from the Barents Sea to the Bay of Biscay. Here, as well as in the waters around Iceland, there is great activity by the fishing fleets of Norway, France, Russia, West Germany, Iceland and the United Kingdom. Figure 28 shows the main types of fish caught in the various parts of the area.

It will be seen from fig. 29 that in *Britain* the chief fishing ports are situated on the east coast, close to the North Sea, which is the most abundant source of supply. Apart from these, numerous small fishing villages exist, particularly in the sheltered inlets of Cornwall and the south-west, which provide a sharp

Fig. 30 Fishing boats unloading their catch of herring at Ullapool in north-western Scotland.

contrast in size, prosperity and importance to the east coast ports. Whereas the east coast fisheries are nearer to the industrial centres and are now very largely controlled by companies with sufficient capital to provide up-to-date vessels and equipment, those in the south-west have no markets close at hand and are, in general, made up of a number of much smaller units—often family concerns—with less adequate financial backing. Moreover, in the warmer waters of the south-west a great variety of fish is caught, for some of which there is so little demand that it is, in fact, thrown back into the sea. The fisheries of Devon and Cornwall are thus at a disadvantage compared with those of the east coast, where all of the catch is readily saleable.

In the British catch cod, halibut, hake, whiting, plaice, sole and mackerel are well represented, but a large proportion of the fish landed consists of herrings. Before 1950 most herring landed at British ports were caught in the North Sea; since then a great decline has taken place in this area, probably caused by over-fishing and the lack of any international agreement in the limitation of catches. In this connection it is interesting to notice that during this century the best seasons were 1919 and 1945, following periods of war when the fish had been allowed to multiply. Today 90 per cent of the herring catch comes from the waters between the Outer Hebrides and the Scottish mainland. Ullapool has become a major fishing port and the herring are sent by road to the long-established processing factories at Fraserburgh, Peterhead, Aberdeen and other East Coast ports. Most of the herrings are consumed within the country, either fresh or 'smoked' as kippers or bloaters, but there is a surplus available for export. Great Yarmouth no longer has its own fishing fleet, but remains the chief centre for 'kippering'.

The greater part of *Norway's* catch, composed principally of cod, herrings and brisling (a small herring-like fish), is exported. Bergen is the chief fishing centre, and Stavanger claims to have the largest fish-canning installations in the world. The economy of *Iceland* is vitally dependent on her fishing fleet, which now brings in over 700 000 tons a year. This is the main reason why the country took such a firm stand to preserve unusually wide fishing limits (see p. 65).

Off *France, Spain* and *Portugal* pilchards, sardines, anchovies and a number of other smaller fish are found, while in the Mediterranean Sea the tunny—which sometimes reaches a length of 3 m (10 ft) or more—forms part of the Sicilian and Sardinian catch.

North-western Atlantic. Off *Newfoundland* and the east coast of the *USA* are a number of 'banks' built up by the deposition of sediment from melting icebergs where warm and cold currents meet. The water over these banks is a mere 50 fathoms (90 m) or so in depth, and is immensely rich, particularly in cod. Norwegian, Norman, Breton and Basque fishermen almost certainly visited the banks hundreds of years before the discovery of America by Columbus. Cod-fishing is a vital part of Newfoundland's economy, and large quantities of fish were at one time exported, dried or cured, to the Catholic countries of the Mediterranean area. Nowadays most of it is frozen and sent to the United States and the rest of Canada. Newfoundland's economic and financial difficulties, which in 1949 culminated in her becoming the tenth province of Canada, were to a great extent the result of her heavy dependence on fishing.

North-eastern Pacific. The area of sea off the western shores of America from Alaska to California is said to be the richest halibut ground in the world, and contains, in addition, such fish as herrings, cod and sardines. It is, however, chiefly important for salmon, caught in the Fraser, Columbia, Sacramento, Skeena and scores of other rivers. The salmon are so easily trapped on their journey upstream to the spawning grounds, and the export of canned salmon is so profitable, that there has in the past been considerable over-fishing, with the result that stocks have been sadly depleted. Moreover, the erection of dams for power stations and irrigation, and the blocking of streams in lumbering operations have often prevented the salmon from reaching the spawning grounds at all. Yet in spite of this, salmon represent almost half of the fish caught in the area, and the canning industry sends immense quantities of tinned salmon to Britain and Australia.

North-western Pacific. With her dense population and mountainous country, where so little of the land is suitable for agriculture, *Japan* relies to an enormous extent on the products of her fisheries. Her annual catch from the neighbouring waters amounts to nearly 9 million tons, and although much of her fishing is carried out in small boats and with primitive equipment, many modern vessels are in operation, and organisation is on the whole extremely efficient. The fish in the northern aters waround Sakhalin are similar in type to those around the shores of Britain, but in the warmer waters to the south the catch displays great variety, and includes sardines, tunny and bonito.

Fisheries in other parts of the world, although sometimes of local importance, are in no way comparable with those of the main areas described above. *Russia* participates in the fishing of the North Atlantic and North Pacific, while some of her catch is derived from the inland fisheries of the Caspian and Black Seas, where, among other species, are found bream, anchovies, herrings, salmon and sturgeon, the roes of which form caviare. Fishing in the Great Lakes of North America has now almost ceased, because of pollution, especially in Lakes Erie and Michigan. At one time the fish were caught solely for use as fertiliser! The people of *Australia* are far less interested in fish than in meat, but a small fishing industry, almost exclusively in the hands of Greeks, is carried on in the waters off the south-eastern coasts, and some fish is imported from New Zealand. *Peru* now has the largest fishing industry in the world by weight of catch but not by value (see fig. 25). Other notable countries in the Southern Hemisphere are the Republic of South Africa, South-west Africa and Angola; but commercial fisheries are in general absent not through lack of fish, but from lack of densely populated areas which would provide markets for the catch.

Other products of the sea

Whales

The whale is the largest creature in existence. It is not a fish, but a marine mammal, and is of considerable importance in the modern world, since it helps to provide a wide range of products from lubricants and margarine to cosmetics and vitamins. Whales are equipped with a thick layer of fat or 'blubber' below the skin, which yields an oil known as train-oil.[1] Before the discovery of petroleum oils, this was in general use as a lamp fuel, and during the nineteenth century whales were hunted so persistently by Norwegians, British and Americans that in the northern Atlantic and northern Pacific Oceans they were very nearly exterminated. New uses have, however, been found for whale products, and nowadays expeditions (notably from Britain, Japan and, till recently, Norway) concentrate on the Antarctic waters in search of the biggest of all the various species of whales—the blue whale.

Modern whaling involves few of the dangers and adventures recounted in Herman Melville's *Moby Dick*, and under present-day conditions the whale has, in fact, so little chance of escape that the nations interested in whaling have eventually been forced to come to an agreement, which restricts the length of the hunting season to the period from January to April and sets a quota of 'blue whale units' which may be caught in any one season. The whales are tracked by spotter aircraft, Asdic and echo-sounding apparatus, chased by small 'catcher-ships', and killed by harpoons loaded with explosive and shot from a special gun. The carcasses are then towed back to a centrally placed factory ship where they are swiftly dissected, and the blubber, flesh and bones are processed in rows of boilers below deck. Eventually the fleets of whaling vessels return to base, and the products are distributed all over the world.

The whale oil (or train-oil), which is still the most valuable of the products and amounts to about 10 tons per whale, is used in the manufacture of soap, margarine and lubricants, the bones and flesh are turned into fertilisers, and vitamin-extract is made from the whale's liver. Sperm-oil,[2] which comes from a species of 'toothed' whale, is used in cold cream and cosmetics. The flesh is sometimes used also as fodder, and in Japan refrigerated whale-meat is eaten by humans. The present quota (which is so frequently disregarded that some varieties are in danger of extinction) permits the annual destruction of about 30 000 whales, the products of each one of which amount in value to well over £1 000.

Seals
Another sea mammal which has narrowly escaped extermination is the seal. This, too, was at one time hunted for train-oil, but

---

[1] Nothing to do with railways: 'train-oil' is derived from the Dutch word *traan*, meaning 'oil'.

[2] This is more of a wax than an oil.

it is nowadays killed for its fur and for its pelt, which is used in making such things as saddles for motor cycles, while insulin from the seal's liver is used in treating diabetes. The Pribilov Islands, 320 km (200 miles) west of the Alaska Peninsula, contain about 85 per cent. of the world's fur seals. Hunting in the Islands is now restricted to Americans.

Pearl oysters

These are found in shallow water off the coasts of northern Australia, Ceylon (Sri Lanka) and southern Japan. They are removed from the rocks on the sea bed and brought to the surface by divers (almost all of whom are Japanese), in the hope that they may contain pearls. Actually, this is quite a rare occurrence, but the shells and their inner lining (mother-of-pearl) find a ready market in Japan, where they are made into pearl buttons and used in decorating boxes and as ornaments.

Shellfish

Crustaceans (that is crabs, lobsters, prawns, shrimps, etc.) and *molluscs* (oysters, mussels, clams, etc.) are classed as 'shellfish', although they are not, of course, fish in the proper sense. They are taken from 'beds' in shallow water close to rocky coasts in many parts of the world. Total production amounts to about one-tenth of all the fish caught. In general shellfish supply only local markets, but nowadays shellfish from Chesapeake Bay, from lagoons along the Gulf Coast and from the coastal waters of Oregon, New England and the Canadian Maritime Provinces are distributed throughout almost the whole of North America.

Sponges

Sponges are the skeletons of animals which live in sea water, and attach themselves to the rocks of the sea bed. The best toilet sponges are found over a wide area of the eastern Mediterranean, down to a depth of 200 fathoms (360 m). They are obtained in favourable situations by diving and dredging.

Seaweed

There are thousands of different varieties of seaweed (as, indeed, of sponges), some of which are used—in Japan, for example—as human food. Many shore-dwellers (such as those in Brittany) have for long been accustomed to use seaweed as fertiliser, and at one time it was the world's chief source of iodine.

Minerals

A number of important mineral salts are obtained from the sea.

Chief of these is sodium chloride or common salt, which in many parts of the world is extracted by the simple process of evaporation; and the Dead Sea, which has a greater salinity than any other body of water, is particularly rich in the potassium bromide familiar to photographers. Owing to the difficulty of obtaining elsewhere supplies of magnesium for the aircraft industry, a method of extraction from sea water was devised during the war. The seas and oceans contain vast quantities of many other minerals, but magnesium and bromine (used in photography and medicine) are, as yet, the only ones which it has been possible to extract on a commercial scale.

International control

In the past the acquisition of the resources of the sea was in the nature of a general scramble, in which everyone grabbed as much as he could without giving any thought to the possibility that one day the resources on which he depended might cease to exist. The only limitation lay in the fact that territorial waters within the 'three-mile limit' were agreed under international law to be the private prerogative of the nationals concerned. Recently there has been much dispute between the nations of north-western Europe over fishing limits. In the negotiations which preceded Britain's joining the Common Market the possibility of European fishermen having access to British waters caused much hard feeling among the fishermen of Cornwall, for example. And in 1973 a 'cod war' was in progress in which Iceland tried by a show of force to prevent British trawlers operating within 80 km (50 miles) of her coast. Agreement has now been reached.

The shadow of impending shortage caused by overfishing first appeared over the whaling industry, and spread to the salmon grounds of the north-eastern Pacific. By 1939 the situation was becoming serious, but during the war stocks of fish in the sea were given a little respite while fishermen were otherwise engaged. After the war the onslaught was renewed with the aid of scientific methods of detection and more efficient means of catching the fish. It is clear that present-day investigations into the breeding and migration habits of fish must not lead to further indiscriminate slaughter, but must form the basis on which sensible international agreement can be reached for the continued use of the resources of the seas and oceans.

5

DRINKS AND SUGAR

Water

Water is the simplest and most essential of all drinks, and we who live in modern communities assume that the supply is both pure and unlimited. But in times past this would not have been true—nor, indeed, is it true in certain parts of the world today.

Drinking water is obtained from various sources, such as springs, rivers, wells and reservoirs, and contains a variety of mineral salts derived from the rocks over and through which it has passed since the time when it fell from the atmosphere as rain, snow or hail. Many of these salts are quite harmless, and some of them are considered so beneficial that spas have grown up where people suffering from rheumatism or other complaints can 'take the waters'. But water is so easily contaminated by bacteria from animal and other refuse that nowadays great care is taken to ensure that all taint of infection has been removed by filtering and treating with chemicals. Many of the 'plagues' recorded in history were due to the drinking of polluted water.

Campers who have to rely on springs and streams for their supply of water realise how important it is to boil water before drinking it. But water which has been boiled is less 'tasty' than unboiled water, and there may well be some truth in the suggestion that we owe the discovery of tea to a wise Chinese mandarin, who sought to encourage his people to drink boiled water by urging them to flavour it with leaves from the tea plant. The drinking of wine in Mediterranean countries was originally due not only to the prevalence of grapes, but also to the possible impurity of water, and not so long ago in England light beers were given even to children in preference to water.

Nor is water always as plentiful and cheap as we, in well-watered lands, assume it to be. At one stage, gold-miners in Western Australia were prepared to pay almost as much for drinking water as they would otherwise have paid for the choicest wines. The fact that families in areas of dense population can turn on the tap with every confidence that water will flow is due to considerable engineering achievements and a great deal of careful planning.

Nevertheless, the problem in Britain is becoming acute. In 1830 the average daily consumption per head was 1·8 litres (4 gallons); today it is nearly 23 litres (50 gallons). Half of this is used by industry and the other half by domestic consumers. The problem is accentuated by the fact that the greater part of the population lives in large urban clusters in lowland areas, where rainfall is lowest. Existing supplies from underground sources (deep wells and bore-holes tapping artesian basins, as, for instance, under London), rivers (e.g. the Thames, the Trent and the Severn), lakes (e.g. Windermere, Thirlmere and others in the Lake District) and artificial reservoirs are proving insufficient. Various remedies have been proposed; these have mainly taken the form of additional artificial reservoirs, in some cases produced by damming and drowning whole valleys—a procedure which has met with considerable local opposition—and there have been proposals for the erection of barrages across Morecambe Bay and the Wash. Other possible solutions are the 're-use' after purification of waste water from industry and sewage works, and the desalinisation of sea water. The final comprehensive answer may well be a nationwide 'water grid' similar to those for electricity and gas.

Tea

Tea is thought to have originated in China, possibly under the conditions described on p. 66. It was introduced to England in the early seventeenth century, but did not become cheap enough to be a popular drink until two hundred years later. Now, the British, with an annual consumption of 4 kg (9 lb) per head, are the heaviest tea-drinkers in the world, and take about half the total world production. They are closely followed by the Australians, the New Zealanders and the Dutch, but the people of India and Pakistan, where a great deal of Britain's tea is produced, consume a mere 15 grammes per head.

The tea plant

The tea plant (fig. 31) is an evergreen shrub which is kept pruned to a height of approximately one metre. While it thrives best in a tropical monsoon climate, it can be found growing as far north as Poti in Russia (42° N) and as far south as Magwa in South Africa (29° S). In equatorial areas growth is continuous throughout the year, but in the northerly latitudes the growing season may

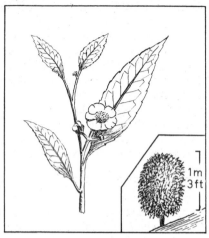

Fig. 31 Leaves of the tea plant.

be as short as five to six months. The plant can be found growing well at altitudes as high as 2 000 m (6 500 ft) in Kenya and as low as 300 m (1 000 ft) in Assam and in Argentina. Since it will not tolerate water standing over its roots, it needs to be grown on hill slopes.

Picking and processing
When the bush gives out normal growth, two or three fresh leaves and the unopened terminal bud are picked every ten to fourteen days throughout the growing season. The technical name for this new growth is a 'flush', each flush providing a slightly different quality of leaf. In China there are only three or four pickings a year, but in the equatorial areas there may be as many as twenty. Tea picking is best carried out manually, and the average tea plucker will pick about 36 kg (80 lb) of leaf per day. With such low outputs labour must be cheap and plentiful if tea is to be marketed at a reasonable price. In some areas where labour costs are high, mechanical plucking is carried out, but the quality of the tea produced suffers very considerably.

There are two main types of tea, *Indian* or 'black' tea, which is the common drink in Britain, and the more highly flavoured China or 'green' tea.

To produce black tea the leaves are first partially dehydrated in a withering process. Next comes the main processing stage, where the leaf is broken open to expose the maximum number of cells to oxidation. This permits the leaf to ferment and thus acquire the characteristic tea flavour. The enzyme causing

Fig. 32 Tea-pickers at work on a plantation in Ceylon.

fermentation is killed by drying the tea at temperatures over 100° C (212° F), a process which also reduces the moisture content of the leaf down to 3 per cent. The dried tea is then graded by size and packed into chests for shipment to the tea-drinking countries. In this condition vast quantities arrive at London Docks to be bought and sold at Sir John Lyon House, the home of the tea trade in the City of London.

China or 'green' tea is produced by applying heat to the green leaf immediately it comes in from the field, thus killing the enzyme before it has a chance to oxidise. The leaf is rolled and dried to produce a specific appearance.

Nowadays most of the world's tea is grown on large estates, and the above processes are carried out under controlled conditions in factories using electrically driven machinery.

Producing areas

Most, but not all, of the China tea comes from the Yangtse-Kiang Basin, where it is produced by peasants chiefly for local consumption, but the growth of Indian tea is carried on almost entirely on large plantations in the Assam hills of north-eastern India, Bangladesh (formerly East Pakistan) and southern India (fig. 33). Second in production to India is Sri Lanka (formerly Ceylon), where tea has been important since blight finally ruined the coffee crop in 1873.

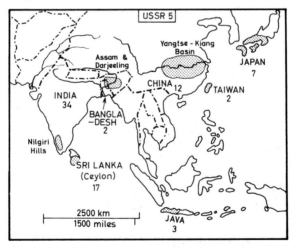

Fig. 33 The world's chief tea-growing areas. The figures indicate percentages of the world's total production of 1 267 000 tons per year. It will be noted that only less than a quarter is grown outside the above areas—chiefly in East Africa. A small amount of *yerba maté*, which is similar to tea, is grown in Paraguay and southern Brazil.

Coffee

The name 'coffee' is thought to have been derived from the district of Kafa in Ethiopia, where coffee has been used as a beverage from time immemorial. A story is told by Arabs that the drink was 'discovered' by a Muslim priest who, noticing that goats which had eaten coffee berries were restless at night, kept his subordinates awake during prayers by dosing them with an infusion made from the roasted and ground seeds. By way of Arabia and Turkey coffee made its way into Europe in the Middle Ages, and by 1700 two thousand 'coffee houses' had been opened in London. Fifty years later, most of these had been converted into clubs and taverns, and the 'bitter, black drink', as Pepys called it, was no longer obtainable only in exclusive meeting-houses, but was being served with meals in inns and at the tables of the nobility. In Britain, although coffee is now more popular than it was a century ago, consumption (1·5 kg [3½ lb]) per head annually) is well below that of tea, and is only one-ninth of the American, Belgian and Swedish consumption.

The coffee plant
The coffee plant (fig. 34) is cultivated for the first six months in a nursery, after which it is transplanted and allowed to grow

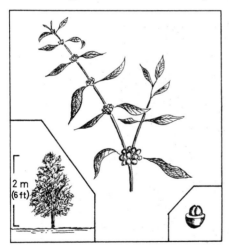

Fig. 34 Coffee berries and leaves.

to a height of 2 m (6 ft) or so, but it does not begin to bear fruit until the fourth or fifth year. It is essentially a plant of the tropical highlands, which needs abundant rainfall with a dry period at the

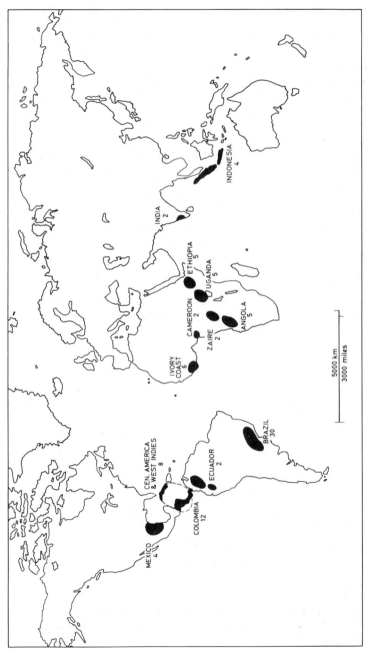

Fig. 35 The world's chief coffee-growing areas. The figures indicate percentages of the world's total production of nearly 4¼ million tons per year. Only a few years ago Brazil's output represented 50 per cent of world production. That it is now only 30 per cent is due almost entirely to the fact that Brazil grows less coffee than formerly; total world production has increased only a little during the last ten years.

time of harvest and temperatures slightly below those required by the tea plant. It is, however, much more susceptible to frost, and during its early growth cannot withstand the direct rays of the sun. In the Yemen in southern Arabia morning mists serve to protect the trees, but in many other areas of production shade is provided by interplanting taller species, such as bananas, maize, or (in Brazil) a type of pea. In due course clusters of dark red berries appear, each about the size of a cherry and containing, beneath a pulpy outer covering, two seeds or 'beans'.

Picking and processing

Like the leaves of the tea plant, coffee berries must be picked entirely by hand, and a supply of cheap labour is, therefore, essential. The pulp is stripped off by machinery, and a certain amount of fermentation is allowed to take place, after which the beans are spread out to dry in the sun for about a week. The beans are still covered by a thin semi-transparent skin called 'parchment', and in this state are often sent to the dealers and shippers as 'parchment coffee'. But sometimes this skin and the tissue below it (known as the 'silver-skin') are removed by the planter before shipment by passing the beans through a mill. Before being used to prepare the beverage known to us as 'coffee', the beans are roasted, the best temperature being 99° C (210° F). At this stage they take on their characteristic colour and aroma.

Producing areas

World production of coffee amounts to nearly 4·5 million tons, a third-half of which comes from Brazil (fig. 35). Here coffee is vital to the national economy and represents 53 per cent of the country's exports. By the late 1930s coffee production in the rich, red soils of the tropical highlands behind São Paulo had become such a profitable occupation that big plantations (called *fazendas*), each containing up to 100 000 trees, had multiplied so rapidly that Brazil was producing more coffee than the rest of the world was prepared to buy. Competition from other countries aggravated the situation, and the Brazilian government embarked on a process of systematically buying and burning a great deal of the coffee, in order to create an artificial scarcity, which, they hoped, would help to raise prices. This state of affairs lasted until 1943, when the government acquired the rights in a patent to convert coffee into 'plastics'.

Although Brazil is by far the world's largest producer of coffee, the best coffee comes from such places as the Yemen, Kenya, Jamaica (where 'Blue Mountain' coffee is produced) and Guatemala.

Cocoa

At the beginning of the sixteenth century the Spanish explorer, Hernando Cortez, found in the course of his conquest of Central America that the Aztecs had a national drink called *chocolatl*,

Fig. 36 Cacao tree, showing pods.

which they prepared from an evergreen tree whose botanical name is *theobroma*[1] *cacao*. 'Cocoa' (a misspelling of *cacao*) was brought to Europe soon afterwards—about a hundred years before the introduction of tea or coffee—but it was not imported in any great quantity until the 'invention' of chocolate some eighty years ago. The USA, West Germany and Britain now lead the world in the consumption of cocoa, some of it in the

[1] *Theobroma* means 'food for the gods'.

form of chocolate and some in the powder form from which the well-known drink is made.

The cacao plant
The plan (fig. 36) resembles an apple tree in size and appearance, and belongs principally to the equatorial low-lands, where a temperature of 27° C (80° F) is maintained throughout the year and the annual rainfall is between 1 250 and 3 750 mm (50 and 150 in). It prefers a deep, rich soil, is very liable to infection by insect and virus diseases and does not bear fruit until several years after planting. Like the coffee plant, it is often protected from the direct rays of the sun by taller plants such as the banana. The cacao tree is peculiar in that the fruit, consisting of bulky pods about 10 cm (4 in) broad and 25 cm (10 in) long and varying in colour from yellow to purple, hang from the trunk and larger branches.

Picking and processing
The pods are cut from the tree and split open, and the seeds or 'beans', twenty or more in each pod, are removed from the surrounding pulp (fig. 37). The beans are then allowed to ferment for several days to remove the bitter taste and to prevent them from going musty later on, after which they are spread out on the ground or in sheds to dry, and packed in bags for export.

Fig. 37 Splitting cocoa pods in Ghana.

At factories in the countries where the cocoa is to be consumed, the beans are cleaned, roasted and hulled (i.e. their skins and husks are removed). The 'cocoa-nibs' produced in this way are then ground to a paste, half of which consists of a fatty substance called cocoa-butter. This is separated from the solid matter, and is widely used in the manufacture of cosmetics, while the remainder is finally ground to the familiar powder. In the manufacture of plain chocolate, powder cocoa is mixed with cocoa-butter, and sugar is added; milk chocolate contains dried milk as well.

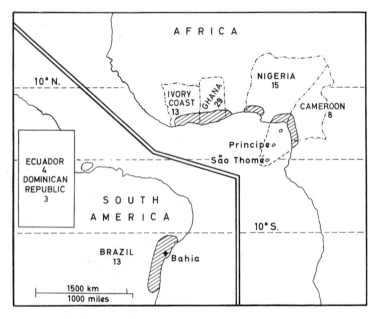

Fig. 38 The world's chief cocoa-growing areas. The figures indicate percentages of the world's total production of 1 422 000 tons per year.

Producing areas

For many years the chief centres of cocoa production lay in Central America and the West Indies, but well over half the world's cocoa now comes from countries bordering on the Gulf of Guinea (fig. 38). At one time Africans from the mainland were shanghaied and forced to work in conditions of semi-slavery in the nearby Portuguese islands of São Thomé and Principe, but the practice was stopped by the refusal of manufacturers to buy Portuguese cocoa. Nowadays in West Africa cocoa is grown not on large European-owned plantations, like so many other tropical crops, but on small-holdings prepared by cutting down and burning the dense equatorial forest. The quality of the cocoa is not always as high as the dealers would like, but the governments concerned are now endeavouring to make the growers take more interest in the improvement of their crops.

Wine

Wine may be produced from a wide variety of fruits, such as raspberries, elderberries and apples; from vegetables like rhubarb and carrots; and even from flowers such as the cowslip; but all the most important wines are prepared from the fermented juice of the grape.[1] The industry is an extremely old one; it is mentioned in the biblical story of Noah, and largely owing to the difficulty of obtaining pure drinking water, wine was consumed on a wide scale by Jews, Egyptians, Greeks, Romans and others in the ancient Mediterranean world. Today it is the national drink of France, Italy, Spain and neighbouring countries, and in this area consumption per head averages 73 litres (15 gallons) a year, but the British, to whom wine until recently was something of a luxury, drink only one-tenth as much, though this is now increasing.

Preparation and types of wine

After picking, the grapes are compressed (sometimes by treading underfoot) to extract the juice or 'must', and fermentation begins immediately the must comes in contact with the yeast which is present in the bloom on the grape-skin. During this reaction the sugar in the juice is converted into alcohol and carbon dioxide, and, after a period varying from a few days to a month or so, the turbid liquid becomes moderately clear. If it is desired to produce 'still' wine, the liquid is run off the dregs or 'lees' into open vats, where a second fermentation takes place. But if a 'sparkling' wine is required, sugar is added and the wine is corked in bottles. In this case the carbon dioxide released by the second fermentation cannot escape, but passes into the wine, giving it an effervescent quality.

The great variety displayed by wines from different areas is due to local variations in the above basic processes, together with variations in the types of grapes produced by different soils and climatic conditions. Claret, for instance, is produced from sandy or alluvial soils and Madeira from volcanic soils; fermentation in port and sherry is stopped by 'fortifying' the wine with

[1] The climatic conditions necessary for the cultivation of grapes (or *viticulture*) are described on pp. 88–9.

brandy, and the Tokay wine of Hungary is made from grapes which have been partially dried on the vine.

The chief types of wine and the regions of Europe in which they are produced are shown in Fig. 39.

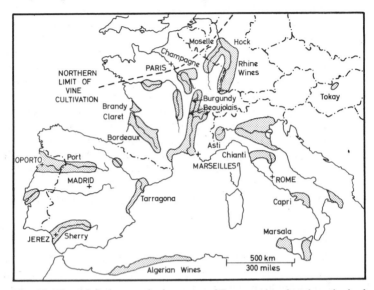

Fig. 39 The chief wine-producing areas of Europe, showing the principal type of wine associated with each area.

Other wine-producing areas

Over 257 million hectolitres (6 000 million gallons) of wine are produced every year, 65 per cent of it in the Mediterranean area, but only one-twelfth of the world's wine enters into international trade. In recent years, however, other regions where a 'Mediterranean' climate permits the cultivation of grapes have been making wines for export—California, the Adelaide district of South Australia, and Cape Province in the Republic of South Africa. Two new and rapidly expanding areas of wine production are the Lake Peninsula of the USA and New York State.

Beer, whisky and cider

Beer

Beer is to the cool temperate lands what wine is to the Mediterranean countries. It is a drink of great antiquity, and details of a recipe for beer-making used by the Ancient Britons are given by a sixth-century writer named Isidorus. Beer can be made from any of the cereals, but barley has generally proved to be the most suitable for the purpose. First of all, 'malt' is prepared by causing the grain to germinate in moist heat, after which it is dried, ground to powder, and boiled in water to produce 'wort'. The nature of the water used in this last process is of some importance, and the particular constituents of water from the local marls and sandstones originally led to the growth of the beer industry in Burton-on-Trent, for example. Nowadays the water used can be 'Burtonised' by the addition of chemicals. Yeast is added to the wort to cause fermentation, and the beverage is flavoured with *hops*. These are the small green flowers of a climbing plant which is trained to grow on a framework of poles and wires, notably in the Weald in Kent. After gathering, for which a temporary labour-force of 'hop-pickers' may be recruited from the towns,[1] the hops are roasted in circular buildings called oast-houses, which form prominent features of the countryside in the above area and in parts of Herefordshire and Worcestershire.

Whisky
Whisky is prepared from wort by evaporating the fermented liquid in 'stills' and condensing the vapour. Scotland and Eire are notable producers—and consumers—of whisky, and exports to the United States of Scotch whisky are five times as great as they were twenty years ago.

Cider
Cider is an alcoholic drink prepared by allowing juice pressed out of apples to ferment in casks. Devon and Somerset are famous producers, also Brittany in France.

Sugar

Sugar, quite apart from the fact that it enhances the taste of many foods and drinks, provides the human body with heat and energy. Although it was probably produced in India in early times, sugar was not generally available in Europe until about three hundred years ago, since it could not be transported over long distances without deterioration. Before this, the only sweetening agent was honey. Nowadays sugar is used by nearly all the world's peoples, and the varying level of consumption is often regarded as a reliable indication of the standard of living.

[1] This occurs less frequently now that machine-picking has been introduced.

The juices of a large number of plants do, in fact, contain sugar; it can be prepared from the maple tree and the coconut palm, for instance, and it has even been prepared from sawdust, but over three-quarters of the world's production of 70 million tons now comes from the sugar cane and the remainder from sugar beet. Sugar was first extracted from beet in 1747, and owing largely to the activities of the Germans, production increased so rapidly in the decade before the First World War that in 1910 more sugar was made from beet than from cane.

Saccharin is related to sugar in only one respect—its sweetening property.[1] It is a product of coal, discovered accidentally in 1879 and is used by diabetics, who cannot take sugar.

The sugar cane

This is a tropical grass which resembles bamboo and consists of woody tube-like stems about the thickness of a man's wrist. It reaches a height of anything from 2·5 to 4·5 m (8 to 15 ft), and is surmounted by long leaves. When the plant is ripe, the stems contain a sap or juice from which the sugar is extracted. Throughout the period of growth, which usually takes a whole year, constant high temperatures—21° C (70° F) or more—are essential, and there must be at least 1 525 mm (60 in) of rainfall or its equivalent in irrigation. A spell of dry weather at the time of ripening is equally essential, otherwise the juice becomes diluted, and the yield of sugar is reduced. Ideal conditions for growth are therefore found in regions where the Equatorial climate begins to give way to the neighbouring Tropical type of climate. In such situations high temperatures are maintained and rainfall is constant, except for a short dry season in which the canes can be gathered. The crop requires a rich soil, but since canes sprout from the same root for five or six years after planting, the soil tends to become exhausted, and the use of fertilisers is necessary.

Harvesting and processing

An important requirement for sugar cane cultivation is an adequate supply of cheap labour. While the plants are growing, there is much weeding to be done, and at harvest-time the task of chopping off the top leaves (with curved knives) is an arduous one in the prevailing steamy heat (fig. 40). The West Indies are now very largely populated by the descendants of Negroes taken from Africa to the New World to work on the sugar plantations; in Natal labour was originally provided by Indians who migrated to South Africa; and at one time 'Kanakas',[2] from the South Sea

[1] Saccharin is estimated to be 300 times as sweet as sugar.
[2] Kanakas were South Sea islanders who had been kidnapped by unscrupulous sea captains (known as 'blackbirders') and sold to plantation owners.

Fig. 40 West Indian plantation workers cutting sugar cane with long knives called *machetes*.

Islands worked in the sugar fields of Queensland.

Transporting the canes over the muddy ground is by no means easy. Originally bullock-carts, whose wheels had a particularly broad tread, were used, but these are gradually being replaced by light railways.

On arrival at the nearby sugar-mills, the canes are cut into shorter lengths and crushed between heavy rollers to extract the juice, which is then boiled with the addition of a little lime to prevent fermentation. Part of the water in the thick syrup so produced is evaporated; eventually the rest crystallises into raw (or 'brown') sugar, leaving molasses as a byproduct. Molasses is used in the manufacture of rum and industrial alcohol, and in the preparation of tobacco, and, pressed into cakes with the crushed cane, it provides an excellent food for cattle. The cultivation of sugar cane and the extraction of sugar calls for such extensive organisation and such costly equipment that sugar production is nowadays almost entirely in the hands of large corporations with great reserves of capital at their disposal. The development of the industry in Cuba would have been impossible but for American financial backing.

The *refining* of raw sugar is usually undertaken in the consuming country. The liquid formed by dissolving the raw sugar in boiling

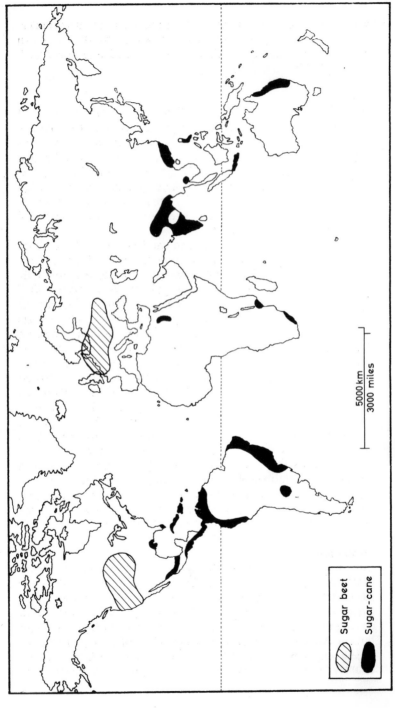

Fig. 41 The world's chief sugar-producing areas.

Sugar beet

Sugar-cane

5000 km
3000 miles

82   Drinks and sugar

water is filtered to remove solid impurities, then run into cylinders packed with 'char' (i.e. bone charcoal), which absorbs the brown colour. The sugar, now 'white', is evaporated and condensed, and the residue is made into 'golden syrup'.

Sugar beet
Sugar beet is a large white or yellow root, a plant of the cool temperate lands, the cultivation of which has often been closely bound up with considerations of military strategy. Beet was originally grown for the extraction of sugar by the French, when, during the Napoleonic Wars, their supply of cane sugar from the tropics was cut off by blockade, and the great expansion of the industry in Germany in the early years of the twentieth century was the result of a desire to be independent of tropical supplies in the event of war.

The crop requires a rich soil, and the *loess* of the Magdeburg region of East Germany, the *limon* of the Paris Basin and the alluvial deposits of the Fens of eastern England are especially productive. At one time a constant supply of labour was essential, for hoeing and weeding between the rows and for lopping off the tops after the roots have been gathered. Where labour costs were high, sugar beet was not, therefore, a very popular crop with farmers, and governments often encouraged beet production by offering subsidies or bounties to those who were willing to grow it. But nowadays little hand labour is needed; weeds are destroyed by chemical herbicides, and the tops are cut from the roots by the same machinery which harvests the crop (fig. 16, p. 32). Moreover, modern varieties of beet have a higher sugar content than the corresponding weight of cane, and, since the consuming areas are close at hand, transport costs are relatively light.

The beet is cut into slices (cossettes) by mechanical knives and processed in very much the same way as sugar cane. There are many useful byproducts, such as molasses, from which in turn alcohol can subsequently be manufactured; and sugar beet pulp, dried and shredded, provides excellent cattle fodder.

Producing areas
In the production of *sugar cane* India leads the world, but since methods of extraction are often primitive and, the population is large, India consumes nearly all the sugar she produces. She is closely followed by Brazil and Cuba who, together with India, account for nearly half of the world's production (fig. 41). *Sugar beet* is grown almost exclusively in the western regions of the USSR, the countries of Western Europe and the United States. Eight per cent of the world's raw sugar (fig. 42) is produced in

Cuba, a large part of whose output was, before the Castro revolution, sent to the USA.

Since sugar production can be increased so easily when it appears that the demand is rising, there is always the danger of overproduction. To prevent the economic distress which inevitably follows in the producing areas when prices fall, a number of international agreements have been concluded over the last forty years, in which quotas have been allotted to the countries concerned, based on estimated world requirements. These agreements have helped to prevent prices from fluctuating.

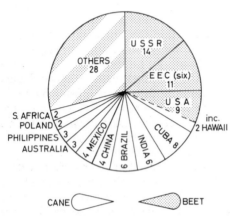

Fig. 42. World production of raw sugar. The figures indicate percentages of the world's total production of 70 million tons per year. It should be noted that the diagram refers to the manufacture of raw sugar, *not* the production of sugar cane and sugar beet.

6

FRUITS, TOBACCO AND SPICES

Fruits

In the diet of the human race fruit has occupied throughout the ages positions of varying importance; and the stages by which the present position has been reached provide an interesting illustration of man's gradually increasing control over his environment. In the life of the early 'food-gatherer', fruit was a necessity, and man could do no more than rely for his food on such fruits as Nature offered. Later, when he had become skilful at hunting animals and cultivating grain, meat and bread-stuffs supplied additions to his diet and fruit was no longer essential. A long period followed in which particular fruits were deliberately cultivated wherever favourable opportunities presented themselves or special needs existed. Dates, for example, are known to have been grown in fertile oases over 4 000 years ago; in Mediterranean lands the olive was at an early stage recognised as a valuable source of oil, and grapes have been cultivated for the making of wine for many thousands of years. It was not until about 1900 that any one part of the world was able to share to any great extent in the fruits of the others; nor indeed until this time did fruit begin to occupy its present place in the diet of the nations.

In the last sixty or seventy years there has been a tremendous increase in the consumption of all kinds of fruit—primarily owing to the all-round improvement of transport facilities. Fruit can now be picked green in tropical or 'Mediterranean' regions and carried in specially built refrigerator[1] ships to the densely populated lands of Europe, for example, so that by the time it comes on sale in the shops, it is ripe and ready for eating. In 1850 bananas were an unfamiliar luxury in Britain, and whereas only fifty years ago oranges and apples were associated with particular seasons, supplies from different parts of the world now succeed one another throughout the year.

Even so, it is doubtful whether consumption would have risen

[1] Fruit is actually maintained at a temperature of about 10° C (50° F): 'cool storage' would be a more accurate term.

so rapidly had not the demand for fruit been boosted by advertisements and sundry forms of propaganda put out by importers and 'marketing boards'. In Britain in the middle 1920s, for instance, a national 'Eat More Fruit' campaign was launched, during which hoardings by the roadside and in railway stations became covered with posters, and schoolchildren were invited to compete for prizes by writing essays on the subject of fruit. Much of this advertisement was government-inspired and highly proper in so far as responsible authorities had by now realised that fruit is an important source of vitamin C and capable of contributing to the health of the nation.

When a sufficiently large demand had been created in this way it became worth while for shipping companies and importers to build special ships, set up storage chambers and generally instal equipment which reduced handling costs and hence the price of the fruit to the consumer. Campaigns of this kind serve to increase not only the quantity of fruit which enters into our diet, but also its variety. The public are, naturally, reluctant to buy things about which they know very little, and quite a large range of unfamiliar fruits exists, such as custard-apples, avocado pears and mangoes, which might well be imported into Britain as cheaply as bananas or grapefruit, if ever a sufficiently large demand were to arise.

One final factor which has led to the worldwide increase in fruit consumption has been the rise in the standard of living which has followed upon industrialisation. After providing the basic necessities of their diet, people in general now have more money to spend on such 'luxuries' as fruit.

Preserving fruit

As a method of preserving, 'refrigeration' makes it possible for fruit to be carried halfway round the world and sold fresh in the shops, but the process is a continuous one, requires special equipment and is economic only for a limited time. When the period of preservation is indefinite, other methods, which are complete after a single initial process, are more practicable. The time-honoured method of preservation is to *dry* the fruit, usually by exposing it to the sun's rays. Being deprived of water, bacteria contained in the fruit are less able to cause deterioration. Raisins, sultanas and currants are produced from grapes by this means. *Jam* and *wine* represent fruit converted into a less perishable form. Nowadays the most widely used commercial method of preserving fruit is *canning*. This process was invented over a hundred years ago by a Frenchman named Appert, and began to be important in the 1870s. Air is excluded from the tin, which is then soldered up and placed in boiling water for a considerable length of time. Any bacteria which are not killed by the heat are rendered incapable of action through lack of oxygen. With the increasing use of commercial and domestic deep-freezing equipment, a method of wide application nowadays is refrigeration at a temperature well below freezing point.

Fruits may conveniently be divided into four main categories—deciduous fruits, citrus fruits, Mediterranean fruits and tropical fruits, although a certain amount of overlapping occurs.

Deciduous fruits
These are the fruits of trees and shrubs which lose their leaves in winter and are grown mainly, but not exclusively, in cool temperate and warm temperate regions.

More *apples* are grown for sale in the world's markets than any other kind of fruit, but only one-twentieth of the total production of 22 million tons enters into trade. France, where part of the crop, as in England, is made into cider, is usually the largest producer, closely followed by the USA.

Pears are cultivated under the same climatic conditions as apples, but only about one-third as many are produced. In France *peri*, a drink similar to cider, is made from 'perry' pears.

Plums, the production of which nearly equals that of pears, are obtained chiefly from the USA, Italy and countries of central Europe. They enter into foreign trade only when dried as 'prunes' or canned.

Fig. 43 Apple orchards near Kamloops, British Columbia.

Cherries are grown widely in Europe and the United States, but since they are a very difficult fruit to pack, only one-fiftieth of the world's production is exported as fresh fruit. Considerable quantities are, however, made into glacé cherries for use in the confectionery trade.

The 'soft fruits' (*strawberries, gooseberries, raspberries, black-currants*, etc.) are of importance locally as fresh fruit or for use in jam-making.

Tomatoes, though used as a vegetable, are in fact a fruit, of South American origin. Their popularity has increased enormously in the last sixty years, and local supplies in Britain are considerably augmented by imports from the Canary Islands and the Channel Islands.

Citrus fruits

These are fruits with a thick, waxy skin which prevents transpiration and enables them to survive in conditions of drought, and are native to Monsoon and Warm Temperate East Coast lands, but the chief areas of commercial production are now situated in 'Mediterranean' regions.

Oranges, which grow on a small, bushy tree about 3 m (10 ft) high, are thought to have come originally from China, but have for centuries been grown in the warmer parts of the Mediterranean area—often with the help of irrigation. The names 'Jaffa', 'Tangerine' and 'Seville' suggest three such producing regions. In the last few decades the production of oranges has become important in several other areas, such as South Africa and south-eastern Australia, but half the world production of over 28 million tons is now grown in the United States (in California, Texas and, more recently, in Florida), with Brazil as the second largest producer.

Lemons originated in India, but nearly half of the world's lemons now come from California and Sicily.

Grapefruit have become popular only in the last fifty years. The United States produces (in California, Texas and Florida) 70 per cent of the world's supply, a great deal of which, unlike that of oranges and lemons, is canned or processed in some way.

Limes and *citrons* (from which 'candied peel' is made) are further examples of citrus fruits.

Mediterranean fruits

Grapes are essentially a fruit of the 'Mediterranean' regions, but may be grown outside these areas provided that average temperatures of 18° to 21° C (65° to 70° F) are maintained throughout the summer, with a long dry period in which the grapes can ripen.

It is for this reason that viticulture is possible in sheltered situations as far north as the Rhine Rift Valley. The grape vine has a particularly long root, which enables it, during the summer drought, to draw water from a great depth, and it thrives on a poor, chalky soil, but it is especially subject to such pests as *phylloxera*, which a hundred years ago did widespread damage in France.

More than 85 per cent of the world's production of grapes (52 million tons) is devoted to wine-making (see p. 77), which accounts for almost all of the grapes grown in southern Europe. Overseas exports of fresh grapes are mainly confined to dessert types, chiefly from South Africa to Britain. Dried grapes amount to 3 million tons; *raisins* now come principally from California; *sultanas*, formed by drying small 'seedless' grapes, come from Asia Minor; and *currants*[1] almost entirely from Greece and Australia.

Olives are the fruit of a typically 'Mediterranean' plant, which will be described in more detail under the heading of 'vegetable oils' (see p. 99). When ripe they are black and lustrous, and resemble small damsons. Some are eaten as fresh fruit in the countries of origin, others are taken from the tree while still green and pickled with spices.

Peaches and *apricots* are also produced in warm temperate regions—particularly California, South Africa and south-eastern Australia. As it is difficult to prevent the fruit being bruised in transport, both peaches and apricots enter into trade either dried, canned or frozen.

Nectarines are a variety of peach which have no down on their skins.

Figs are of considerable antiquity in the eastern Mediterranean, where locally they are eaten as fresh fruit. They have a very thick skin, and are difficult to pack, hence most of them are dried for export. Figs were introduced into California many years ago; most of the crop is canned or made into syrup.

Tropical fruits
Bananas are the fruit of a plant which grows to a height of 3·5 to 4·5 m (12 to 15 ft) and is a large-scale tropical variety of the English plantain (fig. 44). The hollow 'stem' is actually composed of tightly packed leaves, which at the top fan out rather like the leaves on a coconut palm. On each plant the fruit forms in a single compact bunch made up of 100 to 200 separate bananas. Since the plant requires high temperatures and plentiful rainfall throughout the year, it is cultivated chiefly within 15 degrees of the Equator. For centuries various types of bananas

[1] The word is a corruption of *Corinth*, near which 'currants' were first produced.

$3\frac{1}{2} - 4\frac{1}{2}$ m (12–15 ft)

Fig. 44 Banana plant.

Fig. 45 Preparing bananas for shipment. The bunches of still green bananas are split into groups (or 'hands') and carefully laid in cardboard boxes.

have been the staple diet of many groups of tropical natives, but cultivation for export, which depends on highly scientific methods of transport and marketing (fig. 45), is carried on in plantations owned in many cases by European corporations. Brazil, Ecuador and India together provide nearly half of the world's total production, which now exceeds that of apples, but the chief exporting countries are Jamaica and Honduras. In the Canary Islands a type of small, sweet banana is produced with the help of irrigation.

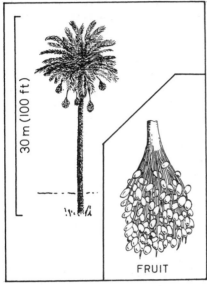

Fig. 46 Date palm, showing (inset) a bunch of dates.

Pineapples grow close to the ground, in the centre of a group of thick, spiked leaves about one metre long. The plant came originally from Brazil, but is now common in most of the tropical and subtropical lands, where it thrives best near the sea. The greater part of world production, half of which comes from the Hawaiian Islands, is canned. Pineapple-growing in Malaya suffered severely during the Japanese occupation, but the industry has now recovered and is once again thriving.

Dates are essentially a product of oases in those parts of the tropics which are classified as 'hot deserts', but they are now grown rather more widely. The date palm (fig. 46) consists of a thin trunk, at the top of which is a cluster of long, feathery leaves. It attains a height of about 30 m (100 ft) and lives to a great age. To the desert-dweller dates, which form in bunches of 200 or more, each bunch weighing from 14 to 18 kg (30 to 40 lb), represent the only available foodstuff, and Arabs have long been accustomed to dry them in the sun or grind them into meal for future use. Imports of dried dates to the temperate lands come mainly from Iraq and North Africa.

Nuts
These are, of course, a type of fruit, in which an edible kernel is surrounded by a tough shell. Many different kinds (such as Brazil nuts, chestnuts, almonds and walnuts) enter into commerce, and are valuable sources of nutriment (for pea-nuts see pp. 104–5).

Commercial fruit-growing
In the foregoing account detailed description of the factors which have led to the development of commercial fruit-growing in each of the areas mentioned would have been impossible. Some factors of fairly general application are, however, briefly indicated below.
1. *Local relief and climatic conditions* are often of supreme importance. In the British Isles, for instance, it is essential that apple orchards should be situated clear of valley bottoms, where frosts are more frequent than on rising ground, and shelter from strong or cold winds is equally important. In certain areas of Europe, vines can be grown only on hillsides facing south; in the tropics, pineapples do better close to the sea; and so on.
2. *The availability of labour.* During the period of growth, a constant supply of labour is often required for weeding, tying up, pruning, etc., and, later on, for gathering the fruit. Bananas, for example, must be picked and placed in cold storage on the ships within a matter of hours.
3. *Soils.* Mixed or sandy soils are often an advantage, since, in general, they lighten the work.
4. *Capital, refrigerator ships and cold storage installations at docks* are a vital necessity in connection with tropical fruits.
   The above list is by no means exhaustive. It should, however, suggest a number of other 'common-sense' considerations for which space is not available here.

Tobacco

The history of tobacco-smoking is an interesting one. American Indians were discovered by Columbus inhaling the smoke of dried tobacco leaves placed in a forked cane, and about the same time it was the custom of natives in the West Indian islands to roll the leaves into a kind of cigar. Smoking was popularised in England about 1585 by Sir Walter Raleigh and Sir Francis Drake, but during the next century smokers were persecuted, and in Turkey even executed! After the Great Plague of 1665 the habit regained popularity, as smokers were considered immune; tobacco was used as incense and disinfectant, and was prescribed for all kinds of complaints. But soon after this a duty was for the first time imposed on tobacco by the British government. When the taking of snuff became customary in the second half of the eighteenth century, smoking declined, but came into favour again about 1800. Nowadays, whatever view may be held about its pleasures or its dangers, it must be acknowledged that smoking is a world-wide habit upon which a major industry is based, and that the tax on tobacco provides governments with an easy method of a raising a substantial part of their income.[1]

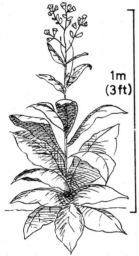

1m
(3ft)

Fig. 47 Tobacco plant.

The tobacco plant

The plant is an annual, which reaches a height of about one metre, and bears small pink or white flowers and a dozen or more large leaves (fig. 47). It thrives best in a subtropical climate, but is extremely adaptable and is, in fact, cultivated on the Equator and, as a summer crop, as far from 'home' as the north of Sweden. The plant requires constant attention throughout the period of growth. The seed, which is so small that 25 000 can be contained

---

[1] In Britain, for instance, the tax on tobacco provides the government with over £1 150 millions a year, about 6 per cent of its ordinary income.

in a teaspoon, is sown in fertilised seed-beds covered with muslin to protect them from frost and heavy rain. When all risk of frost has passed, the young plants are transferred to specially prepared fields. Constant weeding and hoeing are essential, the flowers and suckers are cut off, and tarpaulins may be spread over the plants if the sunlight is too strong.

Harvesting and processing

When the leaves are judged to be mature, they are removed, hung in sheds to dry, 'cured' in a stream of hot air and 'dressed' with cider, molasses and various concoctions about which considerable secrecy is observed. Eventually, packed in hogsheads of about 450 kg (990 lb), they are ready for dispatch to factories, where they are processed further and blended to make them suitable for pipe- or cigarette-tobacco or for making cigars. Before being manufactured and sold, tobacco is often kept 'in bond' for as much as two and a half years. The type of plant, the soil, the climate and the different methods of processing the leaves all lead to an immense variety of flavours and grades of tobacco, most of which are named after the countries or districts in which they grow.

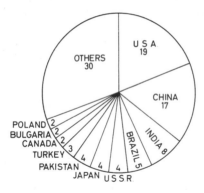

Fig. 48 World production of tobacco. The figures indicate percentages of the world's total production of about 4·5 million tons per year.

Producing areas

World production of tobacco (fig. 48) is about 4·5 million tons, but since many of the largest producers consume most of their own output, only one-fifth of it enters into international trade. Nearly one-fifth is grown in the USA, in the states of North and South Carolina, Kentucky, Georgia and Virginia. This last-mentioned state gives its name to the chief kind of tobacco used in making cigarettes. Nowadays more tobacco for 'Turkish' cigarettes is grown in northern Greece than in Turkey itself, while Cuba and Sumatra specialise in the production of cigar leaf. What were formerly known as 'Empire' tobaccos came from Malawi and (before the application of sanctions) from Rhodesia.

Spices

Under the heading of 'spices' may be included all those vegetable substances which, on account of their pungent taste, are used in flavouring or preserving food.

Although today they are common enough in every kitchen and provide interesting additions to a variety of foods, they are no longer as important as they were when, in the days of the first Queen Elizabeth, they formed the only available method of improving the taste of salted beef. Moreover, as a means of preservation pickling in spices was preferable to salting, which was liable to produce scurvy unless plenty of green vegetables were eaten as well. In those days, and for a considerable time afterwards, the produce of the 'Spice Islands'[1] made up a large part of the trade between East and West. In the monsoon lands of Asia, spices have always been useful in that they have introduced variety to the monotony of daily dishes of rice, as, for instance, in the case of Indian 'curry'. Since the invention of the domestic refrigerator, spices are now chiefly important in temperate lands as ingredients of sauces and pickles.

Pepper, the commonest of all spices, is produced from the 'peppercorns' or berries of a climbing plant native to the hot, wet forests of southern India, but it is now cultivated mainly in Sarawak and Indonesia. The berries when ripe are red in colour, but turn black as they are dried. 'Black pepper' is the result of grinding the seed together with the pulp or outer skin surrounding it; the more usual 'white pepper' is made by soaking off the pulp and grinding the seed alone.

Chillies and *capsicum* are the pods of a dwarf plant found in South America, Mexico and India. They are eaten fresh or dried, and when ground form Cayenne or 'red' pepper. *Paprika* comes from a tree belonging to the same family.

Cloves are the immature buds which grow in clusters on the ends of the branches of an evergreen tree, which reaches a height of about 15 m (50 ft). They are dried in the sun and exported for use as a flavouring in pies and puddings, or for the manufacture

[1] *The Moluccas*, a group of islands in the East Indies.

of oil of cloves. The bulk of the world's supply now comes from Zanzibar and the neighbouring island of Pemba off the east coast of Africa, but production in the Malagasy Republic is increasing rapidly.

Ginger is derived from the root of a tropical plant which grows to a height of about one metre, and resembles a mass of tangled reeds. The dried roots form 'brown ginger'; 'preserved ginger' is made by soaking the portions of root in syrup. India, China, West Africa and Jamaica are the chief producers.

Nutmegs and *mace* both come from the fruit of an evergreen tree, also about 15 m (50 ft) high, which originates from the Bandas, a group of islands in Indonesia. The fruit is about the size of a small apple, and when ripe its outer covering (or pericarp) splits open, exposing the seed. This is composed of a soft outer layer, which is dried to form mace, and a very hard inner layer, like a walnut shell, containing the kernel or nutmeg. The world's supply is now obtained from Indonesia and from Grenada in the West Indies.

Cinnamon is the yellow-brown bark of a small tree native to Ceylon (Sir Lanka).

Pimento or *allspice* is the dried, unripe fruit of a tree related to the clove, and comes mainly from Jamaica.

Vanilla is produced from the pod of an orchid which grows in Mexico.

Other tropical spices are *cardamons, cassia* and *cummin.*

Although almost all of the spices come from the tropics, several important ones are grown in the temperate lands, the most notable being *caraways, aniseed* and the more familiar *mustard*, which was used as a condiment by the Anglo-Saxons!

7

VEGETABLE OILS

Man must have discovered the existence of fats and oils[1] at quite an early stage in his development. In cutting up and cooking the creatures which provided him with food, he could hardly fail to notice the *animal oils*. These were almost certainly the first types of oil to come within the bounds of his experience, and some examples have already been mentioned in the chapters of this book which deal with cattle and fish. Later on, he must have realised that the fruits and seeds of certain plants also contained oil, which could usually be extracted by the simple process of compression. Such *vegetable oils* have throughout the ages been used for a variety of purposes from food and lubricant to illuminant and soap. The discovery in the second half of the nineteenth century of *mineral oils*, from the rocks of the earth itself, added to the range of available resources, but caused no reduction in the demand for oils of the other two kinds. Soon after this the demand for vegetable oils began to rise, and it has continued to rise ever since.

The modern importance of vegetable oils

There are two main reasons for the present importance of these oils:
1. Fats are one of the basic foods essential to health, and by about 1875 population in the industrial countries had increased to the point at which there were not enough animal fats (butter and lard) to go round. Attention naturally turned to vegetable oils as an alternative or supplementary source of supply.
2. In a series of remarkable achievements modern chemists have not only overcome most of the objections to the use of vegetable oils as foodstuffs, but have also found for these oils industrial uses undreamt of fifty years ago.

[1] There is no essential difference between a fat and an oil. An 'oily substance' which is liquid at normal temperatures is referred to as an 'oil'; when it is solid at normal temperatures, it is called a 'fat'.

The history of margarine—a commodity to the making of which a large proportion of the world's vegetable oils is now devoted—provides an interesting illustration of both the above points.

Margarine

In 1869 a French chemist named Mège-Mouriés took out a patent for the manufacture of a butter substitute concocted from purified beef fat, water, milk and finely chopped cow's udder. Since the substance had a pearly appearance, he chose for it the trade name 'margarine', from the Greek word *margaron*, meaning 'a pearl'. Mège-Mouriés himself was not very successful at exploiting his invention, but the process was taken up by three Dutch butter merchants, Jan and Henri Jurgen and Simon Van den Bergh, and within a few years the manufacture of margarine had been extended to England and the USA. Margarine (or 'butterine', as it was originally called in England) did not at first provide an alternative to animal fats so much as a means of eking them out. The use in their place of such vegetable oils as those obtained from the coconut palm, groundnuts, etc., was open to two major objections: their taste and aroma were often unpleasant, and they melted at too low a temperature. The first difficulty was gradually overcome by improved methods of refining, but the second was not conquered until 1909, when a process was perfected in which hydrogen atoms are 'injected' into the molecules of the 'fatty acids' of which oils are very largely composed. In this *hydrogenation* process, oils are hardened into fats which remain solid at normal temperatures. As a result, margarine manufacturers were no longer dependent on supplies of animal fats, and the demand for vegetable oils increased sharply.

Since 1909 many other advances have been made in the technique of processing and refining oils. Perhaps the most remarkable of these has been the process of *fractionation*,[1] in which an oil is split into 'fractions', each with a different chemical structure, and each suitable for a specific purpose. Thus soya bean oil, for example, can be split into two separate oils, one of which is suitable for making margarine and the other for making paint.

Such developments as these make it possible to understand and appreciate the multifarious uses of vegetable oils which are described in the following account of the plants from which they are obtained.

[1] Compare 'fractional distillation' of petroleum (see pp. 234–7).

Principal sources

Olive oil

The olive tree flourishes only in countries with a 'Mediterranean' climate (fig. 49). It was first mentioned in recorded history about 1700 BC, but was certainly cultivated very much earlier than this, and not only provided the Mediterranean peoples in ancient times with fresh fruit, 'cooking-fats', 'butter' and 'soap', but to a large extent does so even today. The olive can survive on limestone and poor gravelly soils, and in conditions where the rainfall is as low as 205 mm (8 in) a year, but it is not very tolerant of frost, and long sunny summers are essential. When fully grown, it is about the size of an apple tree; the leaves are slender, glossy and silvery-green in colour, and the fruit, which is not plentiful until fifteen years after planting, resembles unripe damsons. If adequately cared for, a tree will continue for centuries to bear 14 kg (30 lb) or more of olives every year.

The oil is extracted from the fleshy part of the fruit—often by 'machinery' that has not been improved in design or efficiency for thousands of years—and requires no further processing or refining. In the more modern crushing-mills the fruit is compressed a second time, and the resulting lower-grade oil is dispatched to soap-making factories. Olives have lately been introduced into California and Argentina, but Spain and Italy account for nearly three-quarters of the world's production of about 1·25 million tons of olive oil, and almost all of the remainder comes from other countries bordering the Mediterranean Sea.

Coconut or copra oil

The coconut palm grows on hot, wet coastal lowlands within 15 degrees of the Equator, and is found chiefly in the tropical Pacific islands and southern India (fig. 49). It is thought to have been spread from its original home in the Malay Archipelago by the drifting of coconuts, which are impervious to seawater. To the natives of these areas the coconut palm is a kind of 'universal provider', since it supplies them with food and drink, and to a certain extent with clothing and shelter; to the peoples of the temperate lands it supplies the materials for a wide range of manufactured products from mats and margarine to cattle-cake and soap.

When fully grown the tree reaches a height of about 25 mm (80 ft), and every year bears 50 or 60 fruits resembling dark green rugger balls (fig. 50). Each of these fruits weighs anything up to 5·5 kg (12 lb), and consists of a thick outer layer or husk, which yields the brown fibre or *coir* used in making mattresses, ropes,

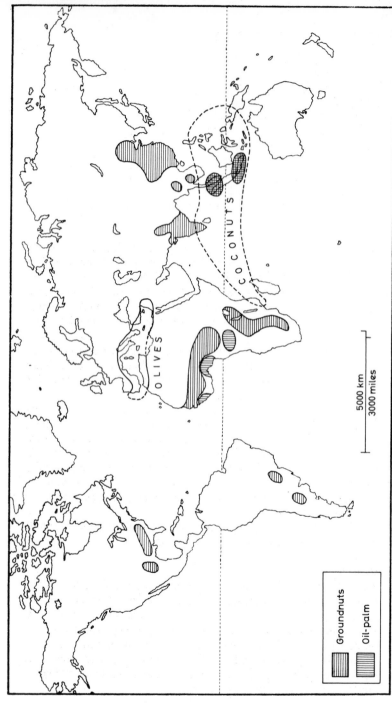

Fig. 49 The chief growing areas of plants from which vegetable oils are obtained.

COCONUTS

OLIVES

5000 km
3000 miles

Groundnuts

Oil-palm

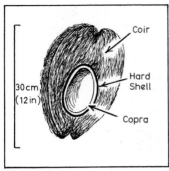

Fig. 50 Sectional drawing of the fruit of the coconut palm.

brooms, 'coconut matting' and many other things. Inside the husk is the seed or kernel—the familiar fairground coconut. The 'meat' lining the hard shell is removed, dried in the sun or in kilns, and exported as *copra*, which, when crushed, yields about two-thirds of its weight in the form of an extremely valuable oil. Since coconut oil (or copra oil) has such excellent lathering properties, it is widely used in the manufacture of toilet soap, but considerable quantities go to make margarine and cooking-fats, while the residue after crushing is sold as cattle-cake. Small amounts of copra are shredded to make desiccated coconut for use in the confectionery trade.

These by no means exhaust the possible uses of the coconut-palm. The 'milk' contained in the nut provides a sweet, refreshing drink; the shells are used as drinking vessels and as fuel, and since they take a very high polish, can be made into buttons and ornaments; the leaves of the tree can be used as thatching or elephant food; the stalks make fences and tool handles; and the powdery mass in which the coir is embedded provides humus for the growth of orchids.

World production of copra is about 3·5 million tons, over half of which comes from the Philippines and Indonesia.

Palm oil and palm-kernel oil
The oil palm in its wild state is a tall tree very much like the coconut palm in appearance (fig. 51). Its original home is the hot, equatorial forests of West Africa, but it was taken to Malaya and Indonesia about a hundred years ago—against the advice of government officials, who saw little point in introducing a rival to the coconut—and by 1925 the oil palm had become a highly productive crop there as well as in such countries as Nigeria and the former Congo (now Zaïre).

Fig. 51 An oil palm.

The fruit grows at the top of the tree in tight bunches of 800 or more, each individual fruit looking like an orange-coloured plum, with a short, spiky, outward-pointing stalk (fig. 52). So firmly are the bunches attached to the tree that they can be removed only by an axe; and although field labourers are extremely swift and skilful at 'walking' up both the oil palms and coconut palms, with a rope looped round themselves and the tree trunk, it is wasteful of time and manpower if climbing is necessary to remove the fruit. Special types of dwarf trees have therefore been produced for growth in plantations, so that the labourers can reach the fruit from the ground.

The complete fruit consists of two main parts—the flesh or pericarp, and an inner seed, which resembles a miniature coconut, except that the space within the hard shell is entirely taken up by the kernel. Both the flesh and the kernel yield oils.

Palm oil, which is orange-yellow in colour, is produced by first boiling and pulping the fruit, and then compressing it. Traditional methods of crushing are often extremely primitive, and include treading underfoot and various simple forms of tourniquet,

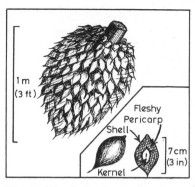

Fig. 52 The fruit of the oil palm.

Fig. 53 Soap-making. When fats and vegetable oils are broken down with an alkali (caustic soda, for example), soap and glycerine are produced. This process of 'saponification' takes place in large, heated pans, from which the hot liquid soap passes to the chilling roller seen below. As it comes off tnis roller, it is cut while still slightly warm into long, thin ribbons, and passes into the 'five-roll mill', where it is plasticised before being compressed into a long continuous bar. This is cut first into lengths and then into 'billets', which after cooling and 'skin-drying' are now ready stamping wrapping.

but more efficient, scientifically designed oil-mills are now being increasingly used. Although palm oil is widely used by the local inhabitants in the preparation of food, large quantities are exported and sold for manufacture into such products as soap (fig. 53) and margarine, and for use in the making of tinplate (see p. 201).

Palm-kernel oil is quite different from palm oil; it is a white fat obtained by crushing the hard, black kernels. This operation is impossible without special apparatus, and it is therefore performed in factories in the consuming countries, where the oil, after being bleached and deodorised, is used in making soap, margarine and cooking-fat.

Groundnuts

Groundnuts (or pea-nuts) are the seeds of a small plant of the pea and bean family, which spread during the sixteenth century from its original home in South America and the West Indies to nearly all parts of the tropical world. The plant was introduced into West Africa by slave-traders, who fed their Negro captives on groundnuts on the journey across the Atlantic.

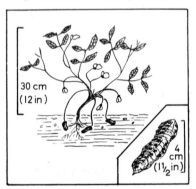

Fig. 54 Groundnut plant.

The plant is an annual, which throughout its growing season of four months requires moderate rainfall and an average temperature of about 27° C (80° F). It produces small, yellow flowers, not unlike sweet-peas, which after fertilisation bend over towards the ground (fig. 54). Their stalks at this stage lengthen rapidly, and thrust into the soil the immature seed-pods which form in place of the flowers. These soon develop into fully grown nuts several centimetres below the surface. To save shipping space the loose, withered-looking shells are usually removed before the nuts are dispatched to the crushing-mills, where about 40 per cent of their weight is extracted in the form of an oil, which is used in making margarine, cooking-fats and a host of other commodities. The residue after crushing provides a cattle-cake very rich in protein, and is also the raw material from which an artificial wool fibre called Ardil was at one time made.

The chief producers of groundnuts are India and China, who themselves consume most of their own output; the main exporters are the Republic of Mali (formerly part of French West Africa) and Nigeria, but the greater part of the world's imports is obtained from a large number of separate areas. A British attempt between 1947 and 1951 to plant 3 million acres of groundnuts in Tanganyika (now the mainland section of Tanzania) failed, largely on account of deficient rainfall and difficulties encountered in the making of roads. Had it succeeded, it would have raised the standard of living in Tanganyika and increased the supply of oil to Europe.

Other sources

Soybeans are the seeds of a leguminous[1] plant which bears brown pods containing 'beans' similar in size and appearance to the peas grown in Britain (fig. 55). They require a slightly cooler

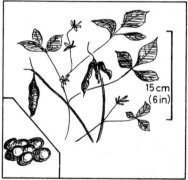

15 cm
(6 in)

Fig. 55 Soybean plant, showing (inset) a group of beans about full size.

climate than groundnuts, and although richer in protein, they have an oil content of only 15 per cent. For thousands of years they have provided the peasant of northern China with many of the requirements of his daily life, such as food, fertilisers, bedding, lamp-oil and soap; but only in the last fifty or sixty years have the virtues of the soybean been appreciated in the western world. Recently, however, the crop has been introduced to many countries with long, hot summers, and in the USA production has increased so rapidly that today the United States and China together contribute over 90 per cent of the world's supplies.

[1] i.e. of the pea and bean family.

Soybeans now provide a remarkably wide range of products. The bean itself is used in the manufacture of a flour (which resembles ground almonds), soy sauce, adhesives, paper size, textile fibre, 'plastics' and even cortisone for the treatment of arthritics; the oil is used not only in cooking-fats and margarine, but also as a 'drying oil' in paints, varnishes and printing-ink; while the residue provides nutritious cattle fodder.

Cotton seed. The cotton plant is, of course, grown chiefly for the fibre (see pp. 134–5), and a hundred years ago the small black seeds which are removed when the cotton is 'ginned' were regarded merely as a nuisance. But nowadays an oil is extracted from them which makes an excellent frying oil, and is used in the manufacture of margarine, lipstick and metal polish. World production is about the same as that of groundnuts or soybeans. Cotton seed is widely used in the USA, but only small quantities are imported into Britain.

Linseed oil is produced by crushing flax seed (see pp. 145–6). Since it has the property of oxidising on exposure to air, it is known as a 'drying oil', and when spread evenly over the surface of wood, forms a thin elastic film which acts as a preservative. Linseed oil is the chief ingredient of many paints—the pigment is added principally for decorative effect—and it is also used in making linoleum, oilcloth and printing-ink, as well as for oiling cricket bats. The world's largest producers are Argentina and the USA.

Tung oil (or *Chinese wood oil*) is expressed from the nuts of the tung tree, which is a native of China. It has very good 'drying' properties, and has recently come into prominence as a substitute for linseed oil. Until thirty years ago China was the only producer, but tung trees are now being cultivated in Florida and Argentina.

Castor seed is produced by a perennial plant which sometimes reaches a height of 6 m (20 ft), and is cultivated in tropical regions. Castor oil has certain medicinal uses and is one of the raw materials from which sodium ricinoleate, used by dentists for treating gum troubles, is manufactured; it is an excellent lubricant where particularly high temperatures are developed; and is an ingredient of certain plastics, soaps and enamels. The residue after crushing is rich in proteins, but cannot be used as fodder, since it contains a poison which can be fatal to cattle. It is, however, used as fertiliser.

Rape seed is obtained from a plant related to the cabbage, and is grown chiefly in warm temperate regions. It enters into human diet in the East, and its oil is used as a lubricant and for 'quenching' steel plates.

Sesame seed comes from a small tropical plant with pretty bell-

Fig. 56 A crop of sunflowers in Bulgaria.

shaped flowers. It yields half its weight in an oil which closely resembles olive oil.

Sunflower seed was at one time eaten by peasants in Russia and eastern Europe, but it is nowadays crushed to produce oil for making margarine, soap and lubricants.

8

TIMBER

Trees are not only a source of food and drink; they also provide mankind with timber. In the three preceding chapters our main concern has been the fruit and the leaves; we must now turn to the material of which the trunks and branches are composed.

World distribution of forests

Generally speaking, Nature clothes the earth's surface with trees wherever rainfall is adequate and evenly distributed throughout the year—provided, of course, that the soils are deep enough to accommodate the roots and capable of holding water. In mid-latitude regions an annual fall of 500 mm (20 in) is sufficient, but in the tropics, where evaporation is greater, 2 025 mm (80 in) are necessary for the full growth of forest. There are some exceptions to the rule. In many monsoon lands, for example, so much rain falls during the summer months that forests prevail despite the dry winter season, and in 'Mediterranean' areas, where hardly any precipitation occurs in summer, much of the vegetation merits the description of, at any rate, 'woodland'. Here the trees have developed certain characteristics which enable them to survive the summer drought. Their roots may be long enough to reach down to water-saturated layers of the soil, or their leaves may be waxy or covered with hairs, so that transpiration of moisture is retarded.

In high latitudes and at high altitudes temperature also is important in controlling the distribution of forests. In common with almost all plants, trees cease to grow when the temperature falls below 6° C (43° F),[1] and they cannot survive at all unless there is a period of at least three months in every year during which the average temperature is above this figure. But the chief importance of temperature is that it controls the size and type of tree.

[1] In this connection 6° C (43° F) is described as a 'critical' temperature. Another 'critical' temperature is 0° C (32° F).

Fig. 57 shows the distribution of forests as Nature intended. It must, however, be remembered that many of the areas depicted on the map are now regions of forest in name only. In western and southern Europe particularly, trees have throughout history been ruthlessly cut down to clear the ground for grazing, cultivation and the spread of population.

Types of trees

Other things being equal, trees grow more rapidly and to greater heights and produce more luxuriant foliage in warm environments than in cool ones. This is due not only to the fact that higher temperatures speed up the chemical processes of growth, but also to the fact that a longer period is available in the year during which the growth of the tree can continue. The influence of temperature is more clearly seen in the shape and character of the leaves and the manner in which the tree conducts itself throughout the year. On this basis, two main types of trees may be distinguished.

1. Broad-leaved trees

These, as their name implies, have broad, flat leaves similar to those of the elm, oak and beech, and grow wherever the average temperature remains above 6° C (43° F) for at least six months of the year. In the tropics and in warm temperate environments, where this 'critical' temperature is exceeded throughout the whole twelve months, the habits of the trees do not display any particular rhythm. In fact, different parts of the same tree may be in leaf, flowering, bearing fruit and casting off their leaves all at the same time. Such trees are therefore referred to as 'broad-leaved evergreens'. In cool temperate regions, such as the British Isles, where winter temperatures fall below the critical figure, the broad-leaved trees adjust themselves to the situation by casting off their leaves in the autumn and 'sleeping' till the return of warmer conditions in spring. Trees which regularly discard their leaves in response to a seasonal rhythm are described as 'deciduous'.[1]

2. Coniferous trees

Coniferous (i.e. cone-bearing) trees generally represent an adjustment to colder conditions, and are found mainly in the northern hemisphere. Their leaves consist of long, narrow

[1] All trees are in a sense deciduous, since they must eventually cast off their leaves at one time or another. The term is, however, properly confined to trees which drop their leaves at a certain season.

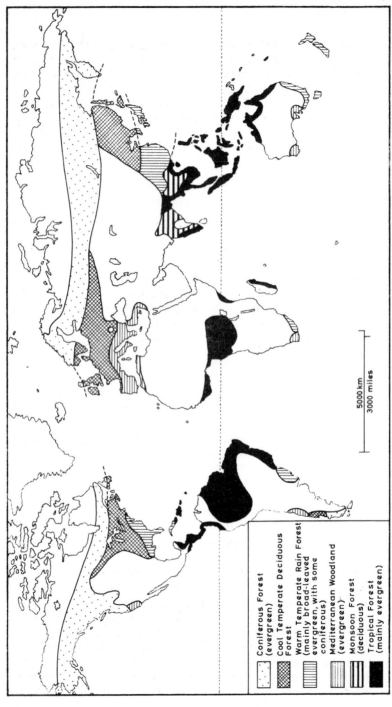

Fig. 57 World distribution of forests.

Coniferous Forest (evergreen)

Cool Temperate Deciduous Forest

Warm Temperate Rain Forest (mainly broad-leaved evergreen, with some coniferous)

Mediterranean Woodland (evergreen)

Monsoon Forest (deciduous)

Tropical Forest (mainly evergreen)

5000 km
3000 miles

'needles' or 'spines', which reduce transpiration to the minimum, and since the trees cannot complete their full annual cycle of growth within the comparatively short summer, they retain their leaves throughout the winter, and are therefore described as 'evergreens'. At the first signs of warmer conditions, they are thus already equipped to resume the process of growth. Their conical shape, and the shape of the needles themselves, prevent the branches from being broken down by accumulations of snow.

Types of wood

Commercially, timber falls into two main categories—hardwoods and softwoods.

Hardwoods
These are obtained mainly from the broad-leaved trees, and are, in fact, usually both heavy and hard; but this is not always the case. Poplar is an exception among the temperate woods, while balsa is a tropical 'hardwood' well known to model aircraft builders for its properties of lightness and softness. Obechi is another soft 'hardwood'.

Softwoods
Softwoods come from coniferous trees, such as the fir, spruce and larch. They are lighter in weight and softer than hardwoods, and have a more open texture. The term 'deal' is popularly applied to softwood timbers in general, but is more accurately reserved for the wood of the spruce (white deal) and the Scots fir (red or yellow deal).

Uses of timber

To our remote ancestors forests were a mixed blessing. They were useful in that they provided fuel and an easily worked material for the construction of implements, furniture, boats and so on, but they were also a hindrance, since they often stood in the way of grazing, cultivation and the spread of population. In western and Mediterranean Europe, and in many parts of North America, vast numbers of trees have throughout history been burnt down or felled simply to clear the ground for man's expanding activities. And in the tropics cultivators have always waged incessant war against the trees. But within the last hundred years it has been realised that we can no longer afford to cut down forests and use up timber unless steps are taken to replace them. The world's remaining forests are now recognised as an important source of wealth, which must not be allowed to fail, and nations in most parts of the world are, therefore, careful to plant fresh trees to replace those they have cut down. The 'robber economy' of yesterday has changed to the practice of *reafforestation* today.

Timber has three main uses:

Timber as fuel
Although in many parts of the world coal, petroleum and hydro-electricity have taken the place of wood as a fuel, a surprisingly large proportion of the world's timber is still used for this purpose.

Timber as constructional material
As a material for a wide range of constructional purposes, wood has many advantages which have recommended it to man throughout the ages. It is easily cut and shaped, it is strong for its weight, is a good shock absorber and a good insulator against heat and cold. For this last reason alone it makes an excellent material for the construction of houses in particularly warm or particularly cold climates. On the other hand, it is inflammable and liable to attack by insects and fungi. In the main structure of ships, bridges, harbour installations, houses, offices and factories, wood has given place to iron, steel and concrete, but vast quantities of timber are still required for other parts of the construction, as well as for railway sleepers, pit-props and telegraph poles.

For the making of smaller items, such as articles of furniture, crates and packing-cases, the demand is greater than it was formerly. The amount of plywood produced is now twice the pre-war output, and since the war there has been a steady increase in the export of 'furniture' timbers from tropical regions—in particular, West Africa.

Timber as raw material
Approximately one-fifth of the world's timber is made into wood pulp (see pp. 118–20). The wide use of timber for this purpose is a development of the last seventy years or so. Smaller quantities are used for a number of other industrial processes; for example, the manufacture of turpentine, resins, disinfectants, certain dyes and cellulose for paint and rayon.

The chief producing areas of the various kinds of timber are discussed in the remainder of this chapter.

Tropical and monsoon forests

Immense reserves of hardwood timber are contained in the tropical lowlands of South and Central America, Africa, South-east Asia and Indonesia, where conditions of great heat and humidity lead to the luxuriant and abundant growth of forests. Although some parts of the monsoon areas have been cleared by generations of cultivators, much of these forests has remained untouched until recent years.

Commercial exploitation

Exploitation of the timber is restricted by the following considerations:

1. The hot, steamy atmosphere leads to difficulties in health, labour supply, sanitation, etc.
2. Thousands of different species of trees exist, only a few of which are commercially valuable.
3. The trees occur in 'mixed stands', i.e. groups of trees consist of many different varieties. In order to procure one particular tree, it is often necessary to fell several others. This wastes time and adds to the expense of lumbering.
4. The tangled undergrowth and swampy ground often make transport to the sawmill extremely difficult.
5. The forests are situated far from consuming centres in the temperate lands, and bulk and weight influence the cost of overseas export.

The exploitation of tropical timbers is therefore confined to those which have such special qualities as make them saleable in spite of their high price. *Teak* provides a good example. It is remarkably straight grained, has great structural strength, is hard and free from knots, and cuts into planks of great length and width; it impedes rust, and is highly resistant to fire, water and boring insects. These qualities have made teak a desirable wood for use in shipbuilding and the construction of railway coaches, in panelling and so on. It comes principally from the Arakan Yoma region of Burma, where elephants are trained to lift the heavy tree-trunks, which are then floated down[1] the River Irrawaddy to the sawmills at Rangoon. *Mahogany* comes chiefly from British Honduras and Mexico. It is a difficult wood to work, by reason of its 'double grain', but since it has an attractive colour and takes a high polish, it is much in demand for household furniture. Various other 'mahoganies' come from other tropical regions. Further examples of tropical timbers are

[1] Teak in growth is heavier than water. Before it will float, it has to be 'killed' by cutting off some of the bark.

ebony, a finegrained pitch-black wood from Africa and south-eastern Asia; *rosewood*, from West Africa and Brazil; and *greenheart*, which has properties and uses similar to those of teak. Many tropical timbers are used in making veneers (thin slices applied as decorative facings to less attractive woods).

The near-exhaustion of many of the traditional furniture woods from temperate deciduous forests (walnut, oak, etc.) has since the war led to a growing export to Europe of 'substitute' woods, often with unfamiliar African names. One of the most widely used 'new' timbers is *afrormosia*, a brownish-yellow wood resembling teak.

Timber products

Besides timber, the tropical forests yield also various timber products, amongst which may be mentioned:

Tannin, which softens hides so that they are converted into leather (see p. 152). This comes from many different types of tree in all kinds of climates, but the chief tropical source of tannin is the *mangrove*, a tree which grows on swampy coasts.

Copal, a resin from certain trees in Zaïre and elsewhere, which is used in making varnish.

Lac, a sticky, resinous material deposited by insects on the twigs of trees in South-east Asia, which is used in the manufacture of lacquers and enamels.

Chicle, from which chewing-gum is made. It oozes from cuts made in the bark of *zapote* trees in Central America.

Camphor, which is produced by distilling shavings of wood from camphor trees.

Rubber is a tropical 'timber product' of such importance that the whole of the next chapter has been devoted to it.

Warm Temperate rain-forests

These are found in such areas as south-eastern Australia, North Island of New Zealand, Natal and southern Brazil. Since rainfall is distributed fairly evenly throughout the year, they probably resembled in their original state the forests of tropical regions, but many parts have been cleared for cultivation or habitation. As in the tropics, the trees exist in a great variety of species. Most of them are broad-leaved types (deciduous or evergreen according to situation), but certain kinds of coniferous trees are also found.

The *kauri pine* is peculiar to New Zealand. It has a very straight stem, grows to a great height (sometimes to 55 m [180 ft]) and was for many years valued for use as ships' masts. It also yields *kauri gum*, a resin which is found in the fossil state in ground once occupied by forest. It is used in making varnish. *Pitchpine* is a conifer, native to the south-eastern USA, which provides not only timber but also resin and turpentine. *Quebracho* (or 'break-axe'), which grows in the forests of Paraguay, and *wattle*, found in Natal and many similar areas, are both important sources of tannin.

Mediterranean woodland

Very little now remains of the evergreen woodland which once covered much of the regions around the Mediterranean Sea. Throughout history the trees have been progressively and deliberately cut down to make room for settlement and crops, and destroyed by accidental fires in the dry summer season and by the depredations of goats. One of the few remaining trees of economic importance is the evergreen *cork oak*. Every ten years or so the bark is carefully removed in slabs which may weigh as much as 16 kg (35 lb), and processed so that it becomes the 'cork' of commerce. Although now to some extent superseded by plastics for use in sealing bottles, cork is also ground into small pieces and used in the manufacture of linoleum.

In the western United States a few stands still remain of the so-called 'mammoth trees' (*Sequoia gigantea*), some examples of which are over 3 000 years old and over 90 m (300 ft) in height (fig. 58). Another variety of sequoia, the *Californian redwood*, of which rather more remain, provides excellent timber. In the 'Mediterranean' parts of Australia are a number of *eucalypts* or 'gum trees'. They are evergreens which sometimes reach a great height, and since they have the peculiar habit of turning the edges of their leaves to the sun, afford very little shade. The gum exuded from the leaves gives off an aromatic scent and yields an oil (eucalyptus oil), which is used as a disinfectant and was at one time popular in the treatment of the common cold. Their hardness and their capacity for resisting water and insects make two members of the eucalyptus family, *jarrah* and *karri*, particularly suitable for use in making railway sleepers, harbour piles, paving-blocks and flooring.

Cool temperate deciduous forests

Western Europe has been as widely denuded of forest cover as the Mediterranean lands, and in the lowlands only patches of

Fig. 58 A giant sequoia in Yosemite National Park in the state of California. This is one of the oldest living things in the world; it probably began growing about 1500 BC.

the original vegetation remain. In the populous regions of eastern North America a similar clearance has taken place, but southern Chile and parts of eastern Asia have been relatively unaffected by man's activities.

Most of the characteristic hardwood timbers have their own specialised uses—chiefly in the manufacture of furniture, panelling and interior decorative work, and in making such articles as have a greater permanence or value than those made from the softer coniferous timbers. *Oak*, for example, has unequalled qualities of strength and durability; *ash*, being flexible, is ideal for making curved members of chairs and carriage bodies, and for oars and tool handles; *beech* is turned easily on a lathe; and *walnut* warps only slightly and can be finished attractively.

Mountain forests

The slopes of highland regions in most parts of the world are covered with forest growth. The types of tree vary with altitude, and it is, therefore, possible to observe a succession of timbers ranging from tropical hardwoods at the foot to conifers on the upper slopes. In this respect the ascent of a mountain in the tropics much resembles a journey from the Equator to the Pole.

Coniferous forests

Stretching all the way across the northern continents, between the inhospitable tundra regions and the zone of deciduous trees, lies a broad belt of coniferous forest, to which the Russian name *taïga* is sometimes applied. It consists very largely of three species of tree, the *pine*, the *spruce*[1] and the *fir*, although in the southern parts of the belt the deciduous *larch* and *birch* are intermingled with the conifers. No such belt exists in the Southern Hemisphere, since none of the continental masses reaches high enough latitudes.

Commercial exploitation

'The northern forests', as they are often called, are the world's chief source of softwood timber for making a wide variety of products, including pitprops, scaffolding, telegraph poles, crates, boxes, cheap furniture, window-frames, doors and wood pulp, and are the scene of the world's most intensive lumbering activities. Exploitation is much easier here than in the tropical forests for several reasons:

[1] The traditional Christmas tree is a young spruce.

1. There are comparatively few species of trees, all of which are commercially valuable.
2. The trees occur in 'homogeneous stands', i.e. all the trees in a group are of the same kind.
3. The climate, far from being a hindrance, as in the tropics, can in fact be of great assistance in the transport of the timber to the sawmills. The trees are felled in autumn or early winter, when the sap is low and the wood 'crisp', and hauled over the snow-covered ground to the frozen rivers, where they remain upon the ice until the spring thaw carries them downstream to the sawmills (fig. 59).

It must not be assumed that lumbering activities are widespread throughout the entire belt of forest. In many parts the soil is too swampy to produce trees of adequate size or quality, and, in view of the enormous bulk of timber, large-scale exploitation tends to be confined to areas where transport by water is available for most of the journey to the consuming centres.

Producing areas

The four chief areas of softwood timber production within the northern forests are:

British Columbia and the western states of the USA, where on the mountain slopes are found not only the smaller varieties of spruce and fir, but also the lofty *Douglas fir*[1] (or *Columbian* or *Oregon pine*), whose merits were first pointed out in 1824 by a Scottish botanist named David Douglas. It should be noticed that the presence of coniferous trees in this region is due to altitude rather than latitude.

Eastern Canada, where much of the timber is devoted to the production of wood pulp.

The USSR, where recently a great expansion of the timber industry has taken place. The once inaccessible forest areas of northern Siberia are now being opened up to supplement production from the 'older' areas behind Leningrad and Archangel. Russia now provides almost a third of the world's softwoods.

The Scandinavian and Baltic countries, in particular Sweden and Finland. Much of Sweden's production is 'prefabricated' into window-frames, doors and general joinery before leaving the country; while a large part of Finland's output is made into plywood and wood-pulp.

Wood pulp

Wood pulp is the most important of the softwood 'timber products'. From it are made two commodities of considerable significance in the modern world—paper and cellulose 'jelly',

[1] The world's tallest tree is a Douglas fir.

Fig. 59 Logs floating down the Ume River to Umeå in Sweden.

which is used in making such things as artificial silk and cellulose paints. In the manufacture of *newsprint* (the paper on which newspapers are printed) and other cheap papers, logs[1] are crushed under water by heavy machinery, and the resulting paste is rolled out and dried to form thick slabs of 'wood pulp'. These are exported to the consuming countries, where they are soaked and rolled out again, this time into sheets of paper, by machines which are sometimes as much as 30 m (100 yards) long (fig. 60). For superior qualities of paper, the logs, before being pulped, are cut up and boiled under pressure in a chemical solution. By this method the wood is reduced to an even, finely-textured mass. *Hardboard*, used for panelling, doors, built-in cupboards, etc., is made from woodchips by a process not unlike paper manufacture.

[1] Usually from trees which are too small to have any value as timber.

Fig. 60 The 'wet end' of a newsprint machine at Bowater's Kemsley Division in Kent. Fluid pulp (shown at the top of the picture) flows on to a fast-moving sieve of fine wire mesh and is carried forward as a vast, flat layer of dripping fibre at which the two men are looking. The water is extracted by gravity and suction, and the layer becomes transformed into damp and rather weak paper before reaching the stage seen in the bottom left-hand corner of the photograph.

Cellulose 'jelly' is prepared from wood pulp by making a chemical solution of the cellulose which forms the cell-walls of the wood.[1] When forced through extremely fine holes in a 'spinneret'[2] into an acid bath, the solution hardens into filaments which are twisted together to make *rayon* (or artificial silk) yarn. Cellulose also forms the basis of the hard, glossy paints which are sprayed on to car bodies, and is used to give a shiny, transparent surface to articles of furniture and radio and television sets.

[1] Cellulose 'jelly' is also produced from cotton linters (see footnote, p. 149).
[2] So called after the organ in a spider through which it spins its web (see p. 144).

9

RUBBER

Natural rubber

The history of rubber

The selection of imaginary teams is a harmless and amusing pastime in which most of us have at one time or another indulged; and if we set out to choose eleven raw materials to represent the modern world, rubber would certainly be a most important member of the 'team'.[1] Rubber is shock-proof, elastic and an excellent waterproofing material, and although now almost completely superseded by plastics for electrical insulation, it still has a multitude of essential uses. A list of items in which rubber plays a vital part—footballs, tennis-balls and games kit generally, 'plimsolls' and 'Wellingtons', swimming-caps, raincoats, tyres, belts and cables, latex foam, hot-water bottles and ordinary 'elastic', to name but a few—provides an interesting illustration of the changes in man's everyday life over the last hundred years.

The Indians of Peru and Central America realised from quite early times that a milky fluid issued from cuts made in the bark of a certain kind of tree, and discovered, moreover, that by heating this *latex* they could produce a sticky, wax-like substance which could be used for waterproofing. *Caoutchouc*[2] was first introduced into Europe in 1735 by a French explorer named Charles Marie de la Condamine (who had been sent to Peru to measure an arc of the meridian at the Equator), but little notice was taken of the material until the distinguished English chemist, Joseph Priestley, in 1770 pointed out its value for rubbing out pencil marks. Since by this time a certain amount of caoutchouc was being imported from India, it also acquired the name of 'india-rubber'.

For the next fifty years or so rubber remained merely an 'eraser', until in 1823 Charles Mackintosh discovered a method of waterproofing cloth with india-rubber. From that time raincoats have been called 'mackintoshes' or 'macks' after their inventor.

---

[1] You may like to choose the rest of the 'team' yourself. Here are a few suggestions: coal, iron, copper, uranium, cotton, petroleum.
[2] The Peruvian name for crude rubber.

Unfortunately, the first 'mackintoshes' were soft and sticky in summer and hard and inelastic in winter. Many attempts were made to overcome the difficulty, but met with no success until an American inventor, Charles Goodyear, adopted the suggestion put to him by his friend, Nicholas Hayward, that the crude rubber be heated with sulphur and dried in the sun.[1] The process was not completely successful, since it hardened only the surface of the rubber or 'gum', as the Americans call it. Strangely enough, another four years elapsed before Goodyear, in 1844, hit upon the idea of heating rubber and sulphur together in a simple oven—i.e. the modern method of 'vulcanisation'. Meanwhile Goodyear had been reduced to such extremes of poverty that he was forced to sell even his son's schoolbooks.

Until this time world exports of rubber were insignificant, and came mainly from trees which grew wild in the Amazon Basin. In the years which followed Goodyear's invention vast areas were progressively devastated by the native Indians in yet another example of a 'robber economy'. It eventually became evident that supplies of 'Pará'[2] rubber were no longer sufficient, and in 1876 Henry (afterwards Sir Henry) Wickham managed to smuggle out of Brazil several thousand rubber-seeds. These were brought to Kew Gardens in London, and later plants reared from them were successfully transferred to Ceylon and then to Malaya, where the careful cultivation of rubber in European-owned plantations first began. Towards the end of the nineteenth century, in response to an enormous and sudden increase in demand, plantations were set up in Indonesia, and subsequently in West Africa and the Congo (now Zaïre).

This enormous increase was due to two main factors:
1. The invention of the pneumatic tyre, which was so important in the early development of the cycle and car industries.
2. The wide application of electricity as a source of power and lighting, which necessitated vast quantities of rubber for the insulation of wires and cables.

Today world production of what we must now call 'natural' rubber reaches nearly 3 million tons, over two-thirds of it coming from Indonesia and Malaysia, and only a ery small amount from Brazil (fig. 61).

The rubber tree
Latex can actually be obtained from a number of different species

[1] The idea is said to have occurred to Hayward in his sleep.
[2] *Pará*—the name by which Belém, a trading centre near the mouth of the Amazon, was then known to foreigners. It now has a population of nearly 600 000.

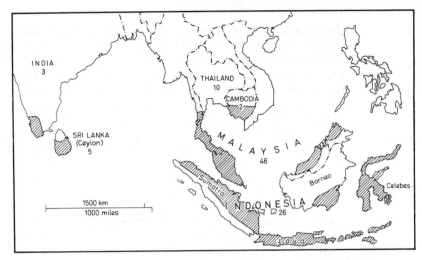

Fig. 61 The areas of South-east Asia which produce plantation rubber. The figures indicate percentages of the world's total production of natural rubber—nearly 3 million tons. The only other notable producing countries apart from those shown above are Liberia (2·5 per cent), Nigeria (2 per cent) and Zaïre (1·5 per cent). Brazil now produces less than 1 per cent.

of trees, but the most satisfactory one for the purpose is the *Hevea brasiliensis*, which came originally from the Amazon forests. The tree needs a fertile soil, bears leaves resembling those of the elm, and when fully grown may attain a height of 20 m (65 ft) or so. A constant temperature of about 27° C (80° F) and rainfall of at least 1 525 mm (60 in), evenly distributed throughout the year, are essential; the tree is, therefore, confined to regions of Equatorial climate.

Tapping and processing
Tapping is effected by making narrow slits in the bark of the tree, and the latex is collected in small aluminium cups placed below the incisions (fig. 62). The flow of latex is Nature's way of healing the wounds, and after about half an hour the liquid coagulates and seals up the cuts. The contents of the cups are collected daily by tappers, and emptied into tanks in the plantation factory. Formic acid is added to make the latex 'curdle', water is excluded by compression, and sheets of 'rubber' are formed by rolling and drying or smoking. At this stage the crêpe rubber used in soling footwear is produced. Latex-foam or foam-rubber, now widely used in upholstery, mattresses, etc. (fig. 63), is made by extracting the water in a 'centrifuging plant'. The effect is similar to that produced by whipping the white of an egg.

Natural rubber 123

Fig. 62 Tapping a rubber tree in a Malaysian plantation. The tapper removes a very thin, sloping strip of bark with his curved knife or *jebong*, so that the latex wells up and runs down the cut into the cup from a small metal spout which the tapper sticks into the tree. (This can just be seen above the tapper's elbow.) The black spots show the amount of each month's tapping.

Subsequent treatment, after the export of the sheets to the manufacturing countries, depends on the purpose for which the rubber is intended. Generally speaking, this is a matter of heating with controlled amounts of sulphur; the higher the proportion of sulphur, the harder the rubber so produced. The hardest kind of all is *vulcanite* (or *ebonite*), which was at one time widely used in making fountain-pens and radio and electrical instrument panels. In the manufacture of car tyres particles of graphite are incorporated in the rubber to reinforce its wearing qualities.

Organisation and production

The cultivation of rubber in plantations involves constant weeding and hoeing, quite apart from the daily collection of latex, and it is no accident that most of the world's plantations were established in the Far East, where an abundance of cheap labour was available. In Malaysia today about half the rubber comes from plantations owned by European companies and half from small-holdings owned by local farmers. A wartime attempt by the Ford Motor Company to establish plantations in South America failed, largely on account of the lack of a local labour supply. The Firestone Company's plantations in Liberia are, however, a thriving concern.

Fig. 63 Making a *Dunlopillo* mattress. Partly 'frothed' latex is poured into a mould, where it remains for about half an hour. At the beginning of this period a vacuum is created in the mould and the latex is cooled to below freezing point. Carbon dioxide gas is then passed through and the temperature raised to above boiling point, thus causing the latex to set and vulcanise. After cooling off, the mattress is stripped from the mould, as shown above.

The world rubber market is subject to periodic fluctuations similar to those which affect the sugar industry, and various agreements regulating production have been concluded in the last forty years in an attempt to keep the price of rubber stable. The increasing use of synthetic rubber after the Second World War introduced further complications.

Synthetic rubber

At the beginning of the war synthetic substitutes for rubber were already being produced experimentally in both Germany and the USA. Under the influence of war conditions production increased at a tremendous rate, and world production of synthetic rubber now appreciably exceeds that of natural rubber. The USA now produces 75 per cent of the world's total supplies (excluding the USSR), West Germany 10 per cent, the United Kingdom 9 per cent and Canada 6 per cent.

Most of the synthetic rubbers are manufactured from petroleum by the process known as *polymerisation* (see p. 237), and each brand has its own particular properties. What is often referred to in the trade as *SBR*[1] or 'general purpose' synthetic rubber has similar properties to natural rubber and replaces it for many uses, car tyres, for example. *Butyl*, which is a little softer than natural rubber, makes better inner tubes, because of its low permeability to air. *Neoprene* and *Perbunan* are not affected by acids and oils, and can, therefore, be used in the manufacture of such things as oil cans. On account of its resistance to flame *Neoprene* is also used for conveyor belts for the National Coal Board. Plant for the production of synthetic rubber is understandably situated close to the refineries whose products it uses. The huge works near Fawley on Southampton Water provides a good example.

World production of synthetic rubber has now overtaken that of natural rubber, as will be seen from fig. 64.

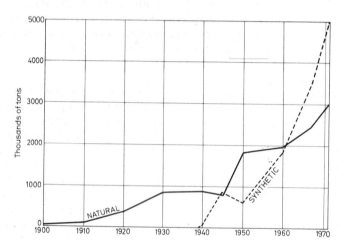

Fig. 64 Graph showing world production of natural and synthetic rubber from 1900 to 1971.

[1] *Styrene Butadiene Rubber*

10

WOOL AND COTTON

Textiles

Man's earliest and simplest 'clothes' were fashioned from the skins of fur-bearing animals, and even today we wear animal skins as fur coats, leather jackets, kid gloves and suède shoes. But most of our present-day articles of clothing are made from woven materials of one kind or another. Such materials are described as textiles (from a Latin word meaning 'to weave'), in the manufacture of which two essential processes are involved:

1. Spinning

The habit of idly twisting things between finger and thumb—a form of 'doodling'—was probably as common with early man as with his civilised descendants; and in this way he may have accidentally discovered that a tuft of wool from a sheep's back could, by the action of pulling and twisting, be drawn out into a long strand. This pulling and twisting motion is the basic feature of the process of spinning, by which the tangled fibres of wool, cotton, etc., can be rearranged so that they all lie more or less parallel to one another in the form of a thread. Nowadays, of course, the operation is performed in factories by complicated machines, but before the Industrial Revolution spinning was done with no more elaborate equipment than a foot-operated spinning-wheel, or even by only a simple distaff (a cleft stick holding a supply of wool) and a spindle on to which the thread was wound as it passed from between the fingers. Since a deft touch was obviously required, spinning was essentially women's work,[1] as may, indeed, be gathered from the word 'spinster'.

2. Weaving

This consists of interlacing the threads of 'yarn' formed by spinning the fibres so as to produce a piece of cloth or 'fabric' (fig. 65). Weaving was, no doubt, originally performed in a process similar to darning, by laboriously carrying the cross-

[1] The female side of a 'family tree' is known as the 'distaff' side.

threads or 'weft' over and under a 'warp' of parallel threads fixed on a rough framework. But eventually a simple *loom* was invented, in which alternate members of the warp could be raised or lowered together, and the weft formed by passing a shuttle loaded with yarn from one side of the work to the other. Some of the looms used in woollen mills in remote parts of Wales and Scotland—or in school handicraft rooms—are only slightly more complicated than the equipment operated by weavers of former times.

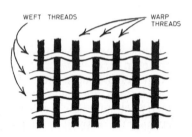

Fig. 65 Weaving — in which the fabric is produced by interlacing warp threads and weft threads.

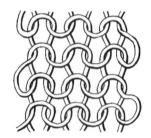

Fig. 66 Knitting—in which a continuous length of thread passes through loops made on the previous row.

Knitting differs from weaving in that a single continuous length of yarn is used in place of the warp and weft (fig. 66). Each 'row' of the fabric consists of a series of loops formed by running the thread through the loops of the previous row. In 1589 a Nottinghamshire clergyman named William Lee invented a 'framework knitting' machine capable of knitting at 600 stitches a minute (i.e. about six times the speed of an experienced hand-knitter using the familiar 'needles' or 'pins'); but it was not until about 1830 that a machine was devised (by a French inventor) by means of which a circular fabric could be made,[1] such as is now used for vests and stockings, for instance.

Types of fibres
Textiles are made from three types of fibres.
1. Animal fibres, such as the wool of sheep (fig. 69), the Angora goat, the alpaca and the camel. There is no biological difference between hair and wool; but wool has two important characteristics by which it is distinguished from hair (and indeed all other textile fibres). Wool fibres are covered with extremely minute 'scales' like those on a fish (fig. 68), which make it possible to compress

[1] Thus was carried out mechanically the operation of knitting 'on four needles'.

Fig. 67 A crofter in Stornoway in the Outer Hebrides weaving Harris tweed. The loom is operated by a treadle; it is owned by the weaver himself and the work is carried out in his own home using yarn supplied to him by the local spinning plant.

a mass of wool into a material known as 'felt' without the process of weaving. Moreover, the fibres are not straight, but finely curled; a woollen fabric, therefore, contains a vast number of tiny air-cells, which, since air is a poor conductor, forms a barrier to the passage of heat. It is this insulating layer rather than the actual thickness of the material which imparts warming properties to a woollen garment.

Fig. 68 Greatly magnified view of part of a wool fibre. The scales on adjacent fibres interlock, so giving strength to the thread. The sectional view (on the right) shows the dark core of the fibre, which, if not neutralised in the operation of bleaching, causes a white wool fabric to turn yellow with age.

2. *Vegetable fibres*, such as cotton and linen.
3. *Man-made fibres*, such as rayon, nylon, Terylene and so on. The first of these (rayon) did not come into wide use until after 1920.

The two fibres which form the subject of this chapter are the ones most commonly used for clothing.

Wool

Although woollen garments have always been of great importance to nearly all peoples of the temperate zones,[1] wool represents less than one-tenth of all the fibres used in industry. It may be obtained from a number of animal species, but by far the chief of these are sheep.

Sheep

Much has already been said about the climatic conditions in which sheep thrive and about the cross-breeding of sheep over the last 150 years, which has led to the development of modern varieties. It is sufficient here to remind the reader that breeds designed specifically for wool-bearing are found more particularly in drier regions, where the pastures are not so rich as those required for mutton sheep. The mid-latitude grasslands of the southern hemisphere, which now produce two-thirds of the world's wool, are ideal for the purpose.

Classification of wools

Wools vary in the thickness, strength, lustre, curliness and length of the tiny fibres or 'staples' of which they are composed, but, broadly speaking, they fall into three main categories.

Merino wool. This is 'long-stapled',[2] curly, lustrous and fine but strong, and is sometimes referred to as 'Botany wool'. It represents about a third of all the wool produced, and is used chiefly in the manufacture of high-quality textiles for clothing. The Merino breed of sheep, from which it is obtained, originated in the Atlas region of North Africa, and was introduced to Spain in the Middle Ages. From there it spread to other countries of Europe and later became the basis of the wool-producing flocks reared on the grasslands of the southern hemisphere.

Crossbred wool. The flesh of the Merino is, however, extremely poor, and quality and weight of fleece have been in some cases sacrificed by cross-breeding with English types of sheep in an attempt to produce more profitable dual-purpose animals. Crossbred sheep tend to yield a less desirable quality of wool with a shorter staple. Of the world's total output of wool 45 per cent is of this kind.

Coarse, 'low' or carpet wool. As the name implies, this is used principally in the manufacture of carpets. It is really a byproduct of mutton production, and is composed of short, thick fibres.

[1] The significant exceptions are the Chinese and the Japanese.
[2] Wool staples vary in length from 2·5 to 30 cm. The longest staples of all are obtained from the fleeces of Lincoln sheep, which have been known to produce fibres 57 cm (23 in) long.

Wool-producing areas

Australia contains about 175 million sheep (representing 16 per cent of the world total), half of them in parts of the Murray-Darling Basin which are too dry for the cultivation of grain or the rearing of sheep other than Merinos. The sheep-runs are of enormous extent, so that in the prevailing conditions of near-drought pastures have the chance to recover. Moreover, the danger of soil erosion as a result of overgrazing (see p. 171) is always present. Australia produces one-third of the world's wool, and three-quarters of her output is of the Merino type, the remainder being made up of 'crossbreds' (fig. 71).

New Zealand, since she experiences a higher rainfall than the sheep-rearing regions of Australia, specialises in the production of mutton, and the commonest breeds are, therefore, English Lincolns and Leicesters and the 'home-bred' Corriedales. Practically the whole output of wool from New Zealand, amounting to 12 per cent of the world total, is crossbred wool. The greater part of it is exported to England to be manufactured in the West Yorkshire.

The Republic of South Africa. Conditions in the sheep-rearing areas of the High Veld of Transvaal and the Orange Free State closely resemble those in the Murray-Darling Basin of Australia, and farmers are confronted by similar hazards. The rainfall is unreliable, many sheep-runs have been permanently ruined by soil erosion and at times the grass over wide areas has been consumed within a matter of hours by swarms of locusts. The sheep are chiefly Merinos, and South African wool (5 per cent of world output) is only slightly less highly esteemed than Australian.

Argentina and Uruguay. At one time 'River Plate' wool was considered 'dirty' and of generally inferior quality, but flocks have been so improved by the importation of English breeds of sheep that now the pampa regions contribute about 9 per cent of the world's supply.

USA, UK and USSR. Vast numbers of sheep exist in the Northern Hemisphere and considerable quantities of wool are produced, mainly from dual-purpose animals, in the USA, the UK and the USSR. Britain's wool is almost entirely of the crossbred and carpet types. Although the fleeces of English Lincoln sheep yield high-quality wool with an exceptionally long staple, only the United States makes any significant contribution to supplies of the Merino type. The basic distinction between these areas and the wool-producing regions of the southern hemisphere lies in the fact that the latter are exporters, engaged

Fig. 69 Sheep-shearing on a lonely croft in the Island of Skye. Here the work is done in a field, using hand-operated clippers rather like garden shears without handles, the blades of which spring apart when the pressure of the shearer's hand is released.

Fig. 70 Sheep-shearing Australia. Here shearing is carried out by travelling teams of professional shearers, who work in a covered shed using clippers similar to those used by a hairdresser.

to only a small extent in the manufacture of their own produce, whereas the former are essentially manufacturers, absorbing not only local supplies of wool but also the greater part of the output from the Southern Hemisphere.

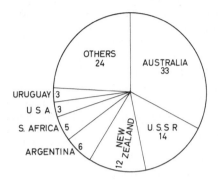

Fig. 71 Annual production of raw (greasy) wool by the chief producing countries. The figures indicate percentages of the world's total production of nearly 3 million tons per year.

Woollen manufactures

In its natural state, wool contains a certain amount of grease.[1] This forms the sheep's protection against moisture, and can readily be detected by squeezing a tuft of raw wool between the fingers. Wool is nearly always exported 'in the grease' (i.e. before the grease has been removed), otherwise, when compressed into the customary 140 kg (300 lb) bales, the fibres would matt together in transit and subsequent treatment would be made more difficult.

In the manufacture of woollen textiles, the first operation is the washing or 'scouring' of the wool to remove the grease; and an adequate supply of soft water, which will lather properly, has always been an essential factor in the siting of woollen-mills. The use of the word 'mill' to describe the factory in which textiles are made is, incidentally, a reminder that water was also used at one time as a source of power, just as it was in the building where flour was 'milled'. *Lanolin*, a waxy substance used in antiseptic ointments, is made from the purified grease.

After scouring, the fibres are ready for spinning and weaving. The many different types of fabric which may result from these two processes have led to a high degree of specialisation within the woollen industry, but two main branches may be recognised according to the type of yarn produced.

[1] The actual amount of grease varies, but on the average represents about half the weight of the raw wool.

Worsteds[1] are high-quality yarns made from only the longer fibres (or 'tops'), after the shorter fibres (or 'noils') have been removed in the process of 'combing'—an operation originally performed by hand with an instrument which was, in fact, similar to an ordinary hair comb. Worsted yarns are tightly twisted, and fabrics made from them (certain gabardines, serges and baratheas, for example) present a smooth appearance in which the pattern of the weave can be detected.

Woollens are yarns made from the shorter, thicker fibres. Fabrics made from such yarns (e.g. flannel) have a looser, more hairy appearance than worsteds, since the threads have not been twisted so tightly. After weaving, woollen cloths are 'felted' by compressing between rollers, so causing the fibres to interlock and concealing the pattern of the weave.

'Shoddy' and 'mungo' are the lowest qualities of woollen yarn. They are made by tearing up cast-off woollen garments, woollen rags, tailors' 'clippings', etc., and respinning the fibres.

Other wools

Besides sheep, a number of other species of animals yield wool.

The *Angora goat* is a native of Asia Minor, which is now reared successfully on the Karroos of South Africa. Its wool, known as *mohair*, consists of long, silky fibres and is used in making rugs, imitation furs, coats and jumpers. (It should be noted that Angora wool is the hair of the Angora *rabbit*.)

The *Kashmir* (or *Cashmere*) *goat* belongs to the Himalayan regions. Its downy undercoat (which grows only in winter) makes costly Kashmir shawls and carpets. The fleece weighs only about 9 g (3 oz) as against 3 kg (6 lb) in the case of the average sheep.

The *camel* yields hair which is employed not only for the bristles of paint brushes, but also (usually in combination with other fibres) for making coats, shawls, blankets, carpets, etc.

The *llama, alpaca, vicuña* and *guanaco* are natives of South America and provide limited supplies of very fine, soft, resilient wools.

Cotton

The plant from which cotton is produced was known in India nearly 3 000 years ago, and in the fifth century BC the Greek traveller Herodotus referred in his *History*[2] to a plant which

[1] Worsteds took their name from the village of Worstead in Norfolk, where a group of Flemish weavers settled in the twelfth century.
[2] Herodotus's *History* was really more of a 'Geography'.

bore what he called 'tree-wool'. It was not, however, until the Industrial Revolution that cotton became important as a textile material. Today, despite the increasing use of man-made yarns, it is still one of the cheapest and most abundant of textile fibres.

The cotton plant

The type of cotton plant most widely cultivated is an annual shrub about 1·25 m (4 ft) high. It requires a rich soil and grows best in subtropical regions where the annual rainfall is between 500 and 1 000 mm (20 and 40 in), with a hot, dry season in which the crop can ripen. It is particularly sensitive to frost, and temperatures must be above freezing point throughout the whole of its growing period of 200 days. The cotton plant bears pale yellow flowers, resembling nasturtiums, which gradually turn to pink and then dark red; in due course they fall, leaving green seed pods or 'bolls' like large filbert nuts in appearance (fig. 72). Soon these burst open and fluffy balls of lint or 'cotton-wool' are revealed, consisting of fibres, which are attached at their bases to hard, black seeds.

Fig. 72 Cotton plant, showing flower and lint ready for picking.

Types of cotton

Cottons, like wools, vary in the length and quality of their staples. Four main types enter into commerce:

Sea Island cotton. This derives its name from the fact that it was first cultivated in the small islands which lie off the coast of Georgia and South Carolina. It has since been introduced to Florida and parts of the British West Indies, and is the most highly esteemed of all cottons. The staples average 41 mm (1·6 in) in length and sometimes are as much as 65 mm (2·5 in) long. Only small quantities of Sea Island cotton are, however, produced.

Egyptian cotton is mainly of the 'Sakel' variety (or varieties bred from it). Its staples are long and silky, and it is the finest of the cottons which are cultivated on a wide scale. Egyptian cotton is only slightly inferior to the Sea Island type.

'*American*' *cotton* (as it is known in the trade) was introduced to the USA from India towards the end of the eighteenth century. In the United States the plant yields fibres about 25 mm (1 in) in length—slightly longer than in the 'mother country'.

Indian cotton, although somewhat improved in recent years, is coarser and shorter in staple, and makes only inferior fabrics.

Problems of cultivation

Soil erosion has in recent times become a major problem in many areas of cotton cultivation. In parts of the south-eastern United States, for instance, cotton has been grown continuously on the same soils for nearly three hundred years; and in spite of the use of fertilisers many of these soils are becoming exhausted and powdery—a condition which has been aggravated by constant, but very necessary, weeding and hoeing between the rows of plants. Water, streaming over the surface of the ground after the sudden bursts of rain which are a common feature of the climate of the cotton belt, is liable to wash away vast areas of soil.

The boll-weevil. The cotton plant is subject to attack by a number of insect pests and diseases, but the most damaging is the boll-weevil.[1] This is a small grub which on emerging from the egg, laid by the female in the cotton bud, eats its way through the entire bud, destroying it completely. The boll-weevil is a prolific breeder, and a single pair, unchecked, can produce 12 million grubs in one season. It entered the USA from Mexico in 1892, and the whole of the Cotton Belt is now liable to attack. Spraying the plants with poison, often from low-flying aircraft, is the only effective safeguard. In other parts of the world a similar pest, the pink boll-worm, is an equal menace.

Labour supply. Cotton buds on a single plant do not all burst at the same time, and it is therefore necessary for labourers capable of enduring the enervating heat of the subtropical summer to make daily rounds of the plants, picking off the fluffy masses of 'lint' from the open bolls. The first mechanical 'picker' (which worked on the same principle as a vacuum-cleaner) was invented in 1904, but until recently machine-picking (fig. 73) had been an economic proposition only in such exceptional areas at the irrigated cotton-lands of Arizona, where the bolls do, in fact, open at more or less the same time. Moreover, if cotton is to be produced cheaply enough to sell in the world's markets, it is impossible

[1] The word 'boll-weevil' was at one time a term of extreme abuse among American Negroes.

Fig. 73 A mechanical cotton-picker at work. In the U.S.A. 85 per cent of the crop is now harvested by machinery.

to pay field-labourers high wages. In the early days of cotton-growing in the USA, the problem was solved by the importation of slaves. In Africa and Asia the difficulty is less acute, but in Queensland, where the work of picking is done by white labourers, the Australian government pays a bounty to the plantation owners to offset the increased costs.

Ginning

Before cotton can be manufactured, it is necessary to separate the seeds from the lint, in the process known as 'ginning'. This was a slow and laborious operation, performed mainly by hand, until 1793, when an American inventor, Eli Whitney, devised a 'saw-gin', which removed the seeds mechanically and greatly speeded up the preparation of cotton for manufacture (fig. 74). The first part of the word 'saw-gin' refers to the fine-toothed, circular saws on to which the lint was fed, and the second part of the word is a shortened form of 'engine'. Whitney's invention gave an enormous incentive to cotton-growers in the United States, and marks the beginning of America's rise to a position of supremacy in cotton production. The state of South Carolina was so grateful to Whitney for his invention that it voted him a prize of £10 000![1] Ginning is almost always performed in factories close to the cotton fields, before the lint is compressed into

[1] Whitney then turned his inventive genius to the improvement of firearms, and died in 1825, having amassed a vast fortune. The basic principle of the saw-gin is said to have occurred to Whitney when he saw a cat thrusting its paw through the holes in a fence surrounding a chicken-run!

bales for dispatch to the manufacturers. The seeds make good fertiliser if ploughed back into the ground in preparation for the next year's crop, but they are usually crushed to extract the oil (see p. 106).

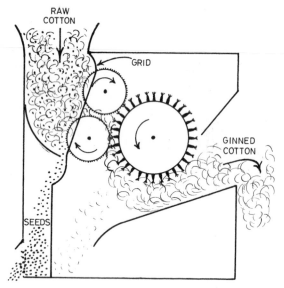

Fig. 74 Diagram illustrating Whitney's saw-gin.

Cotton-producing Areas (See figs. 70 and 71.)
The *USA* now provides about one-fifth of the world's cotton. The crop was originally grown in Georgia and South Carolina, but with the exhaustion of soils in the 'old' cotton lands, cultivation has since spread westwards to the lower Mississippi, to the 'black prairie' soils of Texas and more recently to California. Besides supplying her own very considerable cotton industry, situated chiefly in the north-east,[1] the United States contributes 50 per cent of the world's total exports of cotton.

For the last three centuries cotton has been of such importance in the economy of the south-eastern states that it is sometimes referred to as 'King Cotton'. It has also had an enormous effect on the human geography not only of America, but of the western world in general. The presence of vast numbers of Negroes, descendants of the slaves forcibly taken from West Africa to work in the cotton fields of the 'Deep South', has created in the United States an acute racial problem, and has, moreover, had a marked influence on the music of the last sixty years or so.

[1] The number of mills in the Cotton Belt itself is increasing rapidly.

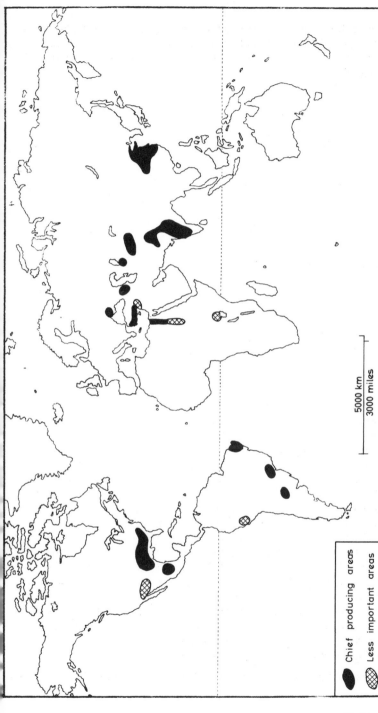

Fig. 75 The world's chief cotton-growing areas

Chief producing areas

Less important areas

5000 km
3000 miles

Cotton 139

Russia, with 17 per cent of world output, is now the second largest producer of raw cotton. This comes mainly from the Turkestan area, and is sent to Moscow and other industrial centres for manufacture. *China's* output (from the lower Yangtse-Kiang region) has declined during the last ten years.

India and *Pakistan* provide 14 per cent of the world's cotton. It is grown on the black, volcanic soils close to Bombay and also, with the help of irrigation, in the Punjab. Although recently improved, the cotton is short-stapled and of poor quality.

Other producing areas include *Egypt* (where crops on the Nile Delta have a yield twice as high as that of the USA and three times that of India), *Mexico* and *Brazil*.

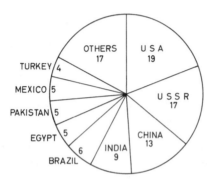

Fig. 76 World production of raw cotton (ginned). The figures indicate percentages of the world's total production of 11 million tons per year.

Cotton manufactures
The history of cotton textiles before the seventeenth century is rather obscure. It seems reasonably certain, however, that although the art of spinning and weaving cotton was known to people of the tropical regions at quite an early date, the fabrics produced were coarse and quite unlike those we are accustomed to use and wear ourselves. This is not really surprising, since cotton fibres are the shortest[1] of all textile fibres, and only the fact that they are flat and twisted makes it possible to spin them at all (fig. 77).

Cotton was first brought to England in 1298, for the making of candle wicks, but until the middle of the eighteenth century it was better known on the Continent than in Britain. In the next fifty years events moved rapidly. Whitney's invention of the saw-gin led to an enormous increase of raw cotton in America,

[1] Some varieties of cotton plant yield fibres only 5 mm long.

and a remarkable series of technical developments[1] in Britain made it possible not only to manufacture into fabrics all the cotton that America could supply, but also—and this was just as important—to spin and weave much finer threads than ever before. From about 1785 steam power began to be applied to textile machinery, and the Lancashire and Lanarkshire coalfields became established as the chief cotton-manufacturing areas of the world.

Fig. 77 Greatly magnified view of part of a cotton fibre. Until the plant has reached maturity, the fibre is filled with sap and resembles an inflated inner tube. The 'tube' becomes flat and ribbonlike after the sap has receded (see sectional view on right).

The cotton industry, like the woollen industry, was originally divided broadly into factories which were concerned mainly with spinning and those in which the weaving, dyeing and finishing processes were carried out (fig. 78). In Lancashire this division was particularly marked, but it is far less so today. Since the 1914–1918 War the cotton industry has suffered a great decline, due basically to developments in Japan, India, Pakistan and Hong Kong, where at first cheap labour and later modern, highly efficient machinery dealt crippling blows to many of Lancashire's obsolete and outmoded mills. There was, moreover, the competition of man-made fibres. The number of workers employed in the cotton industry today is only one-third of what it was fifteen years ago, and the present tendency is for the now more diversified operations to take place under one roof.

Cotton fabrics
These exist in a wide variety. The advantages of cotton (many of which it shares with linen) are briefly:
1. Unlike wool, it is not liable to shrink, nor is it subject to attack by moths.
2. It is stronger wet than dry; it will, therefore, stand up to repeated laundering.

[1] Amongst these were the following inventions:
Hargreave's spinning jenny (named after his daughter), which enabled one operator to handle a number of spindles, and thus caused the old spinning-wheel to be discarded (invented 1764, patented 1770).
Arkwright's water-frame, an improvement on Hargreave's spinning jenny, which was originally driven by a horse. Later, an improved version, known as the 'throstle,' was brought out (patented 1769).
Crompton's mule, another improved spinning-machine, principally important because it spun finer threads (invented 1779).
Cartwright's power loom—another textile invention by a clergyman (invented 1785).

Fig. 78 The weaving shed at Courtauld's cotton factory in Skelmersdale, Lancashire.

3. It can be made into thin fabrics which are cool and pleasant to the touch and which take an excellent finish.

On the other hand, cotton is easily creased—a disadvantage now largely overcome by impregnating the fibres with resin, so as to form a 'drip-dry' finish or by combining it with man-made fibres, notably polyester (p. 150).

11

SILK AND OTHER FIBRES

Silk

Silk is an animal fibre extruded from two tiny holes (or 'spinnerets') in the head of a caterpillar popularly known as the silkworm. The discovery of the art of spinning the frail, glossy filaments into thread and weaving from it fabrics of silk is attributed to a Chinese lady named Si-ling-she, who lived nearly 5 000 years ago, but it was not until the early days of the Roman Empire that the secret of silk production became known in Europe. And for centuries silk remained, in the western world, the 'aristocrat' of textiles. As recently as 1920 silk was in value (but not, of course, in quantity) one of the chief fibres used in making clothes. For many types of garment (particularly stockings) silk has now been replaced by nylon and other man-made fibres, but in the last ten years or so there have been increasing signs of a return to silk as a fashionable material for dresses.

Three-quarters of the world's present requirements of raw silk—which, despite a recent increase, stand at barely two-thirds the pre-war—figure are met by the combined output of China and Japan; and the latter country, although the largest single producer of silk textiles, still has a considerable surplus of raw silk for export to the USA and the traditional European centres of manufacture in Lyons, Milan, Krefeld and Zürich.

The silkworm

A number of different kinds of wild moth can be used for making silk,[1] but the species of silkworm most valuable commercially is the *Bombyx mori*, which feeds on the leaves of the white mulberry tree (fig. 79). The cultivation of the silkworm (*sericulture*) is possible in all of the many regions in which the mulberry tree grows, but since the mulberry is more productive and the insects are more prolific breeders under warm, dry conditions, it is, in fact, generally confined to subtropical and 'Mediterranean'

[1] Silk made from the fibres produced by wild moths (which feed on oak leaves) is known as *tussore* (or *tussah* or *tussur*). *Shantung* is a kind of tussore silk.

regions. Moreover, the rearing of silkworms 'in captivity' and the reeling of the threads calls for such an abundant supply of cheap and patient labour that it tended over the centuries to remain very largely the work of the wives and daughters of Chinese and Japanese peasant farmers.

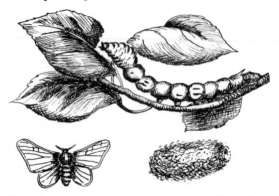

Fig. 79 *Bombyx mori*, showing larva, mulberry leaves and cocoon.

Sericulture

The eggs (of which the female deposits about 500) are laid in autumn, and are hatched out in the following spring, just as the mulberry is coming into leaf. From each egg emerges a caterpillar about 12 mm long, which for the next month feeds so voraciously[1] on the mulberry leaves spread out for it on large trays that it eventually grows to a length of 7·5 cm (3 in). On approaching the chrysalis stage, it mounts up on the twigs of mulberry and begins to spin its cocoon. Out of its two spinnerets proceed slender filaments of a sticky substance, which join together and harden, forming a flat thread; and by moving its head from side to side the caterpillar winds the thread around itself until it has become completely enclosed. If left to itself, a moth with pale grey wings would in about three weeks' time bore its way out of the cocoon, cutting the silk fibres across as it did so. In order to prevent this, most of the chrysalises are stifled in a heated oven, a few of the finest specimens being held back so that they can breed and provide sufficient eggs for the next year's crop.

Reeling

Each cocoon has now to be unwound. Although a cocoon may contain up to 1·6 km (1 mile) of silk fibre, normally only 360 to 450 m (400 to 500 yd) of it is strong enough to be 'reeled' off in a

[1] The caterpillars from 45 g (1·5 oz) of eggs eat in a month one ton of mulberry leaves—the crop of about three dozen trees!

continuous filament. This process may be carried out either by hand or in factories called 'filatures' by allowing the fibres to be taken up by reels revolving slowly overhead. Since single fibres would be too thin for weaving, it is customary to wind sometimes as many as twenty of them together, so as to form a thicker, stronger thread. At this stage the fibres are still rather sticky, and readily combine. Finally the thread is given a slight twist in the operation known as 'throwing'. The remainder of the cocoon comes away in a number of shorter, weaker filaments; these are combed and spun in the same way as wool to provide a yarn described as 'spun silk'.

Silk fabrics

Various special types of fabric may be made from silk.

Satin is a fabric so woven that the warp threads appear on one side only, thereby presenting a smooth, glossy surface.

Sateen is similar to satin, but is usually of lower quality. The bright surface of sateen is formed by the weft threads.

Velvet is a fabric in which the warp threads have been looped over fine wires and subsequently cut into tufts, so as to produce a 'pile', resembling the grass of a freshly cut lawn.

Plush is like velvet, but has a longer and less dense pile.

Damask was originally made only from silk, and takes its name from the town of Damascus.

It is nowadays common for silk fabrics to be imitated by using other fibres either wholly or in part.

Flax

Linen is the fabric made from the fibres of the inner bark or 'bast' of the flax plant, the seeds of which have already been discussed as the source of linseed oil. One of the oldest of fabrics, it is mentioned in the Bible, and is thought to have provided the wrappings of Egyptian mummies, but with the increasing use of cotton over the last two hundred years, the importance of linen for articles of clothing and general purposes in the home is now greatly diminished. In fact, nowadays a great deal of what is called 'household linen' is actually made of cotton.

Flax grown on rich, well-drained soils in cool or cold temperate regions produces the best fibre, and cultivation has always been concentrated on the North European Plain. The location of some of the historic centres of the linen industry is revealed by the names of certain types of fabric—*cambric* (from Cambrai in north-eastern France), *silesia* (a material used by tailors for pockets and sleeve linings) and *holland* (a coarse linen fabric), in addition to *Brussels lace* and *Irish linen* (from the Belfast area).

The flax plant is slender, rather like a cereal, grows to a height of about one metre and bears pretty, blue flowers[1] (fig. 80). It is sown in spring, and three or four months later is pulled up by hand, so as to obtain the maximum length of fibre. The stalks are then 'rippled' with combs to remove the seeds, and 'retted' (i.e. rotted) to get rid of the resinous matter, by soaking in water (nowadays in tanks) for several weeks. It is particularly important that the water used for this purpose should be 'soft', and the

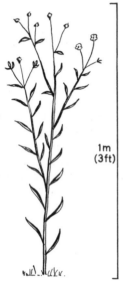

1m
(3ft)

Fig. 80 Flax plant.

peculiar quality of the waters of the River Lys is one of the factors which led to the establishment of the linen industry in Belgium. After 'grassing' (or drying), the woody core is removed by 'scutching' (or beating)—an operation originally performed by means of a hammer-like instrument, but now done on machines with revolving blades. The longer fibres (or 'line') for the manufacture of linen fabrics are next separated (by 'heckling') from the shorter ones (or 'tow'), which are used in making ropes and twine. Linen is spun and woven in much the same way as cotton, but there is one very noticeable difference between the two fibres. Whereas cotton fibres are only about 2·5 cm long, linen fibres may reach a length of 60 cm (2 ft) or more.

[1] Shorter varieties of flax are grown for their flowers in English gardens.

Hemp

Hemp is the general name given to a number of vegetable fibres used in making ropes, string and twine.

True hemp

True (or 'soft') hemp is a member of the nettle and hop family. It grows under much the same conditions as flax, but attains a greater height, and the stem contains a coarser, stronger fibre, which was at one time widely used in making canvas for ships' sails. Nowadays its chief use is in the manufacture of the softer kinds of string. The Indian variety (called *sunn-hemp*) provides a substitute for jute, and the dried leaves, which have narcotic and intoxicating properties, may be chewed or smoked as 'hashish'.

Tropical 'hemps'

Tropical (or 'hard') hemps are not really hemps at all, and the fibres are obtained from the leaves, not the stems.

Abaca or *Manila hemp* is related to the banana and the plantain. The fibre is more difficult to work than that of true hemp, but it is stronger, and has the useful property of being able to resist seawater; hence its use for ships' hawsers. It also makes the better kinds of 'white' string. The name is derived from Manila, the capital of the Philippines which provide 90 per cent of the world's supply.

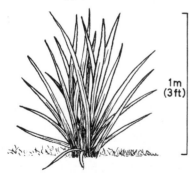

1m
(3 ft)

Fig. 81 Sisal plant.

Sisal hemp is a plant which in appearance resembles the ordinary flag iris (fig. 81). It came originally from the Yucatan Peninsula of Mexico, where it is known as *henequen*, and within the last seventy years has been successfully introduced into Tanzania and Kenya, where it now forms an important crop. Sisal might well be called the 'carving-knife plant', since the long leaves from which the fibres are obtained have such sharp edges and deadly points that in Africa labourers are reluctant to work in the plantations for fear of injury. The coarse, yellow, 'whiskery' string used in wrapping heavy parcels is known in the trade simply as 'sisal', and when dyed and woven into a coarse textile, it makes hard-wearing mats.

Other vegetable fibres which serve similar purposes are:

Phormium tenax (originally called *New Zealand flax* or *hemp*) which comes from the leaves of a plant related to the lily.

Ramie (or China grass)

Esparto grass exported from North Africa for use in the making of high-quality paper.

Raffia (or *bass*), obtained from the leaves of a palm in Madagascar.

Kapok, a brittle fibre, which surrounds the seeds of an equatorial tree. This was formerly used in pillows and mattresses, but, since it is remarkably buoyant, it is now used chiefly for padding life-belts.

Jute

Jute is the humblest and weakest of all the fibres; yet, reckoned by weight alone, world output of jute is second only to that of cotton and well exceeds that of wool. Two-thirds of it comes from the hot, tropical swamps of the Ganges Delta, and at one time Dundee was almost the only manufacturing centre.

A slender, reed-like growth, surmounted by leaves and yellow flowers, jute is the tallest of all the fibre crops, reaching a height of over 3 m (10 ft). It is planted in early spring and cut down at the end of the summer by labourers who are often obliged to work in almost one metre of water. The stalks are 'retted' and 'scutched' in much the same way as flax.

Jute has for centuries been woven into 'gunny-cloth' by Indian peasants and used for clothing, but although it was first brought to the notice of British manufacturers in 1795, it did not become an important commodity until forty years later, when an enterprising Dundee merchant recognised in jute an inexpensive substitute for hemp. In the ensuing years, vast amounts were imported into Britain, principally to Dundee, and made into sacks for carrying grain, sugar, flour, coffee, potatoes and so on. Today, in spite of the growing use of thick paper bags (for packing sugar and cement, for example) and the modern practice of handling grain in bulk, jute is still indispensable in the transportation of a wide variety of foodstuffs and raw materials. It also has important uses in the manufacture of carpets, linoleum and roofing-felts, and in the furniture and boot and shoe industries.

Man-made fibres

In the field of textiles the most remarkable development of recent years has resulted from the invention of 'man-made' fibres. These fall into two main categories—regenerated fibres, made by the chemical treatment of vegetable raw materials, and synthetic fibres, produced entirely from chemical substances.

Regenerated fibres

The first regenerated fibre to be developed on a commercial scale was made in 1889 by Chardonnet, who forced a thick solution of nitrocellulose through tiny holes in a metal plate, so producing fine, brilliant filaments similar to those of real silk. Being a kind of gun-cotton, it was, however, extremely inflammable, and the workmen in Chardonnet's factory 'called it "mother-in-law silk", since the present of a dress made of it was an effective means of disposing of a troublesome relative'.[1] Three years later Cross and Bevan invented what has since become the main process for making what used to be called 'artificial silk'—the *viscose* process, in which the fibres are 'spun' from a solution of cellulose obtained from wood pulp in caustic soda and carbon disulphide.[2] Certain difficulties were involved in the process, which were not finally overcome until 1905, when it was first developed commercially by Courtaulds. By 1914 viscose silk had captured 80 per cent of the market. During the First World War a solution of cellulose acetate in acetone was widely used as 'dope', a kind of weather-proofing varnish applied to the wings and fuselages of aircraft, and after the War, in order to keep the existing plant occupied, the *acetate* process of manufacturing artificial silk was initiated by Dr Henry and Camille Dreyfus. The dope was forced through 'spinnerets', as in the viscose process, and since acetone is extremely volatile, the cellulose acetate immediately solidified into a dry fibre.

By 1920 artificial silk had become popular, and in 1924 (in an effort to forestall misrepresentation) was given the name of *rayon*. In 1929, when world production of real silk reached its peak (just over 60 000 tons), the output of artificial fibre was three times as great. Nowadays a distinction is made between viscose rayon and acetate, and nearly 3·5 million tons of these fibres combined are produced each year, chiefly by the USA, the United Kingdom, West Germany and Japan. The demand for

[1] F. Sherwood Taylor, *A History of Industrial Chemistry* (London, 1957), p. 256.
[2] Originally the cellulose was obtained from cotton linters—the thin fibres of cotton which still adhere to the seed after it has passed through the gin.

real silk, after gradually shrinking to about one-fifth of what it was in 1929, has now recovered (p. 143). Triacetate (*Tricel*) is similar to acetate, but was not manufactured in Britain until the 1950s, when suitable chemicals became available; it is now made in only three other countries.

Although not, of course, a fibre, another viscose product which may conveniently be mentioned at this point is the transparent wrapping material, *Cellophane*. It was invented by a Swiss chemist in 1908, and first became popular in 1923, in America.

A number of 'protein' (as distinct from 'cellulose') fibres has been invented (e.g. *Fibrolane* from milk casein, *Ardil* from groundnuts), but these are no longer in production.

Synthetic fibres

These (like synthetic rubber) really come under the heading of 'plastics'—i.e. substances formed as a result of polymerisation (p. 237). They are derived by complicated chemical processes from the byproducts of coal and petroleum (nowadays almost entirely the latter).

One of the first moves in the search for a commercially useful synthetic fibre composed of 'large molecules' similar to those occurring naturally in cellulose was made in 1928 by the du Pont Nemours Company of America, when they engaged Wallace Hume Carothers, a lecturer at Harvard University, to carry out research into the subject. Carothers succeeded in producing a polymeric substance known as a polyamide, which was given the name of *nylon* when (three years after Carother's death) it was put on the market. The new fibre was first used almost exclusively in making ladies' stockings—with which the word 'nylons' is now practically synonymous—but its uses have expanded rapidly to include a wide range of articles from petticoats to pan-scrubs (fig. 82). Originally manufactured from coal-tar products, nylon now depends almost entirely on petroleum products, as indeed do all the other fibres mentioned below.

Since the war many other similar polymer fibres have been invented, some of which have different names in different countries or when produced by different manufacturers. For instance, *Terylene*, the first of the polyester fibres, which was discovered in the laboratories of the Calico Printers' – Association at Accrington and developed on a commercial scale by Imperial Chemical Industries Ltd, is called *Dacron* when manufactured in America. *Perlon* is a German variety of nylon, while *Bri-nylon* and *Celon* are trade marks of British varieties.

Acrylic fibres are based on a petroleum chemical, acrylonitrile, usually made from natural gas. Examples are *Acrilan, Courtelle,*

Fig. 82 Nylon thread being wound on to reels at the ICI factory in Gloucester.

Orlon (UK) and *Dralon* (West Germany). Modacrylics are as yet developed on only a moderate scale, but are a particularly valuable member of the synthetic group of fibres. For example, *Teklon*, the result of a major research project by Courtaulds, satisfies the statutory requirements for flameproof fabric, and is used in making children's dressing gowns and theatre curtains. With a core of glass fibres, it is proving especially practical for firemen and racing drivers and their mechanics. Another group of synthetic fibres calls for brief mention. Elastofibres, based on polyurethane, a flexible material now used in making paints and varnishes, behaves like natural rubber, and has become an important way of providing elasticity in corsetry and swimwear.

Production

Man-made fibres, with very few exceptions, are made by forcing a viscous liquid chemical substance through tiny holes in a nozzle or 'spinneret' and solidifying the filament from it by various means (heat, for example). The resulting filaments are produced in two different forms:

1. *Continuous filament yarn.* Either a single filament (monofilament) or from say twelve up to several hundred filaments according to the type of fibre and the denier (or, as it is now often called, decitex), are collected to form a continuous yarn, more or less ready for the weaver or knitter to turn into a textile fabric.

2. *Staple fibre*. Thousands of filaments are brought together from a number of spinnerets to form a thick rope-like structure called a tow. This is cut into lengths and the mass of cut fibres is baled and sent to spinning mills for processing on textile machinery. Yarns spun form staple fibre make it easier to blend fibres to provide the desired qualities of texture, bulk or elasticity. It is in fact the almost limitless combinations that can be used in producing a fabric for a particular purpose that has given to man-made fibres the wide popularity they enjoy today.

Furs and hides

Although by far the greater part of our clothing is now made from textile materials of one sort or another, furs still help to provide useful garments in colder parts of the world, and leather is used almost universally as a protection for the feet.

Furs
Furs are obtained from an enormous variety of animal species, but chiefly, of course, from those which inhabit the most northerly areas of Canada and Siberia. The finest furs come generally from the coldest and most inaccessible regions, and high quality and rarity combine, therefore, to make them the most expensive. Nowadays the practice of rearing fur-bearing animals in captivity on 'fur farms' has in Canada largely replaced the historic method of trapping them in their natural habitats. The chinchilla, a small rodent found in the higher parts of the Andes, which produces a soft, grey fur of great value, is today being reared even in Britain.

Hides
These too are derived from a wide range of animals, and play a much larger part in international trade than is generally realised. One has only to think of the tremendous amount of leather used in the millions of pairs of boots and shoes which are made and worn out every year by people the world over, quite apart from the amounts used in belting, straps, attaché-cases, gloves, etc. Hides are converted into leather by the process of *tanning*, the knowledge of which was widely dispersed in very early times. Tannin (which is used in the operation of tanning) is an acid found in the bark of almost all trees, but the chief commercial sources now are the mangrove, the wattle and the quebracho. Tannin causes the protein fibres (or collagen) of the hide to swell, and converts them into fibres of 'leather'.

12

FARMING TYPES, METHODS AND PROBLEMS

Nowadays the word 'industry' suggests to most people factories, machinery and towns. This, however, is a comparatively new and specialised meaning of the word. 'Industry' really means, quite simply, 'work', and in this broader sense the oldest and most essential industry of all is farming, the work which provides us with the first basic necessity of our existence—food. In the preceding chapters the emphasis has been on the animals and plants which supply this and other needs; in the present chapter the emphasis is on man himself, and on the various ways in which in different environments he organises his farming activities, the methods he uses and the problems he has to face.

In some environments Nature is generous with her favours, and the farmer's task is easy, but in others, where Nature is grudging, two alternative developments are possible. Man may remain at the mercy of his environment or he may, by the application of thought and the exercise of ingenuity, rise superior to it and build for himself a fuller, richer life. The measure of man's control over his natural surroundings is shown in each of the broad types of farming which are described below.

Tropical farming

Peasant farming
In the hot, wet forests of the tropical regions conditions are adverse to cultivation. Despite the rank, luxuriant growth of natural vegetation, soils are generally poor, having been leached of their most valuable constituents by the heavy rainfall. The native cultivator lives under a *subsistence economy*, in which he seeks to provide food only for himself and his family; but in order to do this, he is often forced to burn down the existing vegetation to make a clearing in which to grow his few simple crops (such as yams or bananas). Since the soil, fertilised by the ashes, soon becomes exhausted, he moves on after a year or two to make another clearing on a fresh site. This practice is called *shifting agriculture*.

In some parts of the tropics (West Africa, for instance) it is becoming increasingly more difficult to find patches of ground which have not been occupied before, and *sedentary* (or settled) *agriculture* is now more common. In such circumstances, farmers probably grow besides their staple crop *cash crops* (cocoa or rubber, perhaps) for sale to traders. With the money obtained by selling this additional produce, they frequently buy such things as bicycles and record-players.

In the tropical grasslands agriculture in general gives way to *pastoral farming*, in which the rearing of animals is the chief occupation, and very often, particularly in regions bordering on the deserts, the peoples are *nomadic*, following their flocks or herds in search of pasture. Agriculture is, however, to some extent practised along more or less the same lines as in equatorial regions, and in more highly organised communities such cash crops as cotton, coffee or groundnuts may be grown in addition to subsistence crops of maize and millets. The locust and the tsetse fly are deterrents to cattle-rearing in the African savannas, but it may be that in the not too distant future the tropical grass-lands will become important beef-exporting areas, if they can be developed by methods similar to those already adopted in Rhodesia (figs. 83 and 84).

Plantation agriculture

In selected areas of the tropical regions which are capable of yielding commodities of value in world commerce, the business of cultivation was taken over by Europeans. Land was acquired and plantations set up for the large-scale production of such crops as rubber, bananas and sugar cane by more efficient and scientific methods than those employed by the local farmer on his small-holding. These plantations involved a combination of European organisation, capital and equipment with local labour. The peasant farmer thus became a wage-earner, buying the food and other things he needed with the money he received for his work. Today in the developing countries the ownership of the majority of such plantations has passed into the hands of the governments or nationals of the countries concerned.

Oriental agriculture

This is a more advanced type of peasant farming, which is practised in the monsoon areas of South-east Asia. The fertile alluvium in the lower parts of the river valleys has always attracted population, and settlement is so dense that each peasant farmer is confined to a patch of ground no bigger than an English allotment. The Chinese peasant in particular displays a patient skill born of

Fig. 83 In an attempt to conquer sleeping sickness in Boswana, a painted fly-trap is here being used to determine which colour most attracts the tse tse fly.

Fig. 84 Locusts swarming in East Africa.

centuries of adversity. His methods and his equipment are still in many cases crude by European standards. He has no room to keep animals, beyond pigs and poultry; he maintains the fertility of his tiny patch by the constant application of sewage and domestic refuse, and by a primitive system of rotation succeeds in growing a number of different crops each year without impoverishing his soil.

The present Chinese Government has now, however, organised the rural population into large, co-operative groups called 'communes', which display features of both the Russian *Kolkhozes* and the Israeli *Kibbutzim* (p. 158), and has embarked on a number of large-scale undertakings involving flood control, irrigation, reclamation and reafforestation.

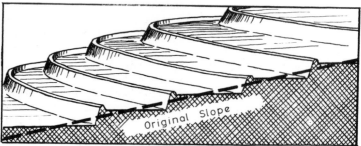

Fig. 85 A terraced hillside. In parts of India the retaining walls are known as *bunds*.

The oriental farmer is often skilful at irrigating his land and in situations where the pressure of population is very great, hillsides may with infinite labour be rearranged so as to form series of flat steps on which rice or other crops may be cultivated (fig. 85). This is known as *terracing*, and considerable ingenuity is often displayed in controlling the flow of water from the upper steps or terraces to the lower ones. Oriental agriculture is clearly intensive, since high yields are obtained from small areas of ground.

Mid-latitude farming

In the mid-latitude zones subsistence farming is now rare; its place is taken by *commercial farming*, in which the farmer sells the produce from his land and buys with the money he receives the food that he and his family require. Types of farming are highly specialised, each region being devoted to the kind of activity best suited to it.

The mid-latitude grasslands

In the pampas and the prairies, for example, where land was at one time cheap and population scanty, extensive farming is practised. The drier parts are occupied by large herds of sheep or cattle, while in the wetter, more favoured parts the cultivation of crops is predominant. The yield *per unit of area*, whether of meat or grain, is small, but the yield *per man* is high. It should be noted that nowadays in both the pastoral and arable areas more intensive methods are gradually being introduced. The present tendency is for the vast ranches to be subdivided and enclosed, and for nutriment derived from natural pastures to be supplemented by specially grown fodder crops such as alfalfa. The system of *monoculture* (in which the same crop is grown year after year on the same piece of ground) has led to such low yields that the practice of *mixed farming* (in which the rearing of animals is combined with the cultivation of crops) is now becoming common.

North-west Europe and North-east USA

In such regions as these, where population is thickly clustered in communities with advanced, modern standards, it is necessary to make the fullest possible use of the available agricultural land. Farming is therefore very highly specialised, scientific and intensive; good quality and a high yield are the paramount considerations. Animal husbandry and crop cultivation are often combined on the same farm, and as much thought is given to providing the animals with the most suitable pastures as to maintaining the fertility of the land on which the crops are cultivated. On the arable land wide use is made of fertilisers, both organic and artificial, and rotation of crops is almost universally practised. 'European' farming is, moreover, highly mechanised.

Two special systems of agricultural organisation are of particular interest.

Co-operation. In Denmark practically all the farmers find it convenient and profitable to join together voluntarily in associations or 'co-operatives', which act on their behalf in a great variety of matters outside the sphere of actual production. The co-operative buys seeds, feeding-stuffs and fertilisers in bulk, and distributes them to its members, and collects, processes and markets their combined produce. The advantages to the individual farmer are many: his materials cost him less, he has the opportunity to use equipment which he could probably not afford to buy himself, he has no worries about selling his eggs, milk, bacon and so on, and he receives for his produce a pre-arranged price. Variations of the Danish system of co-operation exist in other parts of the world, in Eire, Finland, California and New Zealand, for eaxmple, and, since the war, co-operatives have become numerous among coffee-growers in East Africa.

Collective farming is a product of the Communist revolution. In the USSR nearly all the agricultural land consists of either collective farms (*Kolkhozes*) or state farms (*Sovkhozes*) formed by the compulsory amalgamation of small individual holdings. On a collective farm the labourers live on the land and perform tasks allotted to them by the farm manager. After delivering to the government a proportion of the farm produce as a kind of tax, and paying to the tractor-station the hiring costs of machinery, the workers receive as wages shares of the proceeds from the sale of the remainder, according to the work they have done. In the case of a state farm, hired labourers are directed to the farm at certain times, such as seed-time and harvest. This reorganisation of the agricultural land eliminated the uneconomic methods of the former peasants, and made possible the wide use of machinery. The new methods of cultivation have not resulted in increased yields, but the primary object has been attained—a greater overall production from a reduced labour force. The collective system of farming has spread to Soviet satellite countries (Hungary, Poland and Romania, for instance) and to Israel, where the groups of farming communities are known as *Kibbutzim*.

Mountain areas

In certain mountainous countries animals which have wintered on the scanty patches of lowlands or in byres may be driven up the mountain sides to summer pastures, temporarily free from snow, so that crops can be grown on the land the animals have vacated. This seasonal migration of men and beasts is known as *transhumance*. In central Norway, for example, herdsmen and dairymaids accompany the dairy cattle from the coastal lowlands, where they have sheltered throughout the winter, to summer pastures on the high moorlands or *fjelds*. Here they live in groups of log cabins called *saeters* until the snow returns in autumn. Meanwhile, crops of hay for winter fodder, and perhaps oats or barley, are grown on the lowlands. Switzerland provides a similar example. The cattle are taken from the valleys, first to spring pastures on the lower slopes of the mountains (the *Voralpen* or *Mayen*), and later move up to summer pastures on the *Albe* or *Alpen*, returning, after a further stay in the mayen, to the valleys for the winter. This seasonal movement involves a large section of the village community, and the departure of the herds in early spring is often made the occasion for a public holiday, in which the animals are bedecked with ribbons and bells and various traditional ceremonies are enacted. Transhumance is also characteristic of many other mountain areas, such as the Carpathians, the central Andes and Tibet.

Mediterranean areas

Farmers in areas bordering the Mediterranean Sea are confronted by two major problems—soils which are in general thin and barren, and drought during summer, when the crops are most in need of water. Both plants and men have, however, learnt to adapt themselves to such conditions, and the Mediterranean lands have been the home of a series of important civilisations. Most of the plants are characterised by drought-resisting devices (long roots, fleshy, waxy or hairy leaves) and cultivation in the scattered fertile areas is extremely intensive. Irrigation (often involving terracing of the slopes, as in the *huertas* of southern Spain) is widespread, and crops are carefully selected to fit the seasonal alternation of rainfall and drought. It is usual—as well as more economic—for Mediterranean farmers to produce commercial crops of fruit, for which the climate is suitable, in preference to subsistence crops of grain. Cattle-rearing is virtually impossible in view of the summer drought, and pastoral activities are confined to sheep and goats. Transhumance is widely practised in the highland regions.

Irrigation

Irrigation is the term applied to the artificial application of water to land to which Nature has denied sufficient rainfall for the cultivation of crops. The problem is one both of time and place. Where rainfall is unevenly distributed throughout the year, the problem is essentially one of time, and efforts are directed not only to making use of the water which accumulates in the rainy season before it can run to waste, but also to storing it for use later in the year. In permanently dry areas it is a question of place, and water is brought by canals from where it is plentiful.

Traditional irrigation

Two main methods may be distinguished:
Basin irrigation, in which flood waters are held on the land in shallow basins enclosed by banks. This method has been used by the Egyptians from prehistoric times. Monsoon rains in the Ethiopian Highlands cause the Blue Nile to rise and flood the land bordering the lower White Nile, depositing layers of valuable silt and enabling the farmers to grow crops during the next few months. Basin irrigation alone does not, however, permit the

growth of crops after the flood waters have soaked into the ground or have evaporated.

Perennial irrigation (i.e. 'all-the-year-round' irrigation), in which water is distributed by a network of canals and ditches leading from a river. Irrigation schemes of this kind were in operation thousands of years ago in the upper Indus valley, in Egypt and in the Red Basin of China, the water being lifted from the canals by a variety of primitive devices, such as the *shaduf* or the *sakiyeh*, many of which are still in use today, despite the increasing use of petrol or diesel-driven pumps. In the drier parts of the Mediterranean area mountain streams are tapped by ditches and pipes, which lead the water down to fertile patches in the valleys. The productive *huertas* in southern Spain are part of a remarkable irrigation scheme of this kind originally devised by the Moors, which was to a great extent allowed to fall into disrepair after their departure.

Various other ways of irrigating the land are possible:

Wells may be sunk to enable water to be obtained from saturated rocks below the water-table. These are an important source of water in the upper Ganges Basin, where oxen may be seen patiently hauling over a pulley wheel a rope, to the end of which is attached a leather bucket.

The '*tanks*' of southern India and Sri Lanka are really shallow reservoirs formed by earth dams built across valleys so that water from the monsoon rains is held up and stored. Unfortunately, 'tanks' often dry up when the water is most needed.

Modern irrigation

Irrigation nowadays is no longer a matter for local enterprise, but comes within the sphere of government activity. Comprehensive undertakings often combine the development of arid areas with the production of hydro-electricity, the control of floods and the improvement of navigational facilities, and involve the expenditure of vast sums of money on the building of enormous concrete dams and other major engineering works. Such projects are so costly that poorer countries are usually forced to raise international loans in order to finance them.

A number of dams or barrages (i.e. very wide or complicated dams) principally or solely for the purpose of irrigation have been constructed across the Indus and the Nile and their tributaries.

In 1960 India and Pakistan signed an *Indus Waters Treaty* with a view to the large-scale development of irrigation in the semi-desert area of the Indus valley. This involved extensions to existing schemes depending on the *Sukkur* (or *Lloyd*) *Barrage*, inaugurated in 1932, and in dams at *Kotri* (the *Ghulam Mohammed Barrage*), *Taunsa* and *Gudu*, and the building of a number of

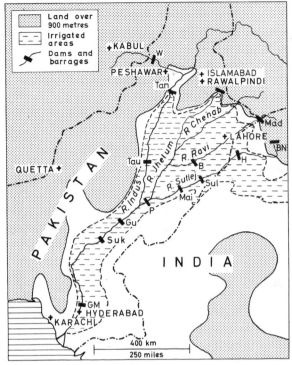

Fig. 86 River control in the Indus valley. Key to names of dams and barrages: **GM** Ghulam Mohammed (or Kotri), **Suk** Sukkur (or Lloyd), **Gu** Gudu, **P** Panjnad, **Mai** Mailsi, **Sul** Suleimanke, **H** Harike, **BN** Bahkra and Nangal, **Tau** Taunsa, **B** Balloki, **Mad** Madhopur, **W** Warsak, **Tan** Tanda, **Man** Mangla.

additional dams on the five rivers of the Punjab.[1] Those already completed are shown in Fig. 86, but there are others still under construction.

A similar series of dams exists on the *Nile* river system (fig. 87). One of the oldest is the dam at Aswan, which has twice been raised since it was built in 1902. By the construction of a new High Dam, 'Lake Nasser' has been created above Aswan. This dam is over 400 km (250 miles) long and has drowned the town of Wadi Halfa. In the Sudan the *Sennar* and *Roseires Dams* hold up the waters of the Blue Nile above Khartoum. Canals lead the water to the Gezira Plain, where 41 000 sq km (16 000 sq miles) of land are now devoted to the growth of cotton and other crops. In 1964 a new dam came into operation on the Atbara River, at Khashm el Girba, where a new town has been created to house the 50 000 inhabitants of Wadi Halfa, whose homes have been inundated by Lake Nasser. Other important dams are at the

[1] *Punjab* means 'five rivers'.

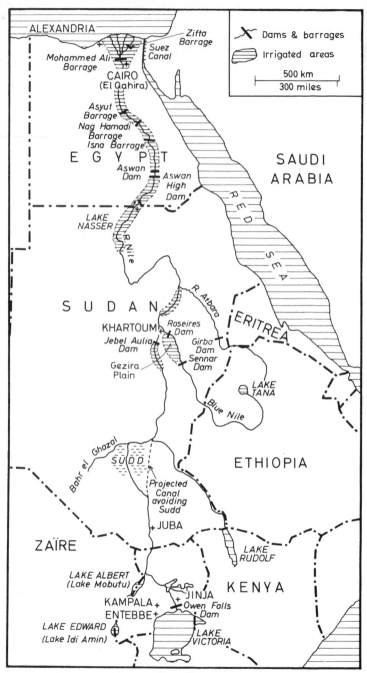

Fig. 87 River control in the Nile valley.

Fig. 88 The Aswan High Dam, officially opened in January 1971. It is 111 m (366 ft) high and, when all its twelve turbines are operating, produces 50 per cent of Egypt's requirements of power.

Owen Falls near Jinja in Uganda, and at Kainji in Nigeria (completed in 1968).

The above examples indicate something of the magnitude of modern irrigation schemes, and have been selected from a large number of projects in parts of the world where rainfall is deficient. Reference should also be made to Chapter 19, where other important schemes are described, in which the control of water for irrigation is accompanied by the generation of hydro-electricity.

Dry farming

In semi-arid areas (where rainfall is between 250 and 500 mm (10 and 20 in) per year) it is sometimes possible to grow crops by means of dry farming. This is basically an attempt to prevent loss of moisture from the ground during one year, while the land lies fallow, so that it will be added to the moisture received in the following year, when the land is put under cultivation. In different parts of the world various methods are adopted to check evaporation during the fallow year; these usually involve keeping the soil in fine tilth (so preventing the baking and cracking of the surface) or covering it with a mulch of straw or even, in some districts, stones.

Reclamation and drainage

From parts of the earth's surface which are too dry for cultivation, we now turn to areas which are too wet. Here also man has achieved a measure of control over his environment, and by various methods of artificial drainage has been able to 'reclaim' from Nature land which was originaly either water-logged or temporarily or permanently under water.

The fertile alluvial lands in the flood plain of a river are particularly liable to periodic inundation, and numerous examples can be found in the British Isles of the time-honoured methods of dealing with the problem. The course of the river is straightened by cutting canals across the meanders, so that the gradient is increased and the water is carried away to the sea more rapidly; a network of ditches allows the excess water to drain off the land, and the banks of the river are artificially raised to lessen further the risk of flooding.

Nowhere in the world are questions of reclamation and drainage so vital as in the *Netherlands*, where the Dutch have always had to protect themselves from both sea and river. Behind a belt of coastal dunes lies an area of rich clay known as Holland (i.e. the 'hollow land') from which the sea has been excluded by lines of banks or 'dykes', while the group of islands which form the province of Zeeland at the mouths of the Rivers Lek, Waal and Maas is similarly protected. Water which accumulates in the *polders* (i.e. the drained units of land within the dykes) is collected in canals and raised to the river or the sea by diesel pumps, which have now almost completely replaced the windmills so often associated with these parts of the Netherlands.

A far more ambitious project than any so far attempted was begun as long ago as 1920, and aims at the reclamation of the greater part of the land beneath the shallow waters of the Zuider Zee (fig. 89). A massive dyke (the IJsselmeer Dyke), over 29 km (18 miles) long and traversed by a motor road and cycle-track, has been built across the opening of the Zee (fig. 90); behind this main dyke four large areas around what is now Lake IJssel have already been 'empoldered'. After draining, the soils are at first too salty for cultivation, and reclamation is not really complete until special grasses have been planted and allowed to grow for a few years. While the roots help to bind the soil together, the dead leaves rot and form humus, and the rainwater washes out the salt.

It is hoped eventually to empolder the whole of the Rhine Delta, and even the Wadden Zee itself by joining up the Frisian Islands into one long dyke, thus reclaiming from Nature land

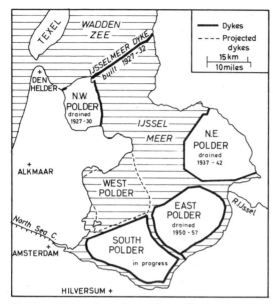

Fig. 89 The reclamation of the Zuider Zee. The West Polder is scheduled for completion in 1975.

Fig. 90 The *Afsluitdijk* or IJsselmeer Dyke—the enclosing dam across the entrance to the former Zuider Zee. The dam is over 29 km (18 miles) long and was completed in 1932.

lost when the sea broke through the line of coastal dunes smoe 2 000 years ago.

The north-eastern Netherlands around Groningen, where patches of waterlogged peat overlie layers of glacial sands, affords an example of a method of reclamation which has been copied in similar regions elsewhere. Trenches are dug, the peat being thrown to one side and the sand to the other; the peat and sand are then mixed and replaced in the trenches with the addition of fertilisers, and a series of ditches is cut to drain away the surplus water.

Fig. 91 The Fens of eastern England, showing soils and boulder-clay 'islands'. In the Great Ouse Protection Scheme completed in 1964 an additional flood relief channel was cut from Denver to near King's Lynn, and in 1971 a cut-off channel was built which supplies Essex with water derived from the eastern margins of the Fens.

In the *Fens of eastern England*, the first serious attempts at drainage were made by the Romans. The remains of a long dyke which they built to hold back the waters of the Wash can still be seen about 30 metres to the right of the road which leads from Boston to Skegness, and throughout the whole Fenland area drainage canals exist which date from the first and second centuries. Most of these works subsequently fell into disrepair, and the Fens again became waterlogged—a mass of pools rich in freshwater fish, the haunt of wild fowl and the refuge of rebels like Hereward the Wake. Only a few 'islands' of dry land[1] remained (fig. 91), on which were built numerous monasteries, abbeys and cathedrals. Between 1651 and 1655 the problem was again tackled in earnest, and an area of land (the Bedford Level) through which flows the River Ouse was drained under the direction of the Duke of Bedford, assisted by the Dutch engineer Cornelius Vermuyden. But it was not until the second half of the eighteenth century that effective drainage of the Fens was accomplished. The water runs off the land into ditches or small canals from which it is pumped into main canals and thus finally led away to the sea. Sluicegates at appropriate points (at Denver, for example) open when the level of water in the canals rises above the level of the sea. Unfortunately, the reclaimed land progressively sinks as the subsoil dries out,[2] and canals well above the level of the surrounding country are a common feature. Efficient pumping installations are clearly essential. As in Holland, the windmills which originally performed the vital task of raising the water to the 'high' canals have now been replaced by power pumps, but canals leading directly to the sea from the higher ground bordering the Fens have been cut to limit the amount of water which drains into the Fens proper.

Fertilisers

It has always been realised by farmers in all parts of the world that soils vary in their fertility or capacity for bearing crops, and that fertility decreases with continued cultivation. But beyond the fact that fertility could be improved or restored by the application of animal or human manure or the ashes of burnt vegetation, very little was known until the last half of the nineteenth century about plant foods in the soil or the chemical and biological processes by which they are absorbed.

In 1843 J. B. Lawes (assisted by J. G. Gilbert) began on his fields at Rothamsted near St Albans[3] a series of epoch-making experiments, which finally demonstrated:

[1] For instance, the 'Isle' of Ely.
[2] About 30 cm (1 ft) in 12 years.
[3] Lawes was knighted in 1882, and at this death in 1900 bequeathed to the nation his fields and laboratories, together with £100 000 for the continuance of soil research. The site of Lawes's original experiments is now occupied by the Rothamsted Experimental Station.

1. that plants in general require from the soil three main elements—nitrogen, phosphorus and potassium;

2. that leguminous plants (peas, beans, etc.), so far from taking nitrogen from the soil, actually give nitrogen to it; and

3. that artificial fertilisers can be made which are as effective as natural fertilisers or 'manure'.

Subsequent research showed how bacteria in the soil 'predigest' the mineral constituents before these are absorbed by the plants. Quite apart from their academic interest, these discoveries did a great deal to allay the prevailing fear that the world's rising population was faced with starvation due to exhaustion of the soil.

The three basic elements mentioned above are added to the soil in the form of various chemical compounds, which fall under three heads.

Phosphates
The first of the artificial fertilisers which followed from the Rothamsted experiments was in the form of 'super-phosphates', i.e. phosphates treated with sulphuric acid so as to make them soluble and therefore more easily assimilable by plants. They were originally made from bones (at Lawes's factory at Deptford, in London), but nowadays basic slag (a byproduct of the smelting of some iron ores), bird-droppings or *guano*, and 'phosphate rock' (a limestone containing phosphorus) are the principal sources.

Nitrates
In the higher parts of the Atacama Desert occur beds of gravel known locally as *caliche*, which contain a cementing material made up partly of sodium nitrate (or Chile saltpetre) and partly of potassium nitrate (also called nitre or saltpetre). Originally these nitrates had been used only for making gunpowder, but by 1850 they had become the world's chief source of nitrate fertilisers, and until 1906, when a method was discovered of extracting nitrogen from the air, Chile had a virtual monopoly of the industry. The chief producers of nitrates are now the USA and the countries of Europe which have well-developed electrometallurgical industries (Norway, for example).

Potash[1]
Wood ash was the only source of potassium salts until 1861, when rich deposits at Stassfurt in Germany were first brought

[1] *Potash*—a term loosely applied to potassium salts in general; derived from the iron pots in which solutions of plant ashes and lime were at one time evaporated.

into production. They are found in association with rock salt in beds which represent the site of an inland sea of past geological times. Until its value as a fertiliser was realised, the potash was thrown away as waste. Alsace and a number of other regions in Europe have similar but less extensive deposits, but the USSR is now the world's largest producer. Potash is also obtained from *caliche* and from several lakes and inland seas.

Rotations of crops

Soil fertility can be maintained without the use of fertilisers by growing different crops in a systematic succession. This is known as rotation of crops, and when a suitable rotation has been worked out for a particular type of soil, it can be repeated indefinitely. The general principle which underlies the practice is that the plant foods which are taken from the soil by one crop are replaced by the others, so that at the end of each rotation the character and quality of the soil are unchanged.

The Chinese peasant farmer long ago discovered from experience that one of the ways in which he could keep his land fertile and secure a high yield was to alternate throughout the year crops of rice, beans, clover and vegetables, but the knowledge of rotation came to Europe very much later. In England the earliest and most elementary attempts at preventing exhaustion of the soil consisted merely in growing grain one year and grass the next, and in parts of Northumberland this simple rotation was still being used at the beginning of the present century. Until about 1600 the most general practice was the 'triennial fallow', a form of rotation which was probably brought to Britain by the Romans. Corn was grown on the same piece of ground for two years,[1] then for the third year the land was ploughed (often several times) but no crops were sown—in other words, the land 'lay fallow'. The soil was thus cleansed and enriched,[2] ready for renewed cultivation (fig. 92).

The introduction from the Continent of two crops, hitherto unknown in Britain—turnips and clover—opened up new possibilities, and soon it became customary to sow these on the fallow. The turnips helped to clear the land of weeds, and the clover (as we now know) put back into the soil nitrogen which had been removed by the grain.

By the middle of the eighteenth century, the so-called 'Norfolk' rotation had been evolved, a 'fourfold shift' which has since

[1] Sometimes corn was grown the first year and beans the second.
[2] Since time was allowed for the solution of potential plant food.

remained the standard rotation for light and medium soils (fig. 93). In the first year wheat is grown; in the second a root crop, probably turnips; in the third, barley; and in the fourth, a leguminous crop, such as clover or beans. It should be noted how in this succession

1. the functions of the various crops are skilfully dovetailed so as to maintain the fertility of the soil;

2. provision is made for the different operations involved in intensive mixed farming. Root crops clear the land and supply winter feed for sheep and cattle; wheat and barley provide poultry food and straw for bedding cattle; clover provides both pasture and hay for fodder; and sheep and cattle manure the ground;

3. the traditional English diet of bread, beef and beer was catered for.

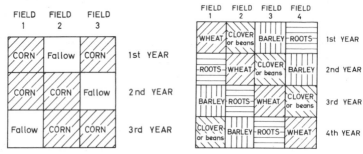

Fig. 92 The triennial fallow.   Fig. 93 The Norfolk rotation.

In other areas of intensive farming, variations of the Norfolk rotation are practised, in response to local needs or conditions. On richer soils it may, for instance, be possible to add another cereal crop, such as oats, thereby making a five-year shift; sugar-beet may replace turnips, and so on.

Soil erosion

It takes Nature about a thousand years to produce 30 cm (1 ft) of soil, yet man by his greed and folly can cause the soil to become so loose and pulverised that in a mere fraction of that time it may be removed by wind or rain in the process known as soil erosion. The world can ill afford to lose potential farming land, particularly since its population is increasing rapidly and many people in backward areas are underfed. This type of erosion seriously affects all of the continents, and is one of the most urgent problems of modern times.

Vegetation not only helps to form soil by creating humus and setting off a whole series of chemical and biological processes; it also helps to preserve it and keep it in place. Roots hold the soil together physically, and the humus, amongst its other functions, absorbs moisture and gives the soil its characteristic texture. Even in dry areas a kind of balance is established under natural conditions which provides sufficient protection against wind and rain, but if this balance is disturbed, soil tends to deteriorate into a mere aggregate of loose rock particles.

The primary cause of this deterioration of what has been called 'the living soil' is man. In many parts of the world he has cut down forests and ploughed up grassland, and then proceeded to cultivate the same kind of crop on the same land. As soon as any particular area has been so exhausted of plant foods that cultivation is no longer profitable, it is discarded; and the dry, dusty remains are liable to be blown away by strong winds or washed away by torrential rain.[1] Examples of destruction of this kind may be found in the USA in the 'Dust Bowl' of the Middle Western states and in the Tennessee Valley, though both are now to some extent rehabilitated. In hilly or undulating country man has foolishly invited soil erosion by ploughing up and down the slopes instead of along the contours, thereby providing channels for the rain-water down which it can transport particles of soil, so hastening the denudation of the upper slopes.

Overgrazing (or *overstocking*) has been a frequent cause of soil erosion in parts of South Africa and south-eastern Australia. If more sheep are allowed to graze over a given area than the land can support, the grass is cropped so short, and the top layers of soil become so powdery as a result of constant trampling, that there is little to prevent erosion in the event of strong winds or heavy rain, to both of which these areas are especially subject.

The removal of vegetation, monoculture, up-and-down-hill ploughing and overgrazing are by no means the only ways in which soil erosion can be encouraged, but all are the result of carelessness or greed in farming.

It will be realised that soil erosion is an embarrassment (at least) to neighbouring areas as well as to those from which the soil cover has been removed. Streams and rivers become turgid or even blocked by material swept into them, sandy windblown dust forms an unwelcome addition to otherwise fertile soils, and may at times be transported by the wind in such quantities as to bury whole farms, buildings, animals and all. In South Africa

[1] The term *sheet erosion* is used when the surface soil is removed over a wide area, and *gully erosion* when the land is scored by deeply-cut run-off channels.

Fig. 94 An example of soil erosion in California.

so serious a position has arisen due to accumulations of dust in reservoirs that supplies of irrigation water are reduced, and the possibility has been envisaged of covering the reservoirs with nylon gauze.

Two questions naturally arise—how may further soil erosion be prevented; and how may areas which have already suffered erosion be restored? Prevention may involve one or more of the following measures: contour ploughing, crop rotation, terracing, the use of manure, compost or fertiliser, the planting of grasses to hold the soil together or of trees to break the force of the wind. The cure of soil erosion is extremely difficult and in many places impossible. It is, moreover, an expensive business, and positive results are really to be expected only from extensive long-term programmes of rehabilitation, such as that undertaken by the Tennessee Valley Authority in America. Temporary local measures consist in planting marram grass (which will grow in sand) in an effort to supply some sort of vegetation cover, filling gullies with brushwood, boulders or other material. If the land is not too badly eroded, it may be possible to plant trees.

So far in this book we have surveyed man's relationship to the living things which enter into his daily life. We have seen examples of his wisdom and his folly, his successes and his failures in his attempts to control his animal and vegetable environments. It is clear that man has achieved his greatest triumphs when he has been prepared to work with Nature and not against her. There need be no end to the fertility of the soil or the abundance of fish, for instance, if man is prepared to co-operate with Nature, but she strongly resents man's robbing without replacing, whether in farming or fishing or in any of his other manifold activities. Man can control Nature, but only with her consent.

13

MINERALS: GENERAL INTRODUCTION

In the modern world of jet-propulsion, television and atomic power, it is difficult to realise that the age of Man the Mechanic dawned barely two centuries ago with the invention of the steam engine. During the intervening years a far more abrupt change has taken place in man's way of life than in any other period of his existence. A remarkable series of discoveries by physicists and chemists concerning the inner structure and properties of the substances which make up the earth's crust has led to a vast expansion of the range of available materials, has revealed new sources of power and has accelerated transport and communications. It will, however, be convenient to define at the outset some of the chief technical terms it will be necessary to use.

Terminology

Unfortunately, it is not easy to find a satisfactory comprehensive definition of the term 'mineral'. Its derivation from 'mine' and 'mining' suggests something dug up out of the earth, and, for all practical purposes, we may describe as *minerals* all those chemical compounds which make up the rocks of the earth's crust. Minerals may by suitable treatment be broken down into chemical 'elements', some of which have a certain lustre, are dense, hard, solid and good conductors of heat and electricity. These are called *metals*. When an aggregate of minerals (i.e. a *rock*[1]) is considered worth mining on account of the presence in it of a metalliferous mineral, it is known as an *ore*; and the relatively worthless earthy matter which accompanies the mineral from which metal will

---

[1] The following are further examples of possible confusion: (*a*) Rocks usually consist of an aggregate of minerals (e.g. granite is composed of quartz, mica and felspar); but some rocks consist of only one mineral (e.g. pure limestone consists only of calcite). (*b*) A few metals (e.g. copper or gold) sometimes occur 'native', i.e. uncombined with other elements. In such cases the metal may also be described as a 'mineral'. (*c*) In trade returns the word 'mineral' is often used very loosely.

subsequently be extracted is described as *gangue*.[1] Metals are extracted from their ores by *smelting*, a heating process which generally involves the chemical *reduction* of the oxide of the metal in a suitable furnace. If only a small proportion of gangue is present in the ore, it may be removed in smelting, but if the gangue is more abundant, it must be disposed of by *concentrating* the ore before smelting.

The importance of minerals

The story of man's increasing control over the mineral kingdom displays two main themes: the discovery of a succession of new materials, and the increasing ability to break down chemically and physically the constituents of the earth's crust. In comparatively early times man learnt to use the rocks in more or less their natural state for weapons and utensils, for building and for pottery; he realised, also, that certain kinds of rocks consisted of ores which when heated would yield such metals as copper, tin or iron, and that some of these metals could be blended to form *alloys*, harder and tougher than the individual metals of which they were composed. By the beginning of the Industrial Revolution he had discovered the value of coal as a fuel and had isolated most of the more familiar metals, but his methods of smelting were crude and inefficient by modern standards.

Events then began to move rapidly. Coal became the chief source of power; improved techniques of smelting led to a vastly increased output of first iron, then steel needed for making bridges, locomotives, railway lines, ships, guns, implements and machines of all kinds; aluminium was discovered, and new alloys were invented; mineral oil (or 'petroleum'[2]) began to be mined, and soon petrol was being used as fuel for the new-fangled 'horseless carriages'.

In more recent years scientific advances have made it possible to break down the materials of the crust still further. Coal, apart from its use as a source of power, can now be made to provide literally thousands of separate commodities of importance, from creosote to saccharin; petroleum yields, amongst other things, 'plastics' and detergents; and the atoms of radioactive metals like uranium can be 'split' to produce atomic power.

---

[1] To rhyme with 'hang'.
[2] *Petroleum*—derived from Greek *petros*, meaning 'rock', and Latin *oleum*, meaning 'oil'.

The distribution of minerals

Although it is within the power of man to control the distribution of animals and plants, he cannot control the distribution of minerals. He must take them or leave them wherever he finds them. Nor indeed can he increase them; he may discover fresh deposits, but ultimately the supply of minerals is limited and exploitation is a 'robber economy'. Whether or not any particular deposit is worked depends on a number of considerations, among which may be noted:

1. The 'grade' of ore, measured by the percentage of metal contained in it. This is a variable factor. It might not be worth while to exploit an iron ore containing only 20 per cent of iron, but a nickel ore with only a 3 per cent metal content is considered rich.
2. The size of the deposit.
3. The presence of impurities (such as phosphorus in iron ore) which may lead to difficulties in processing.
4. The practicability of mining or quarrying operations—the depth of the deposits below the surface, the climate of the area, etc.
5. The location of the deposit in relation to transport facilities to markets.

The occurrence of mineral deposits

Most minerals are found in association with rocks of particular types and ages. This fact is of great assistance to prospectors and mining engineers.

Coal and *petroleum* are found in sedimentary rocks of Carboniferous and Tertiary age respectively.

Iron is one of the commonest ingredients of rocks in all parts of the world, being found in both sedimentary and igneous rocks of every age.

The minerals from which *non-ferrous*[1] *metals* (i.e. other metals besides iron) are obtained nearly always occur in the neighbourhood of igneous rocks. They have been formed principally by liquids or gases rising from underground sources of molten rock (or *magma*) which have at some time forced their way into fissures in the solid rocks above, where, on reaching cooler surroundings, they crystallised in *lodes* or *veins* (fig. 95). Veins usually occupy more or less vertical faults, and may contain more than one valuable ore. For instance, silver, lead and zinc ores are often found together. Some of the contents of the vein may be worthless gangue. Rarely, lumps of 'native' or pure metal may occur.

[1] The Latin for 'iron' is *ferrum*.

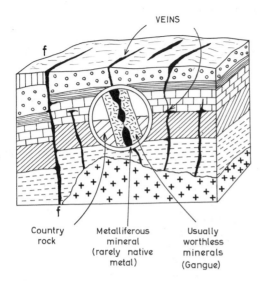

VEINS

f

Country rock

Metalliferous mineral (rarely native metal)

Usually worthless minerals (Gangue)

f

Fig. 95 Block diagram of one method of ore-formation, showing an enlarged view of a vein or lode.

Where surface waters have eroded an exposed vein, particles from it may be transported and later deposited among sand or gravel in *alluvial* (or *placer*) *deposits* (fig. 96). These are derived only from *stable* metals, like gold, platinum or tin, which are capable of resisting weathering; iron would, of course, rust. It was by 'panning out' alluvial deposits that optimistic gold-miners of the last century hoped to make their fortunes.

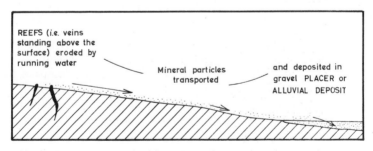

REEFS (*i.e.* veins standing above the surface) eroded by running water

Mineral particles transported

and deposited in gravel PLACER or ALLUVIAL DEPOSIT

Fig. 96 The formation of a placer (or alluvial) deposit.

14

IRON AND STEEL

Iron may be described as the 'framework' of modern industrial civilisation. But although it is the second most abundant metal[1] in the earth's crust, and although it was known and used over three thousand years ago, it was never as popular as bronze for purposes where hardness was essential till the fourteenth century, when a more satisfactory method of smelting was devised. Even so, iron did not begin to assume its present importance until the development of steam power. In the middle of the eighteenth century Britain, then the world's leading producer of metals, made less than 20 000 tons of iron per year. A hundred years later, the annual production amounted to 1·25 million tons, and by 1900 had reached 9 million tons.

The history of iron-making

Most iron ores consist of oxides of iron, and the fundamental process which releases the metal involves heating the oxide with carbon. The carbon combines with the oxygen, forming a gas, and leaves the iron behind.

Before 1350
The earliest workers in iron heated (probably for several days) a mixture of iron ore and charcoal,[2] and were eventually able to pick out of the dying embers of the fire spongy lumps of metallic iron, which could be beaten into shape and used for tools and weapons. These were composed of what we should now call *forged iron*. The more observant ironworkers, noticing that the

---

[1] Aluminium makes up 8·07 per cent of the earth's crust by weight, and iron 5·06 per cent.
[2] *Charcoal*—properly a form of carbon, made by heating animal or vegetable substances with air excluded. Originally the charcoal was provided by the wood burning in the actual fire in which the process was carried out. Later on, charcoal for smelting was specially prepared by burning wood under a covering of earth.

fire burned brighter in a high wind and produced iron more rapidly, came to use some form of bellows to speed up the operation.[1] But in spite of this, the heat generated was never sufficient to melt the iron, the process was extremely slow and only a small quantity of ore could be dealt with at a time.

From 1350 to 1800

It was not until the middle of the fourteenth century that the prototype of the modern blast furnace was invented—i.e. a large furnace into which air could be introduced in such quantities that the iron became completely molten. This was a revolutionary achievement, and was probably due to the efforts of Spanish iron-workers who, driven from their country by the Moors, had settled in the Meuse valley in Belgium. Strangely enough, the *cast iron* (or *pig iron*[2]) produced in this way was brittle, whereas forged iron could be hammered into shape. Scientists have since discovered that when iron melts in a blast furnace, it absorbs from 3 to 5 per cent of carbon, which gives to the metal the brittle property associated with cast iron.

The increased production of iron which resulted from this invention called for large quantities of charcoal, and during the next four centuries many woodland areas in Europe were ruthlessly cleared by charcoal-burners. In England the position became so serious that, in order to preserve supplies of timber for ship-building and other purposes, successive governments were obliged to pass Acts limiting the felling of trees, particularly in well-wooded areas like the Weald of Kent and Sussex, where iron-smelting was at the time concentrated. Declining supplies made it necessary to look for alternative sources of carbon, and although in 1619 an English iron-master named Dud Dudley claimed to have demonstrated that coal could be used in place of charcoal, it was not until the middle of the eighteenth century that coke[3] became widely used in smelting, after its successful application to the process by Abraham Darby in his furnace at Coalbrook-dale[4] in 1735.

[1] Primitive forges of this kind were in use in Japan in 1914, and are still used today in parts of India and Africa.
[2] So called because, as it flows from the furnace, it is run into a number of parallel channels about 1·25 m (4 ft) long known as 'pigs'. The main channel along which the molten iron flows before entering the pigs is called the 'sow'. Strictly speaking, 'pig iron' does not become 'cast iron' until it has been remelted and cast in moulds.
[3] Coal from which the gases and other volatile matter have been extracted.
[4] A village near Shrewsbury; at one time situated on an important coalfield, which is now exhausted.

Fig. 97 Part of the British Steel Corporation's works at Port Talbot.

From 1800 to the present day

One further important development took place before the blast-furnace assumed its modern form (fig. 97). In 1828 James Neilson patented an improvement, in which the blast of air was heated before being forced into the furnace. This reduced the amount of coke needed to produce one ton of pig iron from about eight tons to five. Nowadays the incoming blast is heated by being passed through stoves, which are themselves heated by the hot gases which would otherwise burn at the top of the furnace. By this method rather less than one ton of coke is now needed to produce one ton of iron.

The modern blast furnace

The sectional drawing (fig. 98) shows the main features of a modern blast furnace. The 'charge', consisting of ore, coke and a certain amount of limestone to act as a flux, is hoisted up and fed into the furnace through the double cups and cones, which together form a seal to prevent the loss of the valuable exhaust gases. As the molten iron is formed, it falls to the bottom of the furnace and is from time to time 'tapped' through holes, which are normally kept closed by bungs of baked clay.

Slag, formed by the reaction of the limestone with the earthy gangue, accumulates above the molten iron, and is tapped through

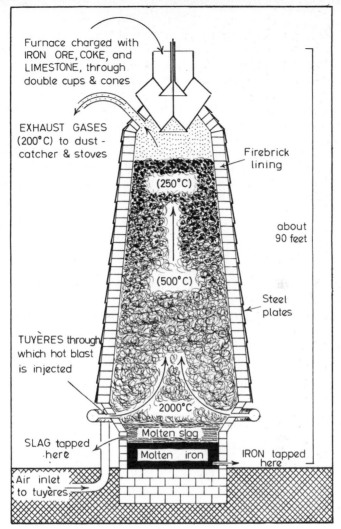

Figure labels:

Furnace charged with IRON ORE, COKE, and LIMESTONE, through double cups & cones

EXHAUST GASES (200°C) to dust-catcher & stoves

Firebrick lining

(250°C)

about 90 feet

(500°C)

Steel plates

TUYÈRES through which hot blast is injected

2000°C

Molten slag

Molten iron

SLAG tapped here

IRON tapped here

Air inlet to tuyères

Fig. 98 Diagrammatic section of a blast furnace.

holes slightly higher up the furnace, and may eventually be used as fertiliser or 'ballast' for filling in the spaces between railway sleepers. A third row of vents accommodates the *tuyères*,[1] through which the blast of hot air from the stoves is injected.

Wrought (soft or malleable) iron

As has already been pointed out, the presence in pig iron of from 3 to 5 per cent of carbon makes it brittle, and cast iron, made by

[1] Pronounced 'tweers'.

re-melting and casting pig iron, is therefore unsatisfactory for objects which may be subjected to sudden shocks or blows. Methods of *refining* pig iron so as to turn it into wrought (soft or malleable) iron, which does not suffer from this defect, were slow and costly, until in 1783 Henry Cort invented the process of *puddling*. This consisted in re-heating the pig iron with iron ore (Fe_2SO_3) in a reverberatory[1] furnace till it became a white-hot, spongy lump.[2] In this state it was 'baled out' of the furnace by the 'puddler', using a long pair of tongs known as a 'rabble'. Wrought iron produced in this way is still used for some purposes, such as chains and ornamental gates, but its place is now almost entirely occupied by mild steel.

Steel

Iron-carbon 'alloys' containing between 0·5 and 1·5 per cent of carbon are called steel. They are harder than cast iron, but less brittle, and although such alloys were known and made at least two hundred years ago, the existing methods of manufacture were slow and expensive, and great difficulty was experienced in controlling the amount of carbon and removing harmful impurities. Steel was confined to such small articles as springs, tools, weapons and instruments. When, therefore, the first metal bridge in Europe was constructed in 1779 at Ironbridge,[3] cast iron was used, and the famous Tower in Paris built by Alexandre Gustave Eiffel 110 years later consists of 7 300 tons of wrought iron girders.

The Bessemer converter

In August 1856 an Englishman, Henry Bessemer, read to the British Association for the Advancement of Science a paper describing a method of steel manufacture which was eventually to revolutionise the industry by making it possible to produce steel in vastly increased quantities at about a fifth of the former cost. Pig iron contains, besides carbon, traces of a number of other elements, such as sulphur, silicon and phosphorus, which are harmful, and manganese, which, since it acts as a 'toughener', is beneficial. In Bessemer's process, the metal is first 'cleansed' of these trace elements by blowing air through the molten pig iron,

[1] In which the metal is touched by the flames but not by the fuel.
[2] The temperature of the furnace was sufficient to melt pig iron (melting point 1 200° C), but not sufficient to melt wrought iron (melting point 1 400° C).
[3] A village only a few Kilometres from Coalbrookdate. The bridge was built by Abraham Darby (see p. 179).

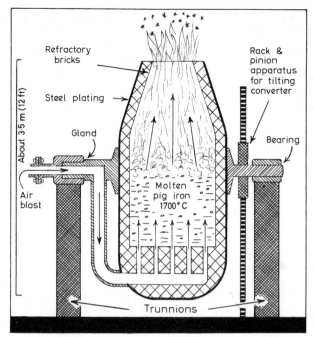

Fig. 99 Diagrammatic section of a Bessemer converter. The force of the air blast holds up the molten pig iron. Hydraulic apparatus for operating the rack and pinion is not shown on the diagram.

and then carbon in the form of anthracite[1] is added later to the required amount. The entire operation takes less than half an hour, and is carried out in a large cauldron or converter, shaped like a huge concrete-mixer and lined with refractory[2] bricks (fig. 99). The flames, sparks and incandescent gases which rise from the converter as the process of oxidising the impurities takes place present a 'firework display' of unparalleled brilliance Bessemer steel originally contained many blow-holes, until his friend, Robert Mushet, suggested that a small quantity of *spiegeleisen* (an iron-manganese alloy) be added to 'quieten' the steel before it solidified. This successfully eliminated the blow-holes and at the same time toughened the metal.

The Gilchrist-Thomas process

There was one element which Bessemer's process did not remove—phosphorus. This is often found as an impurity in iron ore and has the annoying property of making the steel 'cold short' (i.e.

---

[1] A form of 'coal' which consists almost entirely of carbon.
[2] i.e. heat-resisting.

liable to break under pressure or stress). Bessemer steel could therefore be made only from non-phosphoric ores, until in 1878 an amateur[1] chemist named Sidney Gilchrist Thomas, in collaboration with his cousin, Percy Gilchrist, resolved the difficulty by substituting for the silica bricks with which the converter was lined 'basic' bricks, made from crushed dolomite,[2] which absorbed the phosphorus. This is known as the Basic Bessemer process.

The open-hearth process

Soon after the introduction of the Bessemer process, an even more satisfactory method of making steel in quantity was invented—the Siemens-Martin open-hearth process.[3] This, although slower and more expensive than the Bessemer process, has three advantages which have made it until very recently the most widely used method of steel-production. Larger quantities can be dealt with, the operation can be controlled more accurately, and steel scrap can be used as well as pig iron—in fact, the use of scrap is beneficial. The method used is really an extension of puddling, but involves the principle of *heat regeneration*, i.e. the hot exhaust gases from the furnace are used to preheat an incoming mixture of air and gaseous fuel, so that particularly high temperatures can be attained. Figure 100 shows the essential features of the open-hearth furnace. The molten metal forms a pool in a shallow hearth lined with refractory bricks[4] and covered by an arch of similar material. The pairs of chambers or 'regenerators' (AA and BB) contain 'checkerworks' of bricks through which fuel and exhaust gases pass alternately, and mechanism is provided for periodically reversing the circulation over the hearth. Fuel in the form of coal-gas and air is fed through one pair of regenerators (which have previously been heated by the exhaust gases) while the hot gases which leave the hearth pass through the second set of regenerators before rising up the chimney and dispersing. When the first set of regenerators has cooled down and the second set has been warmed up, the flow is reversed.

The carbon content of the steel can be regulated either by stopping the process at the right time, or by allowing it to continue until all the carbon has been removed and then adding the desired amount before the metal is poured out into ingots.

[1] Thomas earned his living as clerk to a magistrate's court in London.
[2] A kind of limestone (consisting of calcium and magnesium carbonate). 210
[3] This was patented in 1867 by Dr Charles W. Siemens, a naturalised Englishman of German birth; and owed a great deal to previous experiments at Angoulême in France by Pierre Martin.
[4] 'Acid' or silica bricks are used ins melting non-phosphoric ores and 'basic' or or dolomitic bricks are used in smelting phosphoric ores.

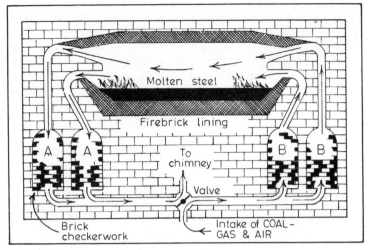

Fig. 100 Diagrammatic section of an open-hearth furnace.

During the windy night of 29 December 1879 the wrought iron bridge over the River Tay in Scotland collapsed as a train was passing over it. From that terrible moment the eventual ascendancy of steel for constructional engineering was assured.[1]

Special steels

About fifty years ago it was discovered that small quantities of other metals (such as nickel, cobalt, tungsten or chromium, for instance) incorporated in steel impart to it special qualities of hardness, resistance to corrosion, etc.[2] In fact, a very wide range of 'special' or 'alloy' steels for particular purposes is now available to designers in every field of engineering activity.

The electric furnace

Although alloy steels can be made by the open-hearth process with a high degree of accuracy, the electric furnace is even more suitable, because extremely high temperatures can be attained.[3] But the cost of the vast amounts of electricity consumed prohibits its use, except in the making of steels of exceptional purity or in situations where electricity is cheap. Two types of electric furnace exist: the metal in the crucible (or brick container) is heated in one by an electric arc drawn (between carbon electrodes), and in the other by the resistance of the metal to a current induced in it.

[1] But the Eiffel Tower, built in 1889, was made of wrought iron!
[2] More detailed mention of these properties is included in Chapter 16.
[3] Probably as high as 3 000° C. Pure iron melts at 1 498° C.

Fig. 101 The BOS 'blow' in progress at Llanwern steelworks near Newport, Mon.

Basic Oxygen Steel-making

In the early 1960s a revolutionary method of steel-making was introduced which has since been adopted in almost all the world's major iron and steel works—the LD (Linz-Donawitz[1]) or BOS (Basic Oxygen Steel-making) process. Whereas in the Bessemer process *air* is blown *through* the molten iron, in the LD process a jet of *oxygen* is directed at supersonic speed vertically *on to the surface*, from which it penetrates deep into the white-hot metal (fig. 101). This new process has several advantages: it is nearly as swift as the Bessemer process, operating costs are low and the steel produced is of open-hearth quality. More than half the world's steel is now made by BOS, and it is calculated that by 1980 this will have completely replaced the open-hearth and Bessemer processes. The two new 300-ton 'pots' at Margam near Port Talbot, opened in 1970, now do the work of the fourteen superseded converters and make steel at £5 per ton more cheaply.

[1] The two towns in Austria where the initial experiments were carried out.

Iron ores

In igneous rocks iron ores are the result of the solidification of magmas containing iron; in sedimentary rocks they are usually due either to the deposition on the beds of lakes and seas of iron minerals which have been dissolved out of igneous rocks in the course of erosion, or to deposition by solutions percolating through pre-existing rocks.

Only four groups of ores are nowadays of commercial significance. These are, in order of importance:

Haematite (Fe_2O_3), a dark-red oxide of iron which takes its name from the Greek word *haema*, meaning 'blood', and contains approximately 70 per cent of iron.[1] It usually occurs in sedimentary rocks of Carboniferous age, and takes a number of different forms, some crystalline, some powdery; and when it consists of small 'lumps' it is known as 'kidney ore'. The Lake Superior deposits are composed of haematite, as are those at Krivoi Rog and Bilbao, and those in the Cumberland and Furness districts of north-western England, which are now almost exhausted. Since 1954 the large-scale exploitation of enormous deposits of haematite in the Knob Lake-Wabush Lake area of Labrador has proceeded apace.

Limonite ($2Fe_2O_3 3H_2O$), a yellowish-brown 'hydrated'[2] oxide of iron, which is formed as a result of the decomposition of other iron-bearing minerals. It contains 60 per cent of iron and is found in sedimentary rocks of Jurassic age. Nodules of limonite are forming even today in swamps and lakes, and at one time 'bog iron ore' was scraped from the beds of lakes with implements which resembled shrimping nets.

Magnetite (Fe_3O_4), a dark-brown or black oxide of iron, which occurs in igneous rocks, and is sometimes referred to as 'magnetic' ore', because it is strongly attracted to a magnet. One variety (lodestone) exhibits magnetic polarity, and mariners' compasses were once made by floating a thin flake of magnetite on a bowl of water. Magnetite contains 72 per cent of iron. The most notable deposits are situated at Kiruna and Gällivare in northern Sweden.

Siderite ($FeCO_3$), or iron carbonate, which is ash-grey to brown in colour and is sometimes known as 'spathic' iron ore. It can occur in association with Coal Measures, and when it contains sufficient coaly matter to enable it to be smelted without additional fuel, it is called 'blackband' ironstone. The Lanarkshire coalfield once contained ore of this type. The most productive siderite

[1] This represents the iron content of the mineral, not the ore in which the mineral is included.

[2] *Hydrated*—containing chemically combined water.

deposits are now found in the zone of Jurassic rocks which stretches from the Cleveland Hills in Yorkshire southwards through Scunthorpe in Humberside to Corby in Northampton-shire. These contain only 30 per cent of iron, but since they lie close to the surface, can be quarried comparatively easily. Most of the Lorraine ores are composed of siderite.

Iron- and steel-producing areas

With the general adoption of coke for smelting, the iron-making industry moved from the woodlands to the coalfields. Since several tons of coke were at that time required to produce one ton of iron, it was clearly more economical to transport the iron ore to the coal than vice versa. Today the situation is more complex. Little difference now exists between the weight of iron ore and the weight of fuel needed to smelt it, so that, all other things being equal, the smelting of ore may be carried out close to the quarries or indeed at any convenient point, such as a meeting-place of coal and ore. New tendencies have, nevertheless, developed in the long-distance transport of iron ore by sea. Nowadays, on the grounds of economy, huge bulk-carriers of 100 000 tons dead-weight are used for carrying ore from, say, Brazil to South Wales. Most new steel works are, therefore, sited on the coast. The planned expansion of plant at Margam is a case in point.

The operation of some of the relevant factors in the location and development of the iron and steel industry may be seen in the following brief descriptions of the world's chief producing areas (figs. 102 and 103).

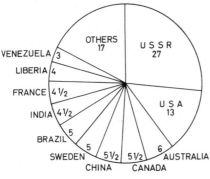

Fig. 102 World production of iron ore. The figures indicate percentages of the world's total output of 395 million tons per year.

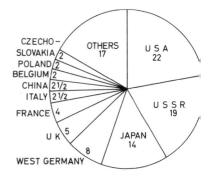

Fig. 103 World production of steel. The figures indicate percentages of the world's total output of 572 million tons per year.

The USA

The USA is the second largest producer of iron ore and the largest producer of steel. Nearly four-fifths of her ores are derived from the immense deposits of haematite[1] which lie west and south of Lake Superior in the Mesabi and other ranges (fig. 119, p. 226). The most important iron and steel manufacturing centres are situated on or near the coalfields of Pennsylvania and the Middle West at *Chicago, Detroit, Cleveland, Buffalo* and *Pittsburgh*. The distance of the iron ore deposits from the coal is offset by the ease with which they can be excavated and the comparatively low cost of transport from Duluth by way of the Great Lakes waterway. Two other major centres of production are situated (*a*) at *Birmingham* in northern Alabama, where in addition to local supplies of good coking coal and limestone are found deposits of haematite and limonite, and (*b*) in the *Philadelphia, Bethlehem, Morrisville* (*Trenton*) and *Sparrows Point* (*Baltimore*) area, where coke from Pennsylvania is used to smelt chiefly high-grade ore imported from Venezuela, Chile, Liberia and the vast new ironfield recently opened up near Knob and Wabush Lakes in Labrador.

The USSR

The USSR is the largest producer of iron ore and the second largest producer of steel. The traditional centre of the industry is in the Ukraine at *Krivoi Rog*, where deposits of haematite are now known to be more extensive than was formerly thought. Originally the ores were taken for smelting to the Donbas (i.e. the *Donetz Bas*in), where ample supplies of coking coal exist, but the whole area has now been integrated into a vast industrial 'combine' and instead of returning empty the ore wagons carry back fuel to blast furnaces at Krivoi Rog. Since the Communist Revolution many fresh deposits have been discovered in other parts of the Soviet Union, and some of these also have been incorporated in 'combines'. The most notable is the *Ural-Kuznetsk Combine*, in which iron and steel industries exist at both ends of the line which joins a group of ore-bodies in the *Ural Mountains* with the Kuzbas (i.e. the *Kuz*netsk *Bas*in) coalfields, over 1500 kilometres to the east. Among these ore bodies is the remarkable Magnet Mountain, composed very largely (as its name implies) of black magnetite.

---

[1] Now within sight of exhaustion. Increasing use is being made of *taconite*, a low-grade ore of which extensive deposits exist in the same area. To reduce transport costs, the ore is first 'concentrated' (see p. 175).

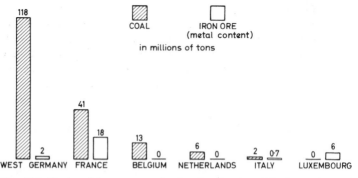

Fig. 104 Coal and iron ore production by the six original members of the European Coal and Steel Community in 1969. It is noticeable that during the last four years the production of coal by the above six countries has fallen by about one-fifth; iron ore production has remained virtually unchanged. (See also pp. 227–9).

The European Coal and Steel Community

None of the steel-producing countries of continental Europe is self-sufficient in both coal and iron (fig. 104). West Germany, for instance, has ample supplies of coal in the Ruhr Basin, but she has to import iron ore to 'feed' her immense steel industry; France, on the other hand, owns in *Lorraine* the second largest deposit of iron ore in the world, but has insufficient coal for smelting. Until recently each country acted independently and in competition with the others, and the movement of raw materials and finished products across the frontiers was often impeded by customs duties and a variety of other restrictions in accordance with national expediency. In May 1950, however, the French Foreign Minister, Robert Schuman, suggested that all these hindrances to economic production should be abolished and that the coal, iron and steel industries of the separate countries should be amalgamated into one vast organisation capable of competing with the mammoth industries of the USA and the USSR. By 1952, six countries (France, West Germany, Belgium, Luxembourg, the Netherlands and Italy) had accepted the Schuman Plan and the European Coal and Steel Community came into operation. The High Authority, aided by the Consultative Committee composed of producers, trade unionists and consumers, has established a common market for coal, iron ore, steel and steel scrap, and abolished frontier restrictions, has tackled the problem of prices and working conditions within the Community, and made various trading arrangements with countries outside it. The chief iron-mining areas and coalfields in the (now enlarged) ECSC are shown in fig. 120 (p. 228) and fig. 121 (p. 229).

Other European centres

Sweden has no coal, but is an important producer of high-grade magnetite from ironfields at *Gällivare* and *Kiruna*, both within the Arctic Circle. All of this ore is exported for use in making steels of especially high quality. Other deposits of magnetite and haematite at *Grängesborg* and *Dannemora* respectively in central Sweden were until 1900 smelted locally with charcoal, but the country's mounting production of steel now relies on pig iron smelted in electric furnaces or in blast furnaces, using imported coke. In the north of Norway low-grade iron ores are mined and concentrated at *Kirkenes*.

Spain produces little coal, but has considerable deposits of haematite ore in the Cantabrian Mountains near *Bilbao*, *Cviedo* and *Santander*. Almost the whole of her iron ore was until recently exported, but in 1955 a huge steelworks was opened at Aviles, near Gijon, and several new integrated plants have recently been established.

Less important ironfields are found in most of the remaining countries of Europe, on either side of the Iron Curtain.

The United Kingdom

By the beginning of the nineteenth century the woodland areas of the Weald and the Forest of Dean had ceased to function as iron-producing regions, and the smelting industry became concentrated in four main areas where deposits of iron ore and good coking coal were found in close proximity (see fig. 120, p. 228):

1. The '*Black Country*' of the South Staffordshire coalfield around Walsall and Wolverhampton, together with the Coalbrookdale and Ironbridge area in Shropshire.
2. The Ebbw Vale-Merthyr Tydfil district of *South Wales*.
3. The southern end of the *Yorkshire* coalfield around Sheffield.
4. The *Lanarkshire* coalfield east of Glasgow.

But increasing demands for iron soon led to the exhaustion of these 'blackband' and 'clayband' ores, and the search for new deposits began. Meanwhile the industry carried on with ores imported chiefly from Spain and North Africa. In the second half of the century two new ironfields were discovered and opened up:

1. In the *Cleveland Hills* of northern Yorkshire. A few kilometres away lay the village of Middlesbrough, which rapidly expanded to become the centre of the great Teesside iron and steel industry, using coal from the neighbouring county of Durham and imported non-phosphoric ores from Spain, as well as the phosphoric Cleveland ores. The local deposits are now almost worked out, but Teesside still produces one-fifth of Britain's steel, using ores from Sweden, North Africa and Lincolnshire.

2. In Humberside around Scunthorpe and Frodingham, where first iron-smelting and later steel-making industries grew up using coke from the Yorkshire coalfield. These ores belong to the same geological sequence as those which were later to be worked near Northampton.

Throughout the whole of the nineteenth century the valuable but limited ores at Cleator, Millom, Dalton and other places in *Cumberland* and *Furness* were being smelted with local or Durham coal.

No other major changes took place until the 1930s, but the following interrelated factors which operated in the meantime may be noted:

(*a*) Since Britain is so small a country, the necessity to carry the ore to the coal was rarely an overriding consideration.

(*b*) The increasing reliance on imported ores.

(*c*) The tendency for the iron and steel industry to move closer to the ports into which the ores were imported. In South Wales, for instance, the industry moved from Ebbw Vale Llanelli and Port Talbot.

(*d*) The tendency for the industry, despite the exhaustion of local ores, to remain where a supply of skilled labour had been built up over the years (e.g. at Sheffield).

(*e*) The tendency, with declining local ores, for the iron- and steel-making industry to be replaced by the manufacture of metal objects (e.g. the Black Country).

In the decade before the Second World War it was realised that most of the British ores were worked out and that much of the country's equipment was obsolete. Large sums were spent on remodelling existing plant, a number of new steel works was constructed (for instance, at Shotton near Chester, and in Ebbw Vale—the latter being intended largely to alleviate economic distress in the area), deposits of 'lean' siderite ore in Northamptonshire were opened up, and a completely new iron and steel plant was built at *Corby*, which grew almost overnight from a small village into a thriving town. Ores from the Corby area now represent 37 per cent of all Britain's home-produced ores. After the war the Steel Development Plan was put into effect, many old works were modernised, an enormous new steel works was built at Margam near Port Talbot, and a similar project was officially opened by the Queen in October 1962 at Newport. Between 1936 and 1960 output of both pig iron and steel more than doubled. The most recent proposals, however, envisage steel production being concentrated at five 'heritage plants' at Margam, Newport, Scunthorpe, Teesside and Ravenscraig near Motherwell, and the eventual closure of Ebbw Vale, Consett, Corby and others.

Other countries

Japan has a rapidly expanding iron and steel industry based almost entirely on imported coke and imported pig iron, iron ore from Australia and steel scrap. With an output of 93 million tons Japan was in 1970 the world's third largest producer of crude steel.

India. The Damodar Basin contains ample supplies of both coal and iron ore. Jamshedpur, 200 km (130 miles) west of Calcutta, is now the centre of an iron and steel industry, which produces more than 1·5 million tons of steel a year.

China. The Chinese People's Republic has expanded the iron and steel centres in Manchuria set up during the Japanese occupation, has increased output from the traditional producing area around Hankow and has established other centres.

Australia is self-sufficient in coal and is now the world's third largest producer of iron ore. She is able to produce all the steel she needs in the Newcastle and Port Kembla districts and more recently, from what is claimed to be one of the largest integrated steelworks in the world, at Whyalla.

South America is deficient in coal, but has large reserves of iron ore. There are (as yet) few iron- and steel-making centres; most of the ores are exported.

Africa (although geological surveys are still incomplete) appears to be rich in iron ore, but relatively poor in coal. Only in the Republic of South Africa has a large, modern iron and steel industry been established; Vereeniging is the chief centre of production.

15

FIVE BASE METALS

Within the iron 'framework' of modern industrial civilisation a wide range of non-ferrous metals performs important specialised functions. Although world production of all these metals is less than one-tenth that of iron, they are, nevertheless, indispensable. The five chief among them are copper, zinc, lead, tin and aluminium.

Copper

Former uses

Copper was probably the first metal used by man. Ancient workings dating from 3500 BC have been unearthed in Sinai and Cyprus (from which the metal takes its name), but long before the art of smelting had been discovered, finds of native copper were being hammered into shape and used as weapons, utensils and ornaments. The ores of copper often occur mingled with those of tin, lead, zinc and other metals, and early peoples had difficulty in extracting pure copper. This, however, was of no great moment, since these 'impurities' produced alloys all now classed as 'bronze', which were harder than copper by itself. Later on, man learnt to control the constituents with a fair degree of accuracy, and until ways were found of making steel, bronze consisting of about 88 per cent copper and 12 per cent tin proved the most serviceable material for knives, swords and axes. Brasses—i.e. alloys of copper and zinc in varying proportions—were known at any rate to the Romans, but were used less widely.[1] Throughout the Middle Ages and afterwards, copper was gradually superseded by iron for most purposes, and in 1800 world demand was so modest that it could be satisfied almost entirely from the rich ores of Cornwall and Spain.

[1] Metallic zinc was not isolated from its ore till about 1 500 years later. The Romans (and other peoples after them) made 'brass' by adding to molten copper a substance which is thought to have been calamine or zinc carbonate, one of the ores of zinc.

Modern uses

During the Industrial Revolution new uses were found for copper, and demand increased so rapidly that it became economic to work ores in the USA and Chile which contained only 1 or 2 per cent of metal. It is, however, as the 'handmaiden of electricity' that copper has achieved its present importance among non-ferrous metals. Pure copper has a higher conductivity of heat and electricity than any other substance except silver, it resists many forms of corrosion and is very 'ductile'—that is, it can be drawn out into a thin wire without cracking. It is clearly a most suitable material for use in transmission lines for power and lighting, in generators, switch-boards, and radio and television sets. Nearly half of the world's present annual output of just under 6 million tons is, in fact, used in this way. The remainder goes to make a wide variety of alloys with diverse applications. Four examples must suffice:

1. *Phosphor-bronze*, containing copper, tin and about 0·3 per cent of phosphorus, makes an excellent material for bearings, such as those required for the 'little ends' in car engines.
2. The *bronze* of which British pennies (both old and new) and other small coins are made consists of 97 per cent copper, 2·5 per cent zinc and 0·5 per cent tin.
3. The cupro-nickel ('silver') of which British 5, 10 and 50 pence pieces are made is an alloy of 75 per cent copper and 25 per cent nickel.
4. *Nickel silver*[1] used as a basis for EPNS[2] tableware usually consists of 65 per cent copper and the rest of nickel and zinc in varying proportions.

Producing areas

Copper ores are widespread throughout the world (fig. 105), and occur in many different kinds of rocks. The largest producer is the USA (chiefly from the states of Montana, Utah and Arizona in the Western Cordillera), followed by the USSR. The Copper Belt of Zambia, Chile (which possesses at Chuquicamata in the Atacama Desert the world's most extensive copper mine), Canada, Zaïre and Peru are all important producers.

Processing

Most of the copper ores now being worked contain only 2 per cent or so of metal, and in order to avoid the cost of transporting vast quantities of useless gangue, copper ores are nearly always

[1] Until 1914 known as 'German silver'.
[2] i.e. electroplated nickel silver.

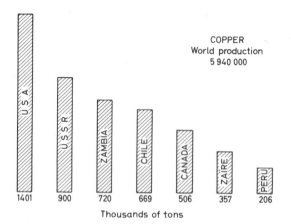

COPPER
World production
5 940 000

Thousands of tons

Fig. 105 Annual world production of copper, showing the leading countries.

'concentrated' near the mines. After a preliminary smelting which increases the metal content to about 66 per cent the ore becomes known as *matte*; if it is also 'Bessemerised' before being sent to the refinery, it becomes *blister copper*, containing 98 per cent metal (fig. 106).

Fig. 106 Removing copper ingots from their casts at a smelting works in Jinja, Uganda.

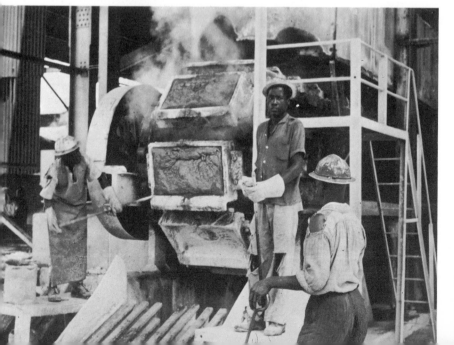

Zinc

Although world output of zinc is now only slightly below that of copper, the metal was unknown in Europe before the sixteenth century, and appears to have been first manufactured in England by a certain William Champion of Bristol about 1740. For the next 130 years or so zinc had few uses, and most of it went into brass for making such articles as thimbles, ornaments and buttons for soldiers' uniforms. But towards the end of the nineteenth century, the demand for zinc rose sharply, and a more satisfactory method of smelting was devised.

Smelting—the distillation process

The difficulty met with in early attempts to smelt zinc was that, since the metal boils at a comparatively low temperature, it turned to vapour, which became oxidised in contact with the air and drifted away as a cloud of white fumes.[1] In the distillation process zinc oxide is first prepared by roasting the ore (zincblende). The oxide is then heated with coke, but the vapour in the furnace is not allowed to oxidise in the air; it is led away into closed containers, where it cools down and collects as liquid zinc. About half the world's zinc is still produced by this method, the rest being smelted, in countries where hydro-electricity is abundant, by an electrolytic process.

Modern uses

Zinc alloys. The rapid growth of the electrical industry towards the end of the nineteenth century called for increased quantities of brass, not so much for wires and contacts as for accessories and fittings which would take a high polish. For such purposes brass containing two parts of copper and one part of zinc is generally most suitable. In the last fifty years zinc has been alloyed with other metals besides copper (aluminium, for instance), and a variety of zinc alloys is now available, which finds many applications, particularly in the car industry. Such components as door-handles, hub-caps and interior fittings are die-cast[2] and coated with a thin layer of chromium.

[1] The temperature at which zinc *boils* is lower than the temperature at which either copper or iron *melt*. It is, therefore, extremely unlikely that zinc ore was accidentally smelted by early man in his camp fire, since the vapour would mingle with the smoke and disappear.

[2] *Die-casting*—a method of casting metals in which the mould, made of steel or cast iron, can be used over and over again. A more modern and more effective method of mass-producing small components is 'pressure die-casting', in which the molten metal is forced into the mould under pressure.

Galvanising. One of the most useful properties of zinc is that it resists corrosion by air and water. About a hundred years ago the practice became widespread of covering articles made of sheet iron or steel with a thin protective coating of zinc. This was originally done in an electrical process known as galvanising, but although we still talk of 'galvanised' wire, 'galvanised' iron buckets and so on, the coating is nowadays applied by dipping the articles in molten zinc or exposing them to zinc vapour. 'Galvanised' corrugated iron, which (despite the increasing popularity of plastic materials) is still used in many parts of the world as a cheap roofing material, provides a further example.

Miscellaneous uses. Zinc is used as roofing material for bays and other projections on buildings, in making collapsible tubes (for toothpaste, etc.), containers for dry batteries and various forms of piping. Zinc oxide provides pigment for paint, and is a constituent of certain antiseptic ointments.

Zinc ores

The ores of zinc are numerous and dispersed throughout the world, with particular concentrations in Europe and North America. Most of them, of which zincblende (or sphalerite[1]) is the chief, occur in association with those of lead.

Producing areas

Until quite recently nearly a fifth of the world's zinc came from the USA, where the so-called Tri-State (Missouri, Oklahoma and Kansas) is the main producing region, but Canada is now by far the largest producer, especially from the Sullivan Mine in British Columbia, followed by the USSR, Australia and the USA. Mexico, Peru and Japan also make important contributions to world supplies (see fig. 107).

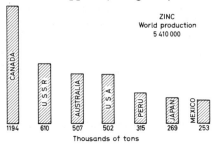

Fig. 107 Annual world production of zinc, showing the leading countries.

[1] *Sphalerite*—from a Greek word meaning 'deceptive'. Lead-miners formerly threw away zincblende as useless, but were often deceived into thinking it was galena, the ore from which lead (and some silver) was obtained.

Lead

Lead ranks with copper as one of the earliest metals known to man. Although it does not occur native, it is easily reduced from its ore, is soft[1] and malleable, and is so resistant to weathering and corrosion that it is almost everlasting. Such properties did not, of course, commend lead to our forefathers for making tools and weapons, but they were quick to find for it other uses. Four thousand years ago it was employed as coinage, for instance, by the Chinese, and the Hanging Gardens of Babylon contained leaden plant-pots. In Ancient Rome lead was used principally for the manufacture of baths and water-pipes, which were made from sheet metal, the joints being soldered by an alloy of lead and tin. The Latin word for 'lead' is *plumbum*, and lead has been associated with plumbing ever since Roman times. It was subsequently discovered that a lead-tin mixture was appreciably hardened by the addition of a small amount of antimony, and when in the fifteenth century printing from movable type was invented in Europe, an alloy consisting of about nine parts of lead with two of tin and one of antimony proved the most suitable material for casting the type.

Modern uses

Nearly a third of the world's present output of lead is used in making the plates of electric storage batteries or 'accumulators'. The second most important use has until recently been in providing a heavy protective sheath for electrical wiring, but 'leaded cable' is now being superseded by PVC cable, in which the outer covering is made of a plastic material (polyvinyl chloride). Lead is used in the building trade for pipes and roof-covering, and since it resists corrosion, it is invaluable in the chemical industry as a lining for tanks containing acid. Alloys of lead include 'soft' solder and type-metal, while the lead compounds, white lead, red lead and litharge, on account of their durability and preservative properties, are important constituents of many paints.[2] Lead tetraethyl (one of the lead salts) gives petrol an 'anti-knock' quality.

Lead ores

The most important lead ore is galena (lead sulphide), which is intimately associated with zinc blende. Galena contains a small amount of silver, but until the middle of the nineteenth century

[1] Lead can, in fact, be cut with a penknife.
[2] But 'black lead', which is sometimes used in polishing fire-grates, and the 'lead' in pencils, both consist of graphite—a form of carbon.

no economic method had been found of extracting it. About a hundred years ago a number of churches in England were given new lead roofs, so that the silver could be recovered from the old ones!

Smelting

The metal is extracted by first concentrating the galena by 'roasting' to remove the sulphur, and then smelting it with coke in a blast furnace. The lead *bullion* so produced is the equivalent of pig iron, and later undergoes a process of refining more with the object of removing the silver than attaining a high degree of purity. Since lead is not used as an electrical conductor, extreme purity is rarely essential.

Producing areas

The USA, whose chief areas of production are the Ozark Plateau in south-western Missouri and Coeur d'Alene and Bingham in the Western Cordillera, have recently resumed first place in world output; Australia, whose output comes very largely from the Broken Hill area, and the USSR both produce almost as much as the USA; Canada, Mexico and Peru also make important contributions (see fig. 108).

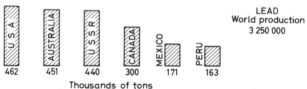

Fig. 108 Annual world production of lead, showing the leading countries.

Tin

From the time of its discovery about 3000 BC until a century ago tin was valued chiefly as an ingredient of bronze. Early peoples made very little use of the metal by itself, although the Romans appear to have used it for brooches and mirrors, and were so far ahead of their times that they could 'tin' copper or bronze saucepans to prevent them imparting an unpleasant taste to food cooked in them. During the Middle Ages pewter, an alloy of four parts of tin with one of lead, was widely used for plates and drinking-vessels, and is still used in making such things as tankards. In 1800 world production of tin amounted to only 9 000 tons, but a hundred years later, when the practice of preserving food in 'tin' cans had become common, 75 000 tons were produced, and today world output is about 225 000 tons, roughly half of which is absorbed by the tinplate industry.

Modern uses

Tinplate. Tin has an attractive appearance and is resistant to corrosion by air, water and most acids. Therefore, when it was discovered that foods could be preserved in sealed containers (see p. 86), tin very soon suggested itself as a suitable material, but since it is also soft and comparatively expensive, it was not practicable to use tin alone. Eventually a method was developed by an Englishman named Peter Durand of enclosing food in 'cans' made of sheet iron coated with a thin film of tin.[1] This combined the rigidity of iron with the corrosion resistance of tin, and made it possible to manufacture on a large scale cheap containers for preserving a variety of foodstuffs. Nowadays mild steel is used in place of iron, and tin accounts for less than 1·5 per cent of the weight of an empty can. The success of Durand's invention led to the popular misconception of tin as something 'cheap and common'. Although this description may possibly suit tinplate, it is certainly not true of tin metal, which is normally about twenty-five times as costly as steel.

The traditional method of making tinplate involves several operations. Sheets of mild steel are cleaned by 'pickling' for about five minutes in dilute sulphuric acid, after which they pass first through a bath containing molten flux (zinc chloride), then through a bath of molten tin, and finally through a bath of hot palm oil, which helps to spread the tin evenly on the steel. Excess tin is squeezed off by passing the sheets between rollers, and when cold the 'tinplate' is polished and packed in boxes for dispatch to the can-making factories. This process has now, however, been largely superseded by a method in which the tin is deposited electrolytically.

One of the most important centres of the tinplate industry is situated in South Wales. Although it now obtains its tin from much farther afield, the industry grew up on the basis of ore from Cornwall, which until a hundred years ago was the world's chief tin-producing area.

Other uses. Tin is also used in 'Babbitt metals', which consist of small quantities of antimony and copper alloyed with tin and which are employed in lining bearings in aircraft and car engines;[2]

[1] The process of coating iron with a protective covering of tin had been known since the thirteenth century, when 'tinplate' (presumably stouter than the modern kind!) was used in making parts of suits of armour.
[2] The 'big ends' of a car engine run in removable shell bearings, each like a divided serviette ring, made of Babbitt metal.

in 'Britannia metal', a tin-antimony alloy of which forks and spoons are sometimes made; in pewter, solders and bronze. So-called 'silver paper' often consists of a very thin sheet of lead covered by an even thinner film of tin.

Tin ore

Most of the world's tin is derived from particles of cassiterite (tin oxide) which have accumulated in alluvial or placer deposits (see p. 177), and are quarried in a comparatively simple operation, either by dredging or by directing a powerful jet of water against the face of tin-bearing gravels. In Bolivia, however, the ore is blasted out of lodes. It is likely that in the not too distant future all the known alluvial deposits will have been exhausted, and it will then be necessary, as is now the case with gold, to search for the parent rock from which the material of the placers was originally eroded.

Producing Areas

Deposits in Malaysia and their continuation in the small islands of Banka and Billiton in Indonesia provide one-third of the world's supply of tin, while lodes in the Potosi district of Bolivia are another important source. Among the smaller producers it is noteworthy that Australia's output (now over 8 000 tons) is steadily increasing, so also is that of the UK (from the reopened Cornish mines), though it is barely 2 000 tons. The USA is almost completely devoid of tin.

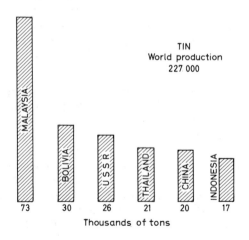

Fig. 109 Annual world production of tin, showing the leading countries. Notice that this diagram has been drawn on a larger scale than the diagrams for copper, zinc and lead.

Aluminium

Aluminium[1] is the most abundant metal in the earth's crust. It is found in several different kinds of rocks (ordinary garden clay, for instance, contains about 25 per cent of aluminium), but in every case the metal is so closely combined with other elements that ordinary methods of smelting are not effective. Aluminium was first extracted from its ore about a hundred years ago by St Claire Deville, who, under the patronage of Napoleon III of France, succeeded in producing, by a laborious and expensive process, a few kilograms of the metal—just enough, in fact, to make forks and spoons for use in the banqueting hall by the Emperor's especially important guests. Less 'favoured visitors to his table were provided with implements of mere silver or gold!

In 1886, however, a Frenchman named Hérault and a twenty-two year old American student named Hall both discovered that aluminium could be produced by passing electricity through a bath of molten cryolite[2] in which aluminium oxide had been dissolved. Although 25 000 'units' of electricity were required to extract one ton of aluminium, this was an extremely important discovery, since it meant that, providing vast supplies of cheap electricity were available, the metal could be produced at a fraction of its former cost. Aluminium is still produced by essentially the same method (fig. 110), refineries being situated close to hydro-electric power stations (e.g. Kitimat—see pp. 254–5).

In Britain two new smelters have recently been built at Anglesey and Invergordon, near Inverness, using power from the National Grid, and a third at Lynemouth, north of Newcastle upon Tyne, using power from its own station, supplied with coal from the neighbouring Northumberland coalfield.

Properties and uses

Aluminium is a remarkable metal. It is light, having a density of only one-third that of steel; it is a good conductor of heat and electricity; and although pure aluminium is not particularly strong, its alloys are stronger than many kinds of steel and considerably lighter. This is obviously of crucial importance in aircraft construction. In its own strange fashion, aluminium is also highly resistant to corrosion, since, on exposure to air, it instantly develops a protective film of aluminium oxide, which can be thickened and hardened by an electrolytic process known as *anodising*.

Aluminium became available to the public about 1900 in the

[1] In America aluminium is called aluminum.
[2] Cryolite is sodium aluminium fluoride (Na_3AlF_6). It is found in nature only on the west coast of Greenland, but is now sometimes manufactured.

Fig. 110 Siphoning molten aluminium from a furnace at Fort William in Scotland. Oxygen liberated from the bauxite by the current passing into the furnace combines with the carbon in the electrodes to form carbon dioxide.

form of saucepans and general kitchen ware, but articles made from it were not altogether satisfactory. They were easily dented, and, owing to impurities left in the metal, tended to corrode and flake badly. It was, however, soon discovered that the hardness and strength could be greatly increased by the addition of small quantities of other metals (in particular copper, magnesium and manganese), and furthermore that such alloys actually became harder with the passage of time. This is called *age-hardening*, and applies to a wide range of aluminium alloys which are now classed as *duralumin*.[1] These are used in vast quantities in making railway coaches, goods wagons, cars, aircraft and ships, as well as domestic articles such as kettles and saucepans, washing machines and vacuum cleaners. Aluminium wire containing a central core of galvanised steel has largely replaced copper wire for the overhead transmission of electricity, as, for instance, in the British National Grid. Since it is lighter than copper wire, the supporting pylons can be spaced farther apart. Minor uses include certain types of 'silver paper' and milk-bottle tops, while aluminium foil is used in cooking and for covering foodstuffs in refrigerators.

Aluminium ores
Although aluminium is now being recovered experimentally from a number of other minerals, the only one of commercial importance is *bauxite* or hydrated oxide of aluminium, a claylike

[1] 'Duralumin' is really a trade-name given to the first alloy of this type by its inventor, Alfred Wilm, of Düren in Germany.

stance named after Les Baux, a village close to Avignon in southern France, from which the mineral was originally obtained. The manner in which bauxite was formed is not very clear, but it is thought that aluminium oxide became concentrated in clays from which other constituents were removed by high temperatures and heavy rainfall in past geological times.

It is necessary to distinguish carefully between bauxite (the ore), alumina (aluminium oxide) and the metal aluminium. Before shipment the ore is treated (to reduce its bulk) by a complex chemical process which yields alumina. On arrival at the smelter, the oxygen is removed from the alumina to produce aluminium. It is this latter process which requires such high temperatures.

Producing Areas

World output of bauxite (fig. 111), of which Jamaica is the chief producer, has more than doubled during the last ten years. Deposits discovered only a few years ago at Weipa in Cape York Peninsula and at Gove in Arnhem Land have been exploited so rapidly that Australia, now in second place, bids fair to overtake Jamaica in the near future. In Europe, Yugoslavia, Hungary and Greece contribute nearly 6 million tons to the world total.

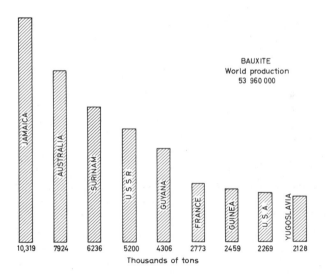

Fig. 111 Annual world production of bauxite. Notice (i) that this diagram has been drawn on a smaller scale than the diagram for tin; and (ii) that, whereas the previous diagrams show the actual weight of metal extracted from the ore, this diagram shows the weight of aluminium ore itself.

16

OTHER MINERALS

Precious metals and diamonds

Gold

On account of its beauty and rarity gold has always been the most highly esteemed of metals. It usually occurs in the earth's crust as 'native gold',[1] but it is also found in minerals known as 'tellurides', and is recovered as a byproduct from the ores of certain base metals, such as copper, lead and zinc. Until comparatively recent times most of the world's gold was obtained from placers, formed by the deposition in river gravels of particles eroded from neighbouring veins or reefs. Once an alluvial deposit had been discovered—and that, of course, was the major problem —it was a fairly simple matter to remove the gold by washing the gravels in a bowl or 'pan'. The heavy gold particles fell to the bottom, and were retained when the lighter materials were poured away with the water. On very rare occasions 'nuggets' or particularly large pieces of solid gold were found among the gravels. The largest of such nuggets ever discovered was found at Ballarat in Victoria, Australia, in 1869 and weighed 2 280 Troy ounces. It was valued at £10 000 and named (naturally enough) 'Welcome Stranger'.

Most of the world's known placer deposits are exhausted, and the opportunity for the individual prospector to make a fortune overnight is even less promising than in the nineteenth century, when a succession of gold rushes took optimistic adventurers to Australia, California and Klondike. Today gold is derived mainly from ores worked at a considerable depth below the surface by large mining companies, and a great deal of heavy and expensive equipment is required for extracting and refining the metal. After crushing and concentrating, the gold is eventually recovered by chemical processes which involve either mercury or potassium cyanide.

Properties and uses. Gold is the most ductile and malleable of all

[1] Actually, 'native gold' contains a very small proportion of silver, and sometimes other metals.

metals. One Troy grain can be drawn into a wire 2 km (1·25 miles) long or beaten into a sheet of 'gold leaf' over half a square metre (6 sq ft) in area. It has an attractive colour, does not tarnish and is resistant to corrosion. These properties together with its great rarity have throughout history led to its wide use for coinage[1] and jewellery. But for both of these purposes pure gold is too soft a metal, and it is, therefore, hardened by the addition of small quantities of alloying elements. The purity or 'fineness' of gold is usually expressed as so many carats. Pure gold is '24 carat', but British sovereigns are '22 carat' and contain 22 parts of gold with 2 of copper.[2] Good-class jewellery is made from probably '18 carat' gold, and fountain-pen nibs are almost always '14 carat', but in these cases other metals (such as silver, palladium or nickel) may be used instead of, or in addition to, copper. Some indication of the composition of the alloy can be gained from its colour: copper imparts a reddish hue, while a high proportion of nickel or palladium produces 'white gold'. 'Rolled gold' is a 'clad' metal, consisting of brass coated with a thin film of 9 carat gold.

Producing areas. Nearly half the world's output of gold is obtained from the 'Rand' (*Witwatersrand*[3]) of Transvaal, a ridge 96 km (60 miles) long, containing 'banket reefs' of quartz conglomerate in which are embedded particles of gold so small that they cannot be seen by the naked eye. Similar deposits discovered in 1951 at Odendaalsrus in the Orange Free State now produce half as much gold as the Rand and may eventually overtake it. The second largest producer is the USSR, followed by Canada, whose output comes mainly from the Porcupine-Kirkland Lake district in Ontario. A large number of other countries (amongst which is Australia) contribute the remainder of the world's supply.

Silver

Throughout most of history silver has been regarded as the second most desirable metal after gold. It has almost equal qualities of ductility and malleability, and provided it does not come into contact with sulphur in any form,[4] it is resistant to most kinds of corrosion. At certain times and in certain countries it has

[1] Nowadays gold as a monetary standard takes the form of ingots or 'bullion', held by the great state banks of the world.
[2] On the continent of Europe and in the United States 'carat' is spelt *Karat*. Articles made of gold are therefore stamped (or hallmarked) 14K, for instance, instead of, as in Britain, 14c (or 14 carat).
[3] Afrikaans for 'White Waters Ridge'.
[4] Sulphur in the smoky atmosphere of towns causes household silver to tarnish, and the sulphur in an egg causes discoloration of silverplated egg-spoons.

actually been as valuable as gold, but over the last five centuries its relative price has dropped steadily, so that now gold is at least a hundred times as costly. It is, therefore, no longer strictly accurate to describe silver as a 'precious' metal. Although silver occurs in the native state, it is obtained principally from argentite (silver sulphide), which is found in close association with the sulphides of lead, zinc and copper. As the world's output of these base metals has increased, so has the quantity of silver produced as a by-product increased also.

Uses. There has, however, been a striking decrease in the amount of silver used for coinage. In the last ten years or so the proportion of world output used for this purpose has fallen from two-thirds to less than one-fifth. Since 1947 all British 'silver' coins have been made of cupro-nickel (p. 195). But considerable quantities of the metal are consumed in various industrial and technical processes. Certain of the salts of silver are sensitive to light and are, therefore, indispensable in the manufacture of photographic plates and printing papers; electroplated ware is made by depositing a thin layer of pure silver on a nickel silver[1] base; and the metal is also used in making 'silver' solders, in backing mirrors and in the chemical, milk and brewing industries for lining tanks and piping.

Producing areas. Since the middle of the seventeenth century the chief source of silver has been Mexico, which today produces nearly 14 per cent of the world's supply. A further 40 per cent comes from mines in the Cordilleran areas of the USA and Canada, and the central Andean states of South America.

Platinum

Platinum is a rare metal which is normally about twice the price of gold. It has a white, lustrous appearance, and is probably best known for its use in jewellery, in which it often forms the 'claws' or settings of diamonds. Most of the world's output of platinum is now, however, used in the chemical, electrical and metallurgical industries, where its high melting point, extreme ductility, insolubility and resistance to corrosion make it especially valuable. It also plays an important part as a catalyst[2] in the 'cracking' of petroleum (see p. 237).

'Crude' platinum as found in nature is almost always alloyed with one of a number of other rare metals of the 'platinum group' (e.g. palladium, osmium, iridium). *Osmium* is the heaviest of all known substances, and *iridium* is the metal with which fountain-

---

[1] Nickel silver is an alloy composed of nickel, copper and zinc.
[2] *Catalyst*—a substance which alters the rate at which a chemical reaction takes place, but is itself unchanged by the reaction.

pen nibs are tipped. Rustenburg in South Africa and Sudbury in Canada produce over four-fifths of the world's 'platinum metals'.

Diamonds

Diamonds are composed of a crystalline form of carbon[1] which is the hardest of all known substances. They are found either, like alluvial gold, in placer deposits or embedded in 'pipes' (i.e. dykes) of igneous rock. Most of them are quite small—only a few 'carats' in weight,[2] and only transparent diamonds are used as gems, for which purpose they are usually cut into many-sided pyramidal shapes to form 'brilliants'. Black diamonds (*carbonado*) and badly coloured diamonds (*bort* or *boart*) are widely used in industry for making abrasives and for 'edging' lathe-tools, rock-drills and the like. Although the fabrication by chemical means of certain grades of industrial diamonds has in fact been achieved, the cost is as yet prohibitive.

Zaïre produces about 30 per cent of the world's diamonds, mainly the industrial varieties. Gem diamonds are obtained chiefly from volcanic pipes, filled with an igneous rock formerly known as 'blue ground' but now as 'kimberlite', in the Kimberley district of South Africa. Apart from the USSR all the other important producing areas are in Africa south of the Sahara.

Ferro-alloy metals

Mention has already been made (in Chapter 14) of certain metals, small quantities of which alloyed with steel impart to it special qualities of hardness, strength, resistance to corrosion, etc. The properties and functions of the chief of these ferro-alloy metals are briefly described below.

Manganese

Manganese is the most important of the ferro-alloy metals, since it is essential as a 'cleanser' in the manufacture of every kind of steel. For this purpose a very small amount of manganese is sufficient, but if the proportion is increased to about 12 per cent, a particularly hard, tough steel is produced, which is especially suitable for rock-crushing machinery and railway points and crossings.

---

[1] Another crystalline form of carbon is graphite (see p. 223).
[2] When used in connection with precious stones (as distinct from gold) the term 'carat' is a measure of weight. Formerly in Britain the carat equalled 0·2054 g, but now Britain uses the international metric carat, which is equal to 0·20 g exactly. The largest diamond ever discovered was the Cullinan diamond, which weighed 3 106 metric carats (i.e. 621g or 1 lb 6 oz).

Nickel

In many of its qualities nickel resembles iron, but it is resistant to corrosion and is not tarnished by foodstuffs. In steel alloys it is amazingly versatile. A small proportion of nickel (4 to 7 per cent) improves strength, ductility and toughness. As the proportion is increased, first 'soft' steels are produced, then non-magnetic steels, followed by 'stainless' steels and steels with a high resistance to electricity.[1] 'Invar',[2] containing 36 per cent nickel, has the remarkable property of being almost completely unaffected by ordinary changes of temperature, and is, therefore, used for making measuring-tapes, precision instruments, etc.

Tungsten

This is obtained from either wolfram or sheelite. It has a higher melting point than any other metal, a very high tensile strength, and extreme ductility and resistance to electricity. Pure tungsten is nowadays the indispensable material for making the filaments of electric light bulbs, while in steel alloys it revolutionised workshop practice when these were first produced about sixty years ago. Machines using cutting tools made from tungsten steel can be run at five times the speed of those on which tools made from ordinary steel are used. Tungsten steels are also employed for armour-plating.

Cobalt

Until comparatively recently the chief application of cobalt was in making blue pigment for staining the glass of church windows and poison bottles; and children's paint-boxes almost always contain a pan of 'cobalt blue'. Nowadays, however, most of the world's output is devoted to the manufacture of cobalt steels, which have remarkable magnetic or anti-corrosive properties, and to the making of stellite (an alloy of cobalt, chromium and tungsten or molybdenum) for high-speed cutting tools and jet engine parts.

Chromium

The most familiar application of chromium is in the car industry for plating bumpers, radiator grilles and other such fittings. But the greater part of the world's chromium is used in making 'stainless' steels for cutlery, general kitchen equipment and chemical apparatus. Such steels were discovered accidentally in

[1] Nickel as an impurity in copper ores had such unpredictable and tantalising effects that German metal-workers in the Harz Mountains at one time suspected the work of the Devil or 'Old Nick'—hence the name 'nickel'.
[2] i.e. *Invar*iable.

1913, when Harry Brearley of Sheffield was endeavouring to make an alloy suitable for gun barrels.

Molybdenum
This has many of the qualities of tungsten, for which it is now widely used as a substitute in the manufacture of high-speed cutting steels and has important uses as a lubricant (Molyslip, etc.).

Vanadium
Vanadium in steel is an excellent 'scavenger' of non-metallic impurities, and renders the metal less liable to fatigue or fracture under shock or stress.

Producing areas
The chief producers of ferro-alloy metals are shown in fig. 112.

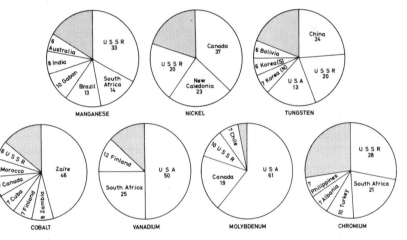

Fig. 112 Annual world production of the chief ferro-alloy metals. The figures indicate percentages of the world's total production.

Other metals

The following metals are also of importance or interest in the modern world. Notable producing countries are indicated in brackets.
Antimony is important as a hardening agent in leaden type-metal and accumulator plates (see p. 199), and is used in a number of alloys (South Africa, Bolivia and China).
Beryllium is a very light metal with a high melting point. It 'strengthens' copper, and is widely used in controlling the speed of nuclear fission (Brazil).

Bismuth forms part of many medical and cosmetic preparations. It has a very low melting point, and is one of the constituents of electrical fuse-wire and of Wood's metal, which melts in boiling water (Mexico, Canada and Peru).

Cadmium has come to the fore only in the last twenty-five years, mainly as a protective coating for iron and steel. It is also used in atomic reactors (see p. 261) (USA).

Magnesium was until 1930 used only for making photographic flashlight powder. Since it is an extremely light metal, it is now particularly important in the manufacture of light alloys for the aircraft industry (the USSR and Czechoslovakia).

Mercury (or *quicksilver*) is the only metal which is liquid at ordinary temperatures. It is the traditional material for the 'columns' of thermometers and barometers, and is used in the 'amalgam' process of refining gold (Spain, Italy and the USSR).

Selenium is a 'new' and fascinating metal with many ingenious uses. When light falls upon it, a small electric current is set up. It is used in sound film apparatus, mechanism for automatic street lighting, burglar alarms, photographic exposure meters, etc. It also gives a ruby colour to the glass of railway signals and traffic lights (Canada and USA).

Titanium has recently become important in the manufacture of paint, since titanium oxide provides a white pigment several times as opaque as white lead (USA and Canada).

(*Uranium, radium* and *plutonium* are dealt with in Chapter 20.)

Industrial minerals

Asbestos
Asbestos is a remarkable mineral in that it occurs as fibres attached to the walls of veins traversing certain igneous rocks, notably serpentine. These fibres are usually about 6 mm long, and can be spun and woven into textiles. Since asbestos has a very high resistance to electricity and a very low conductivity, and since it will not melt, burn or decay, it is clearly the ideal material for the manufacture of fireproof clothing and ropes, theatrical safety-curtains, boiler lagging and a wide range of similar articles. For many purposes, such as the heat-resistant mat on an ironing-board, fireproof roofing-tiles, etc., the fibres are made into 'asbestos cement' and pressed into sheets. Nearly two-fifths of the world's asbestos comes from Thetford Mines and Asbestos in eastern Canada.

Mica

Mica is equally remarkable, and in many of its properties (resistance to heat and electricity, etc.) resembles asbestos. It occurs, however, in hexagonal crystals known as 'books', sometimes as much as 30 cm in diameter and a few centimetres or so in thickness. Each 'book' can be split into hundreds of thin sheets of shiny, more or less transparent material, which is of immense importance in the electrical and wireless industries, since no other known substance has such a high resistance to the passage of electricity. Mica is also used for making 'windows' in furnaces and stoves, and fragments of crushed mica not only provide artificial frost for Christmas decorations but are also being increasingly used under the roofs of houses for insulation against heat and cold. The largest producer of mica is the state of North Carolina in the USA, while the Damodar Valley of northern India supplies most of the remainder.

Common Salt

Common salt (rock salt or halite) is sodium chloride, a food substance indispensable to all living creatures. It is found in nature either in brine (from which in the tropics it is obtained by the simple process of evaporation by the sun) or as a crystalline solid, representing the precipitate deposited on the bed of an enclosed sea or lake of former geological times—particularly the Permian and Triassic periods, when arid conditions were widespread. In some cases these buried deposits (being plastic and under high pressure) have been forced upward in local areas of weakness in the earth's crust, so that they now form 'saltdomes' varying in diameter from 90 to 1 500 m (roughly 100 yd to one mile). A large number of these somewhat peculiar features, from which most of the world's salt is now obtained, occur near the Gulf Coast of the USA. Rock salt is, however, more especially important as one of the chief raw materials of the chemical industry. From it are made soda ash (sodium carbonate) for the preparation of glass, soap and washing-soda; caustic soda (NaOH) is made by the electrolysis of salt; and chlorine (for bleaching textiles, paper, etc.) and the metal sodium are also produced from it. The United States is the largest producer (from the southern states) followed by China and the USSR, and there are notable deposits at Stassfurt in East Germany and in Cheshire in England.

Sulphur

Sulphur is the most important element used in the chemical industry, and is obtained either native in the vicinity of hot springs and volcanoes, in association with salt domes (now the main source) or from iron pyrites ($FeSO_2$), a mineral which in appearance resembles gold[1] and consists of roughly equal parts of sulphur and iron. Large quantities of pure sulphur are used in vulcanising rubber, and in the form of dust it has many valuable applications in controlling insect and fungus pests. But it is chiefly important in the form of sulphuric acid, which is used in practically every branch of the chemical industry, and to a lesser extent as sulphur dioxide (SO_2). The USA produces over half of the world's crude sulphur, while pyrites are obtained mainly from the countries of North America and Europe.

Graphite

Graphite is a soft, black crystalline form of carbon which was probably formed, like anthracite, from organic material which has been converted by intense heat and pressure. It is a relative of the diamond, and as it was originally mistaken for lead, it so acquired the name of plumbago or 'black lead'. Mixed with a special fine clay, powdered graphite provides the 'lead' of pencils,[2] and the making of pencils at Keswick in Cumberland was based on local supplies—now exhausted—in Borrowdale. Most of the world's graphite is used in making large crucibles for melting brass and steel. Other uses are as carbon brushes for electric motors and dynamos, in dry batteries and in powder form as a lubricant where grease would be harmful (in pianos, for example). Graphite is also widely used as a 'moderator' in atomic reactors.

China-clay

China-clay (or Kaolin[3]) is a fine, white clay which has been formed as a result of the disintegration of the felspar in granite, either by downward percolating waters or by ascending gases. Over a quarter of the world's kaolin is obtained from open pits in the South-west Peninsula of England, Dartmoor, Bodmin Moor and St Austell being the chief producing areas. The finest types of kaolin—such as those yielded by the deposits of Devon and Cornwall—are an essential constituent of pottery and porcelain. China-clay is also used as a 'filler', giving body to the pulp from

[1] It has been called 'fool's gold', and was at one time shipped to England from America in mistake for gold.
[2] The name 'graphite' is derived from the Greek word *grapho* meaning 'I write'.
[3] The name 'kaolin' is derived from the Kau-ling or 'high-ridge' range of mountains in China from which china-clay was first brought to England in the eighteenth century.

Fig. 113 Washing china-clay from the pit face with a high-pressure hose at Bowater's china-clay mines in Cornwall.

which paper is made and providing a smooth surface; in toothpaste, pills and poultices, and as a mild abrasive in polishes and soaps. The clay is usually washed out of the decomposed granite by directing a powerful jet of water against the wall of a pit (fig. 113). It is carried away by the water and eventually dries out in shallow ponds, after which it is broken up into rectangular lumps. The conical heaps which are a common feature of the landscape of the areas noted above represent the discarded particles of sand and other impurities which have been separated from the china-clay itself.

(For a description of the minerals used as fertilisers—*phosphates*, *nitrates* and *potash*—reference should be made to Chapter 12).

Rocks of commercial importance

Quite apart from minerals and metals extracted from the materials of the earth's crust, man also makes extensive use of the rocks themselves. Since most rocks are both too bulky and too heavy to be transported over long distances, *building stones* used in the older types of cottages and houses were normally selected from local rocks, usually varieties of limestones (fig. 114) and sandstones, especially those known as 'freestones', which can be shaped and cut in any direction. Among many examples in Britain may

Fig. 114 Quarrying Purbeck limestone in the 'Isle' of Purbeck, Dorset.

be noted the use of oolitic limestone in the Cotswolds. Roofs were frequently made of *slates* (chiefly from Llanberis, Bethesda and Ffestiniog in North Wales) or other rocks which can be split into thin sheets, although nowadays tiles are more common. *Flagstones* (or paving-blocks) were similarly chosen from rocks which can be separated into slabs of regular thickness. Various types of granite and marble have always been used for special buildings and *ornamental work*, and the hard granites of the Penmaenmawr district of North Wales and the Charnwood Forest of Leicestershire provide excellent *road metal* (i.e. fragments of rock used in making roads), while coarse sandstones like millstone grit have wide applications as *millwheels* and *grindstones*.

Where local building stone is not available, *bricks*, made by baking clay, are frequently used. Extensive deposits of Oxford Clay in the vicinity of Peterborough and Bedford have of recent years led to a concentration of the brick-making industry in these two areas. *Mortar* for holding the bricks together consists of a mixture of water, sand and cement (a powder produced by burning clay and limestone together in a kiln). Probably the most widely used of all modern constructional materials, however, is *concrete*, formed by mixing water, sand, cement and gravel, which, in this connection, is described as 'aggregate'. The presence of local supplies of sand, gravel and limestone is at the present time a factor of considerable importance in promoting the development of parts of the world where an urgent need exists for factories, roads, bridges, dams and similar major constructional works.

17

COAL

Early sources of power

It is possible for us here to take only the briefest glance at the sources of power available to man before the invention of the steam engine barely two hundred years ago. In the earliest days man could call only upon the power of his own muscles; but in course of time he found ways of employing the superior strength of horses, asses and oxen to carry his loads and draw his plough, and he devised what to us seem rough, simple pieces of machinery driven by his own hands or feet (the potter's wheel, the loom and the spinning-wheel, for instance), by animals (like the *sakiyeh*, a cumbrous device used for lifting water for irrigation), by the wind (the windmill) and by the force of running water. In fact, at the beginning of the Industrial Revolution the most powerful machine so far invented was the millwheel, in which the energy was supplied by a fast-flowing stream. How recent an event was the inauguration of the modern machine age may well be seen from the fact that in many parts of the world primitive devices are still widely used, and indeed in the more remote parts of even such highly industrialised countries as Britain, 'crude' water power is still used for milling grain, weaving textiles and sawing timber.

Modern sources of power

The Industrial Revolution initiated by Watt's invention was fundamentally based on coal as a source of power. Soon two further sources of power were developed—petroleum and hydro-electricity—to which in the last two decades has been added the energy derived from nuclear fission, or what is generally known as 'atomic power'. A certain amount of thought has been given to the possibility of making use of the rise and fall of the tide and of solar radiation, but little real progress has yet been made in this direction although a tidal power station constructed at the mouth of the River Rance near St Malo in France came into operation 1965, and in 1968 the USSR assembled a similar station on the Barents Sea.

The history of coal-working

Coal has been found in Bronze Age barrows in South Wales, and was probably not unknown to the Greeks and Romans, but until the end of the Middle Ages the chief domestic and industrial fuels were wood and charcoal. In Northumberland, where seams appeared at the surface of the gound, coal was dug up and burnt locally; and by the thirteenth century, owing to the shortage of timber in the south of England, 'seacoale', as it was called, was being shipped to London from the Newcastle area. The number of riverside streets in London named 'Coldharbour[1] Lane' is an interesting reminder of these times. But the introduction of coal as a domestic fuel was delayed, because the smoke was considered poisonous, and there was general consternation when the first Queen Elizabeth decreed that coal should be used on the court fires in place of timber. Two other circumstances must be remembered. The houses of only the very wealthy had proper chimneys—most people had to be content with merely a hole in the roof—and the inadequacy of the roads made it almost impossible to transport coal except by water.

The formation and geological occurrence of coal

Coal is a mineral composed of vegetable matter, representing the compressed remains of former swamp forests, probably similar to those found today at or near the mouths of such rivers as the Amazon, the Ganges and the Mississippi. The fact that coal occurs in seams interbanded with clays, sandstones and other rocks shows that the layers of vegetation must periodically have become choked and buried by sediment as the area subsided. In most cases the process of growth and burial was repeated over and over again, and each stage may well have lasted a million years or more. The thickness of the seams is, of course, an indication of the length of time during which conditions remained the same. Swamp forests were particularly widespread in the Upper Carboniferous period of geological history, and coal is therefore usually associated with rocks of this age, although certain inferior kinds of coal are found in the sediments of Secondary and Tertiary times. Subsequently rocks containing coal were folded and faulted, and many of the original seams were completely worn away in the course of erosion, so that now coalfields are less extensive than formerly.

[1] A corruption of 'coal harbour'.

Methods of mining coal

Three main ways of mining coal are possible:

1. *By adits or 'drifts'*. Where a seam of coal outcrops (i.e. appears at the surface) it is a comparatively simple matter to drive a tunnel into a hillside, removing the coal in the process. In Britain most of the available outcrops have been worked out, although one still occasionally reads of someone living in a Pennine valley who has discovered a seam of coal running across his garden.

2. *By 'opencast' mining*. If a seam lies very close to the surface, it may be possible for mechanical excavators to expose the coal by removing the 'overburden' (fig. 115). Although this is an inexpensive method of 'winning' coal, it may be wasteful of good agricultural land, since, however carefully the overburden is replaced after the coal has been cut, many years elapse before the soil recovers from the upheaval. Nevertheless methods of land restoration are now much improved.

3. *By shafts or pits*. This, of course, is the most usual, the most complicated and the most expensive method of coal-mining.

Fig. 115 Opencast coal-mining in progress at Acorn Bank Site, Bedlington, Northumberland. The large excavating machine which can be seen removing the overburden is called a 'drag-line'. Mechanical shovels dig coal out of the seam and load it direct into the waiting lorries.

Access to the seams is gained by sinking shafts, often to a considerable depth.[1] This in itself is a long and arduous operation, which may take as much as ten years to complete. Before the work of mining can begin, provision must be made for ventilation, lighting and haulage below ground, and pumping equipment must be installed to keep the mine drained of water, quite apart from the setting-up of pithead gear, the building of offices, baths, canteens and so on, and the laying down of railway sidings. As the coal close to the main shafts is removed, 'galleries' extend farther and farther outwards until, as in some of the older pits, the miners may have a considerable distance to travel before reaching the coal face, and in mines such as those of the North-east and Cumberland coalfields in Britain may actually be working under the sea.

Two principal considerations affect the speed and ease with which coal can be worked: first, the thickness of the seams, and secondly, their regularity and freedom from faults. Seams of 3m (10 ft) or more in thickness, such as are found in the coalfields of the USA, not only give the miner more working space, but also make possible the installation of powerful coal-cutting machines. The output per man is therefore much greater in America than in Britain, where the best seams (which are now largely exhausted) are rarely as much as 2 m (6 ft) thick, and where the seams are often contorted and interrupted by faults. In such cases the miner is often forced to work in a confined space with only a pick and shovel, there is less opportunity for the use of cutting-machines, a great deal of time is wasted in removing worthless rock, and the continuity of conveyor belts is frequently interrupted.

As the coal is removed, the roof is shored up by pit-props, formerly made of timber, but now almost always of steel. When a section of the mine is abandoned, the pit-props are usually knocked out and the ground above sinks. This subsidence (which, of course, occurs eventually as the props decay, even if they are allowed to remain) is often a matter of inconvenience at the surface. In many parts of the English Midlands, for instance, the walls of houses on the coalfields may be seen to have been cracked by the settling of the ground, and in Cannock Chase one could until recently see notices by the roadside, 'Caution: Road liable to subsidence'.

[1] The average depth of coal-working in Britain today is about 366 m (1 200 ft). The deepest mine (at Llay Main colliery near Wrexham) reaches a depth of 1 143 m (3 750 ft) below ground level.

Types of coal

Coal is often referred to as if it were a single commodity. Actually many varieties of coal exist which vary in their chemical and physical composition and the purposes for which they are suitable. The vegetable substances from which all types of coal have been formed consisted originally of carbon, hydrogen, oxygen and nitrogen, together with certain impurities, which are left behind as ash when the coal is ultimately burnt. Owing to the passage of time, the pressure of overlying sediments and movements within the earth's crust, the gaseous elements have to a greater or lesser extent escaped, so leaving a higher proportion of carbon. It is thus possible to differentiate coals on the combined basis of carbon content, gaseous content, hardness, colour and age.

Usually seven main types of coal are distinguished. The carbon content of each is shown in fig. 116.

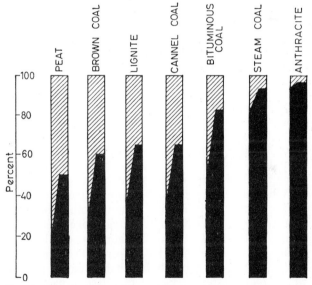

Fig. 116 The carbon content of the various types of 'coal'. (For example, the carbon content of lignite varies between 35 per cent. and 65 per cent.)

Peat. This is the youngest geologically, and is formed as a result of the decay of mossy plants in the bogs of central Eire, the Scottish Highlands and Dartmoor, for example. It is dark brown in colour, contains up to 50 per cent.[1] of carbon, and is heavily

[1] The carbon content of wood is only slightly less. Percentages quoted refer to the coal when dry.

charged with moisture. When cut like turf into large slabs and dried out, it burns with a great deal of smoke, and it has a very low 'calorific value'—i.e. it gives out little heat. Peat is used only locally, and is not really a 'coal' in the commonly accepted sense.

Brown Coal. This is grey or dark brown in colour, is light in weight and reveals signs of the original vegetable structure. It is associated with rocks of Tertiary age, contains up to 60 per cent of carbon, produces a smoky fire and gives out only a moderate amount of heat. Notable deposits of brown coal occur both in West and East Germany, where it is used in specially designed steam engines for the generation of electricity. At Lauchhammer near Cottbus in East Germany brown coal is used for the distillation of oil.

Lignite. A stony kind of coal, blacker and harder than brown coal, but used for much the same purposes: it has a slightly higher carbon content, includes much less moisture and its original vegetable structure is less evident.

Cannel coal. This type appears to have been formed under water from accumulations of drifting vegetation, and contains roughly the same amount of carbon as lignite, but far more inflammable gases. Splinters of cannel (i.e. candle) coal burn like tapers when ignited.

Bituminous (Household) Coal. This is the most familiar variety. It was formed in the Upper Carboniferous period, is black and sometimes lustrous, contains 48 to 83 per cent of carbon and burns with a fairly long flame and a moderate amount of smoke. Its calorific value is more than twice as great as that of lignite.

Bituminous coals which contain a high proportion (perhaps as much as 30 per cent) of gases and vapours are known as *gas coals*. When heated in retorts, they give off their volatile matter,[1] which is collected in the form of (amongst other things) *coal gas*, leaving as a byproduct the 'soft' or gas coke used in domestic hot-water boilers. *Coking coals* contain less volatile matter than gas coals, but since they have the property of softening and fusing on burning, they are particularly suitable for the production of 'hard' *coke*—the essential fuel of the blast furnace. In this case coal-gas is released as a byproduct.

Steam Coal contains 83 to 93 per cent of carbon, and is a superior kind of bituminous coal, which occurs in regions where the seams have been subjected to great pressure, as, for instance, in parts of South Wales. It is hard, black and lustrous, and burns with a short flame; but its most useful quality is that, being very nearly smokeless, it does not readily lead to accumulations of soot in the fire-tubes of locomotives and marine engines,

[1] i.e. matter which readily evaporates.

which would reduce their efficiency. When used in steamships it is known as 'bunker coal'.[1]

Anthracite. Extremely hard, black and shiny, anthracite burns with great heat and hardly any smoke or flame. In the course of geological history it has been subjected to such immense pressure that it is composed almost completely of carbon (93 to 96 per cent). It would be impossible to light a fire in an ordinary domestic open grate with anthracite alone, but it is admirably suited for use in closed boilers or with a forced draught, and is the ideal solid fuel for systems of central heating. There is a definite connection between the fact that in North America large quantities of anthracite are available and the fact that central heating is more widespread in the United States than in any other country. It should, however, be noted that anthracite has now been almost completely superseded for this purpose by oil and natural gas.

Graphite, containing 98 or 99 per cent of carbon, probably represents the ultimate stage in the transformation of vegetable matter under the influence of time and pressure.

The uses of coal

Coal is used for three main purposes:

1. *As a fuel* for domestic heating. This is really an extremely wasteful practice, since the smoke which passes up the chimney contains a vast number of valuable chemical substances.

2. *As a source of power* for driving steam engines, not only locomotives but also stationary engines, many of which are used in power stations to drive dynamos for the production of thermal[2] electricity.

3. *As a raw material.* The two chief products of the 'carbonisation' of coal are coke and coal-gas, but three by-products are released in the process—coal-tar, benzole and sulphate of ammonia. As a result of further chemical subdivision, these may in turn be made to yield over 200 000 different products. A complete list would more than fill this book, and it must suffice to mention only a few examples (fig. 117).

From *Coal-tar*: fuel oils, pitch, disinfectants, antiseptics, aniline dyes, plastics, perfumes and flavouring extracts.

From *Benzole*: motor spirit, weedkiller, aspirin, saccharin and sulphonamide drugs (among the first of which was the M & B group).

[1] Very much less 'bunker coal' is used nowadays, since almost all vessels are oil-driven.
[2] As distinct from hydro-electricity.

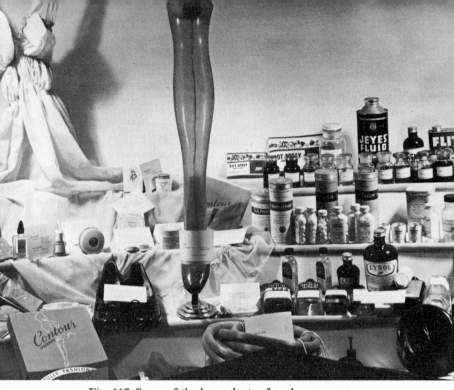

Fig. 117 Some of the byproducts of coal.

From *Sulphate of ammonia*: fertilisers, insecticides, soap, explosives and chemicals for use in refrigerators.

World distribution of coalfields

The world's coalfields (i.e. areas in which coal seams exist at a depth shallow enough to permit exploitation) are situated principally on the edges of belts of rocks of the Upper Carboniferous period which have survived erosion. It would be quite useless to look for coal in areas where more ancient rocks appear at the surface, and although seams may well lie under younger rocks, mining would probably be impracticable in view of their depth below ground. A broad zone of 'coal forests' at one time stretched across Europe and Asia from Britain to Japan and was continued in North America. Remnants of this belt now form the most extensive and most important coalfields of the modern world. The land masses of the southern hemisphere, since they consist largely of ancient crustal blocks, contain few coalfields, and the tropical lands are almost completely devoid of coal.

The presence of coalfields in Western Europe and North America was a basic factor in the early industrialisation of these areas, and since coal was throughout most of the Industrial Revolution the only available source of power, the distribution of coalfields largely controlled the location of industry within the countries concerned, and led to a general redistribution of population. The dominance of 'King Coal' as a source of power has, however, in recent years been limited not only by the exhaustion of many of the older mines, but also by the competition of hydro-electricity, oil, natural gas and nuclear power. The resulting stock-piling of unwanted coal and the closure of collieries have led to great economic and social problems (such as unemployment and the transfer of redundant miners to other jobs and other districts) in the United Kingdom, West Germany, Belgium and the Netherlands, for example.

World production of coal

World production of bituminous coal and anthracite is now slightly more than 2 000 millions tons annually. The USA is the largest producer and supplies 25 per cent of the total (fig. 118), followed by the USSR, China, the United Kingdom, Poland and West Germany. Estimates of the untouched reserves of coal vary, but probably enough remains in the earth's crust to permit consumption at the present rate for over 3 000 years. We may assume that, before the point of exhaustion it reached, coal as a source of power will have been superseded. Over three-quarters of the estimated reserves are situated in the USA, the USSR and China. The only considerable producers of lignite and/or brown coal are East Germany, the USSR, West Germany and Czechoslovakia.

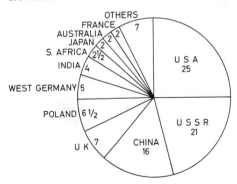

Fig. 118 World production of coal (i.e. bituminous coal, steam coal and anthracite). The figures indicate percentages of the world's total output of just over 2 000 million tons per year.

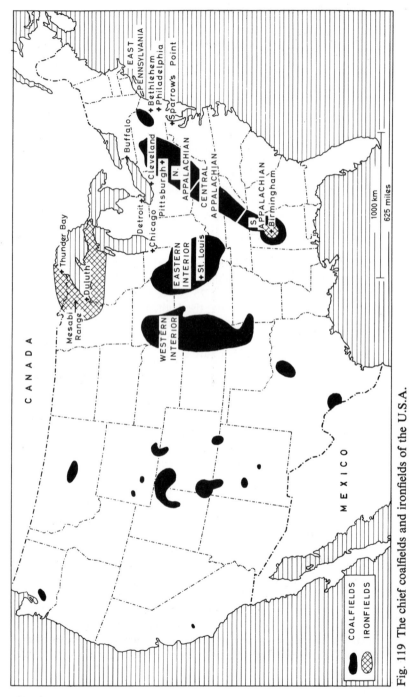

Fig. 119 The chief coalfields and ironfields of the U.S.A.

Chief producing areas

The United States

On the lower slopes of the Appalachian Mountains lie four important coalfields which provide nearly three-quarters of America's output (fig. 119).

The *East Pennsylvanian* field in the north-east is especially noted for its anthracite.

The *Northern Appalachian* field supplies good coking coal, and is, therefore, associated with the iron- and steel-producing region around Pittsburgh and Cleveland.

The *Central Appalachian* field of Kentucky and West Virginia is notable for household and steam coal.

The *Southern Appalachian* field centred on Birmingham in Alabama also provides good coking coal and supplies the local iron and steel industry.

Farther westward lies the *Eastern Interior* coalfield, from which bituminous coal is supplied to Chicago, St Louis and other industrial areas, and the *Western Interior* coalfield. Smaller, isolated coalfields extending as far west as the Rockies are of only local importance.

The USSR

The four main coalfields of the Soviet Union are the *Donetz Basin* or *Donbas*), the oldest of the Russian coalfields, which still supplies about one-third of the country's needs of anthracite and bituminous coal, and supports the iron and steel industry of Krivoi Rog; and the *Karaganda*, the *Kuznetsk* and the *Irkutsk* coalfields, which have developed in the course of Russian industrial expansion east of the Urals.

The *Tula* coalfield, south of Moscow, produces lignite which is used locally for the generation of electricity.

The United Kingdom

Fig. 120 shows the distribution of coalfields in Britain. With the exception of the small Kent coalfield, all lie among the older rocks north and west of the Jurassic escarpment, and on the borders of the uplands. The most productive area is the *Yorkshire, Derbyshire and Nottinghamshire* coalfield, which normally contributes about half Britain's total production. In 1961 Britain's output was 194 million tons, but in 1971 only 133 million. It is noticeable that in the United Kingdom the individual coalfields (or parts of them) have become associated with particular industries—*Lancashire* with the cotton industry, *Northumberland and Durham* with shipbuilding, *South Wales* with tinplate, *north*

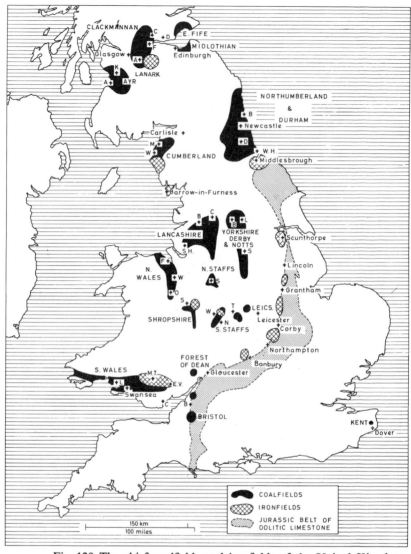

Fig. 120 The chief coalfields and ironfields of the United Kingdom. Places indicated by the initial letters of their names should be identified with the help of an atlas.

Yorkshire with the woollen industry, *south Yorkshire* with steel, and so on. In addition to supplying home demands of bituminous coal, steam coal and anthracite,[1] Britain was for many years a considerable exporter (chiefly of Welsh steam coal), but exports

[1] Britain has only an insignificant amount of lignite—in Devonshire.

(3·3 millions tons in 1970) have now fallen well below the level of 1913, when production reached its peak of 287 million tons. Britain's declining output is a reflection mainly of the fact that less coal is needed as a fuel than formerly.

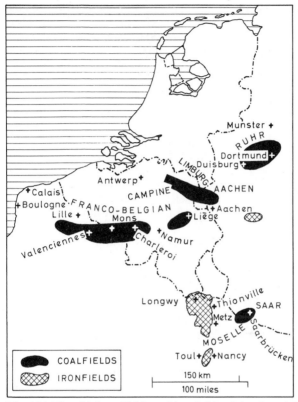

Fig. 121 The chief coalfields and ironfields of the six original members of the European Coal and Steel Community.

The European Coal and Steel Community
The ECSC (figs. 120–1, and see p. 190) operates:

The *Ruhr* coalfield in West Germany, which contains immense reserves of all types of coal (except lignite), and produces the greater part of the Community's output;

The *Saar* coalfield;

The *Franco-Belgian* coalfield, the *Limburg* coalfield in the Netherlands, the *Kempen* (Campine) in Belgium, and several smaller fields, such as *Aachen* in West Germany, and *Le Creusot* in France.

Brown coal is obtained from a large field west of Cologne.

Eastern and southern Europe

The largest European coalfield (and the chief exporter) is situated in *Upper Silesia*. Since the war almost all of this field has been in Polish territory, with the remainder in Czechoslovakia.

East Germany is deficient in bituminous coal, but has large reserves of brown coal north of Zwickau and Karl-Marx-Stadt (formerly Chemnitz) in *Saxony*. Coal is also mined at *Pilsen* in Czechoslovakia. The only coalfield of any importance south of the Hercynian block mountains of western and central Europe is near *Oviedo* in Northern Spain.

It should be noted that coal is absent from Scandinavia apart from a small field in Svalbard (the Spitsbergen Archipelago).

Other coal-producing areas

China has enormous reserves of coal, and great efforts are being made to increase production. Output, largely from an extensive 'opencast' mine at Fushun in north-east Manchuria, increased enormously until 1961, when it reached a peak of 421 million tons; since then production has fluctuated, but now averages about 390 million tons a year.

Japan produces annually about 50 million tons of inferior bituminous coal, but is also an importer.

India is extending her coal production, now about 75 million tons a year, chiefly at Raniganj in the Damodar Basin.

South America has a small output, principally from mines in Chile and southern Brazil.

Africa is deficient in coal, but there are mines in south-eastern Transvaal (Witbank, for example), at Newcastle in Natal, at Wankie in Rhodesia and at Enugu in Nigeria.

Australia obtains most of her coal from the Newcastle area of New South Wales, and in Victoria thick deposits of lignite are exploited.

New Zealand has deposits of low-grade coal at Greymouth and other places on the west coast.

Canada now produces increasing amounts of coal (18 million tons in 1972). Most of it comes from the newly-developed Crowsnest and other Rocky Mountain fields and is exported to Japan via a special terminal near Vancouver.

18

PETROLEUM

On 27 August 1859 a certain Laurentine Drake, employed by the newly formed Pennsylvania Rock Oil Company,[1] became at Titusville, 80 km (50 miles) north of Pittsburgh, the first man to 'strike oil' by drilling a hole into the earth's crust. By the end of the year 'Drake's Folly' had produced 2 000 barrels of petroleum, and oil prospectors, after the fashion of early gold-miners, had begun to flock to the area in the hope of making a quick fortune. In 1950 world production was 516 million tons[2]; it now well exceeds 2 000 million, and besides being one of the chief sources of power, petroleum is also the basis of a wide range of byproducts, amongst which must be included most of that group of modern materials known as plastics (see p. 246) and synthetic rubber (see p. 125). Estimates of reserves of petroleum vary, and the search for new deposits goes on continually, but even so it seems more than likely that known reserves will have been exhausted within the next fifty years. The mining of petroleum is far more of a 'robber economy' than the mining of any other mineral.

The origin, nature and geological occurrence of petroleum

Petroleum is a mixture of various hydrocarbons (i.e. chemical compounds of hydrogen and carbon only). Authorities differ as to the manner of its origin, but it is generally thought to have been formed as a result of the action of bacteria upon the bodies of tiny marine creatures (plankton—see p. 54), which became intermingled with mud at the bottom of seas and lagoons. In addition to pressure, the passage of time and the exclusion of air, heat may also have been a necessary condition for the formation of petroleum. Subsequent earth movements appear to have

---

[1] Drake was an ex-railway conductor, and was popularly known as 'Colonel' Drake—a self-assumed title!
[2] Figures of petroleum production are sometimes quoted in barrels and sometimes in tons. One ton of petroleum is normally equal to between 7 and 8 barrels, depending on the specific gravity.

squeezed the oil and gases[1] out of the original sediments and driven them into porous rocks, particularly sandstones and limestones, where, providing the geological formations were such as to trap them between impermeable layers above and below, they remained available for exploitation. Petroleum is, therefore, usually found in anticlines (or upfolds) in areas of plains, where the strata have been gently folded. More violent folding would have caused fracturing of the sealing layers and allowed the petroleum to escape or evaporate. Below the actual oil, the porous strata contain salt water, while above it there is often a quantity of natural gas (fig. 122).

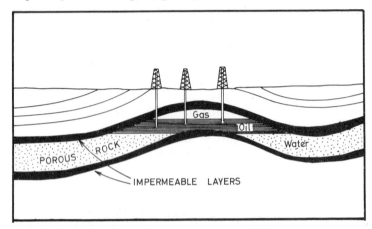

Fig. 122 The occurrence of petroleum in an anticline.

Prospecting and drilling

A detailed knowledge of the geology of a given area is clearly the most valuable aid to oil prospecting. There are few other clues to the presence of oil, although in rare cases a tarry scum, formed by the oxidation of oil leaking from a subterranean reservoir, forms at the surface. In the early days, the general practice was random drilling or 'wild-catting', in the hope of being fortunate enough to 'strike oil'. But nowadays before the expense of drilling is undertaken,[2] petroleum surveyors set off explosive charges at selected points, and can interpret from the

[1] 'Petroleum' is sometimes used to include both crude oil as found in the earth's crust and 'natural gas' with which crude oil is associated, while at other times it refers to crude oil only. It is usually obvious from the context which meaning is intended.

[2] In the USA the cost of drilling a well of average depth is about $100 000.

recordings made on seismographs the nature and arrangement of the rocks in the vicinity. By this means, and with the help of various other ingenious instruments for measuring density, permeability, etc., they can indicate whether the existence of petroleum is likely.

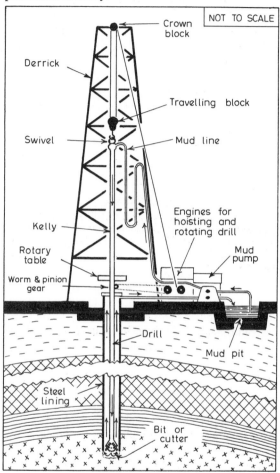

Fig. 123 Rotary drill and derrick.

When a site for drilling has been decided upon, a steel derrick about 35 m (115 ft) high is erected, and machinery for rotating the drill is installed (fig. 123). The drill, to which extra lengths are constantly attached, is in the form of a tube down which mud is forced to lubricate and cool the bit or cutter. The mud passes through holes in the bit and returns to the surface, bringing with it the rock cut away as the work proceeds. Meanwhile tubes of larger diameter are let down into the shaft as a lining. When the layer of impermeable rock which 'caps' the oil-bearing stratum is eventually pierced, petroleum will either flow of its own accord (in which case the well is said to be a 'gusher') or it may be necessary to install pumps to raise the oil to the surface. In any case the pressure will fall as the oil passes out of the underground reservoir. A well once started may go on flowing for years—but there is always the possibility that it will cease within a matter of weeks or even days.

A modern development of great significance—and in the not too distant future of vital importance—is the search for petroleum and natural gas beneath the sea bed, as, for instance, in the North Sea, the Gulf of Mexico, the Persian Gulf and the Bass Strait.

Refining petroleum

The circumstance which led to the drilling of 'Drake's Folly' and the numerous other wells which soon followed it was that America was running short of train-oil (see p. 63). Whales in the North Atlantic had been pursued with such success that they were in danger of extermination, and it was becoming necessary to find an alternative oil for lighting lamps. It was soon demonstrated that by boiling crude oil in a simple still and distilling the vapour which rose from it kerosene (or paraffin) could be produced which answered the purpose extremely well. And until about 1910, this was the only product of petroleum distillation for which any sizeable market existed.

But in the meantime the internal combustion engine had been developed, and the demand was created for the more volatile petrol (or gasoline), which had hitherto been regarded as useless. Moreover, the increasing speed and complexity of modern machinery in general called for a much wider range of lubricants than could be supplied by vegetable oils. It thus became possible to utilise all the various materials which could be produced by splitting up petroleum.

Fractional Distillation
This is the fundamental process by which petroleum is split into its 'fractions' (or groups of hydrocarbons), and makes use of the fact that the various fractions boil at different temperatures. Crude oil is first heated to a temperature of about 430° C (806° F) by being passed through pipes in a furnace; after which it enters

Fig. 124 The oil-refinery at Lavéra in Mediterranean France.

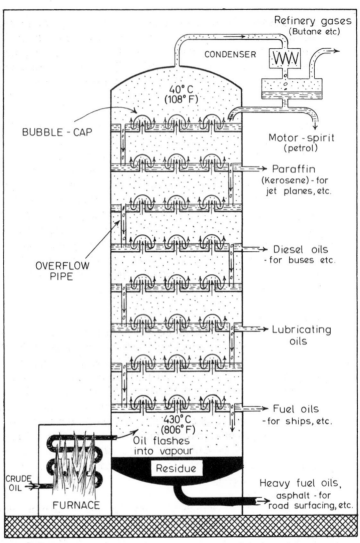

Fig. 125 Simplified diagrammatic section of a fractionating tower.

the 'fractionating tower' (fig. 124) and immediately flashes into vapour. As the vapour rises it is forced by an arrangement of vents and 'bubble-caps' to pass through liquids which in the continuous process of distillation have already condensed on trays set one above the other throughout the height of the tower. Motor-spirit vapours, which have boiling points below about 40° C (108° F), pass out of the top of the tower and are liquefied in a condenser. Other light fractions (such as paraffin) condense on the uppermost trays, while on successive trays beneath lubricating oils and fuel oils collect; at the bottom, where the temperature is about 430° C (806° F), a residue forms consisting of heavy fuel oils and asphalt or, in some cases, wax.

Thermal cracking

The rapid increase in the number of cars during the early part of the twentieth century[1] created an enormous demand for petrol; but since crude oil yields only 10 to 20 per cent of its weight in motor spirit, the oil-refining companies soon found that they were accumulating far more paraffin, lubricating oils and asphalt than they could sell. In 1912, therefore, the process of thermal cracking was adopted, in which the heavy fractions (i.e. those constituents of crude oil which consist of molecules containing a large number of carbon atoms) are subjected to extremely high temperatures and pressures, so that they 'crack' or break down into lighter fractions (such as petrol) which consist of molecules containing a small number of carbon atoms.

Catalytic cracking

It was eventually discovered that more and better motor and aviation spirit was produced if cracking took place in the presence of a catalyst (i.e. a substance which assists a reaction without itself being affected by it). This normally takes the form of pow-dered platinum flowing in the stream of vaporised oil. Periodically the catalyst is removed and the carbon with which it becomes coated is burned off in a current of air. Modern methods of cataly-tic cracking ('cat-cracking') make it possible for oil-refiners to produce enough of each fraction to supply the market without acquiring unwanted accumulations of any one of them.

Polymerisation

This process, in which the simpler hydro-carbon molecules obtained from refinery gases are made to combine so as to form large molecules, is essentially the reverse of cracking. Although it is used in the manufacture of motor spirit, the process is really of more importance in connection with synthetic rubber and plastics.

---

[1] 'While there had been only four automobiles registered in the United States in 1895, that number had risen to about half a million by 1910, and by 1913 had topped the million mark', *Petroleum Refining*, published by Esso Petroleum Co., Ltd. In Britain in 1971 there were over 15 million motor vehicles.

Natural gas

The gas which is found above deposits of crude oil[1] is known as natural gas to distinguish it from gas derived from coal, and consists almost entirely of methane (marsh-gas) and ethane. It sometimes issues from the ground of its own accord, and was until recently used solely for lighting and heating, but the development of polymerisation has made it an important raw material of the chemical industry. The hydrocarbon molecules of which it consists are the simplest of all such molecules, and may be made to combine so as to form the larger molecules of which modern 'synthetic' substances are composed. Natural gas is a commodity of increasing importance. The USA is by far the largest producer, followed by the USSR and Canada, but it is now being exploited in many other countries, including the United Kingdom. The gasfield at Slochteren near Groningen in the northern Netherlands is claimed to be the largest in the world.

Bituminous shales

In certain parts of the world (notably the USA, the Central Valley of Scotland, Estonia and Manchuria) shales exist impregnated with a kind of tar, which is thought to have been formed from oil which leaked out of petroleum deposits many years ago. When heated in great retorts, such shales yield crude oil, which can be converted into petrol, lubricating oil, fuel oil and so on in the same way as ordinary petroleum. The distillation of oil-shales is, however, a comparatively expensive operation, and few countries have so far considered it worth while,[2] but there is little doubt that when existing sources of petroleum begin to fail, the world will turn to the very considerable deposits of bituminous shales which are known to exist in the above-mentioned areas and elsewhere. A particularly interesting deposit of this kind is the 'tar sands' of Athabaska in northern Canada. An economic method of extracting the petroleum has now been devised and production is increasing rapidly.

The transport of petroleum

Oil is an essential commodity in every corner of the world;

[1] Natural gas is often found independently of crude oil.
[2] In Estonia for about ten years after the First World War the shale itself was used as a fuel for locomotives as well as on domestic and factory fires.

without it the London bus, the transatlantic plane and the tractor on an Antarctic expedition would be equally useless. Yet the world's oilfields are concentrated in two or three main areas. Regular and efficient distribution is, therefore, a matter of vital importance. Where it is necessary to transport oil for great distances overland, the cheapest method is by means of pipelines, but the capital cost of installing the pipes (modern examples of which are nearly one metre in diameter) and the pumping-stations which are required at intermediate points is extremely high. In the United States an intricate network of pipelines conveying crude oil, gasoline and natural gas to the consuming areas has a total length of over 480 000 km (300 000 miles), while in the Middle East pipelines carry supplies from wells in the interior to the ports of Baniâs, Tripoli and Sidon on the east coast of the Mediterranean Sea or to Abadan and Bahrein on the Persian Gulf. A particularly important artery of this kind is the 76-cm (30-inch) diameter 'Tapline' (the Trans-Arabian Pipeline), which carries oil from the Aramco (Arabian American Oil Company) concessions to Sidon over 1 500 km (940 miles) away.

During the last decade tremendous developments have taken place in the construction of pipelines in Europe. Notable ones are: the *South European Pipeline* (768 km [480 miles] from Lavéra, near Marseilles, to Karlsruhe), the *Central European Pipeline* (1 000 km [625 miles], from Genoa to Ingoldstadt and Stuttgart), the *Transalpine Pipeline* (475 km [300 miles] from Trieste to Ingoldstadt) and the *Friendship Pipeline* (5 291 km [3307 miles], from Brody in the Ukraine to Schwedt-an-der-Oder in East Germany). New and equally important pipelines for the transport of oil or natural gas have also been constructed in Asiatic Russia and in Canada. The Trans-Canada Pipeline, with a length (as yet) of 6 026 km (3 769 miles), is the longest pipeline in the world. In Britain a network of pipelines is being laid based on a main artery from the Thames estuary to Merseyside.

By sea, oil is carried in specially built ships known as 'tankers', which nowadays rank as the largest cargo vessels afloat (see p. 283). Since it is far cheaper to transport oil by tanker than by pipeline, road or rail,[1] and since petroleum is a comparatively easy commodity to load and unload, sea transport is used wherever possible.

---

[1] It is calculated that in the USA the cost of transporting oil by road or rail is three times as great as the cost of transport by pipeline and seven time as great as the cost of transport by tanker.

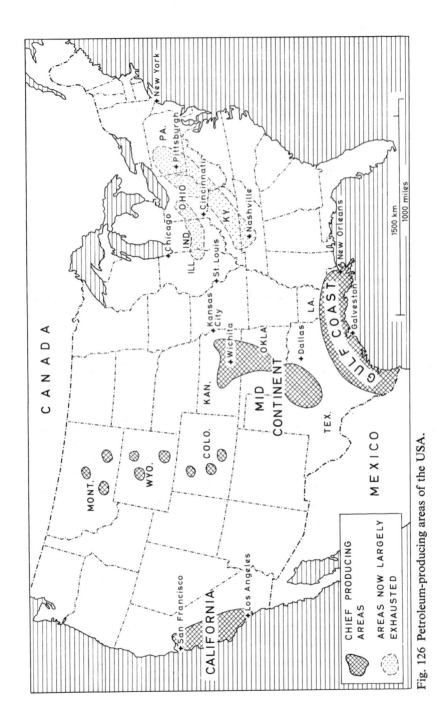

Fig. 126 Petroleum-producing areas of the USA.

CHIEF PRODUCING
AREAS

AREAS NOW LARGELY
EXHAUSTED

240   Petroleum

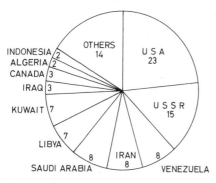

Fig. 127 World production of petroleum in 1970. The figures indicate percentages of the world's total production of 2 334 million tons.

Chief producing areas

The United States
As will be seen from fig. 127, the USA is the world's largest producer of petroleum, but is nevertheless obliged to import oil (from Venezuela) in order to satisfy her requirements. The oilfields of Pennsylvania, Ohio and Indiana, which were the chief producers until about fifty years ago, now yield only a small amount, and the main centres of production today (fig. 126) are the *Mid-Continent* field of Kansas, Oklahoma and northern Texas, and the *Gulf Coast* field of southern Texas and Louisiana. These two areas together contribute about three-quarters of America's output. Almost all of the remainder comes from *California*, which between the two world wars was the chief producing state, and the *Rocky Mountains* region, where widely dispersed oilfields in Montana, Wyoming and Colorado are not yet being developed to capacity on account of their distance from consuming areas.

The Middle East
This area includes four chief producers (fig. 128):
Kuwait, a small Arab sheikhdom near the head of the Persian Gulf, where oil was first produced as recently as 1946;
Saudi Arabia, another newcomer in the field of petroleum, whose principal oilfield is at Abqaic;
Iraq, where output (from Basra, Kirkuk and Mosul) has increased over twelvefold since 1948; and
Iran, which was for forty years or more the only oil-producing country in the Middle East. The organising centre of the Iranian oil industry is at Abadan.

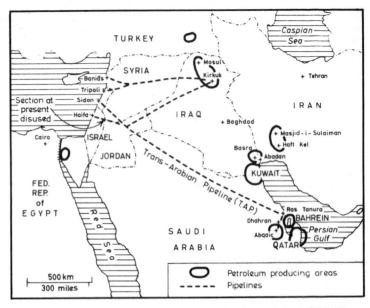

Fig. 128 Petroleum-producing areas and pipelines of the Middle East.

Smaller quantities of oil are obtained from the sheikhdoms of *Qatar* and *Abu Dhabi*, the nearby island of *Bahrein* in the Persian Gulf, from *Oman* and from *Egypt* south of the Suez Canal.

Venezuela
Venezuela, which produces 8 per cent of the world's oil, chiefly from the district around Lake Maracaibo, exports almost the whole of her output to the USA.

The island of *Trinidad* contains an extension of the Venezuelan oilfield, but is more notable for its famous pitch lake (fig. 121), which yields apparently inexhaustible supplies of natural bitumen used in road-making, etc.

The USSR
Oil has been mined in the northern foothills of the Caucasus Mountains since before the beginning of the twentieth century, and abundant supplies from *Baku* on the shore of the Caspian Sea are taken by pipeline (part of which was built in 1900) to Batum on the Black Sea, from which it is shipped to the Donbas industrial region. The comparatively new *Volga-Urals* oilfields centred on Molotov, Ishimbay and Kuibyshev are called by the Russians 'a second Baku' and now supply over three-quarters of the Soviet's Union's petroleum.

Fig. 129 A close-up of the surface of the Asphalt or Pitch Lake in Trinidad in the West Indies. The Lake is the largest deposit of natural asphalt in the world, and has been worked since the middle of the last century, during which time over 8 million tons of asphalt have been removed. The asphalt is refined on the spot and dispatched in wooden barrels or steel drums, chiefly for use as a matrix for road-surfacing materials. It is also used in making roof-coverings, certain special kinds of adhesives, compounds for jointing or lining pipes, and for many other purposes.

Other producing areas

Canada. In 1947 important new oilfields were opened up near Calgary and Edmonton in Alberta. These already supply over half of the country's needs, and now that petroleum is being produced from the Athabasca 'tar sands', Canada exports to the USA. Equally important deposits of natural gas in the same area make Canada the world's third largest producer.

Indonesia. Indonesia is the only part of South-east Asia which makes any significant contribution to the world's supply of oil. In fact, the combined production of all the various territories which are included in an arc from India and Pakistan to Japan and China is less than that of Canada alone.

Africa. Until recently Africa was considered to be devoid of petroleum, but large deposits, both of crude oil and natural gas, have now been tapped at a number of places in the Sahara region.

Pipelines have been laid to the Mediterranean coast, and since 1964 Libya and Algeria have become considerable producers. Important developments have also taken place in Nigeria.

Europe. Europe (excluding European Russia) produces only 1·5 per cent of the world's oil. Over half of her contribution comes from Romania and West Germany.

The United Kingdom. In 1939 deposits of crude oil were discovered at Formby near Liverpool and at several places near Newark, then subsequently in Dorset, Lincolnshire and Yorkshire. The 1970 production of nearly 80 000 tons represents only 0·003 per cent of the world total, but the whole position may soon be revolutionised, when the numerous finds of oil and natural gas under the North Sea come into full production.

In spite of being virtually a non-producer, Britain has nevertheless played an important part in the oil industry for nearly a hundred years. A full discussion of the subject would be out of place here, but the salient points are as follows:

1. From 1850 until 1938 Scotland was the world's leading producer of shale-oil. Until the workings were closed down in April 1962, bituminous shales on the southern side of the Firth of Forth had been producing more crude oil than the wells in Lancashire and the Midlands.

Fig. 130 One of the North Sea drilling platforms which operates near the Shetland Isles.

2. A great deal of the capital needed for the development of oilfields in many parts of the world was provided by British investors.

3. Britain's fleet of oil tankers is the largest in the world.

4. British oil-refineries have a combined capacity greater than that of any other country in Europe. This is largely due to a remarkable programme of expansion undertaken by the three big companies which almost entirely control the import of petroleum. Modern refineries have been built at Fawley (the largest in the Commonwealth), Shellhaven, Stanlow, and other places situated in tide-water locations which permit access by large tankers (fig. 131). The Sydenham refinery in Northern

Fig. 131 Some important petroleum refineries in Great Britain and Northern Ireland.

Ireland, built on reclaimed land in Belfast Harbour, started production in 1965. These refineries are in part fed with crude oil offloaded at other ports and conveyed to them by pipeline; for example, since 1959 some of the oil delivered to the Grangemouth refinery has been offloaded at an 'oil-terminal' specially constructed at Finnart, 16 km (10 miles) up Loch Long on the *west* coast of Scotland. At Bantry Bay in south-western Ireland an oil-terminal has been built capable of receiving tankers of over 300 000 tons.

Plastics

Plastics have already been mentioned in connection with textiles, timber and coal, but since there is an increasing tendency for the raw materials of this new and rapidly expanding industry to be derived from petroleum, main discussion of the subject is included in this chapter rather than elsewhere.

The nature of plastics

Neither the layman nor the scientist has any difficulty in recognising a modern 'plastic', but both have great difficulty in defining the term. In general a 'plastic' may be described as an organic substance which at some stage of its manufacture is capable of being shaped by heat or pressure or both. Some such substances (known as *thermoplastics*) can again be softened by heat, while others (made of *thermosetting* material) cannot. The molecular structure of plastics was not properly understood until about forty years ago, when they were shown to consist of 'big' molecules or *polymers* in which two or more molecules of the same chemical substance combine to form a new compound with a greater molecular weight. In both thermoplastic and thermosetting materials the 'big' molecules are made up of long chains of ordinary molecules, but in the case of thermosetters heat causes cross-linkages to form between the chains, thus destroying their elasticity.

Invention and development of plastics

Although certain naturally occurring polymeric substances such as rubber have been known and used for a century or more, the noun 'plastic' is now, popularly at any rate, reserved for 'synthetic' substances which are the result of processes[1] devised by modern scientists. The first thermosetting substance of this kind was made by Leo Baekeland in 1907, using phenol (carbolic acid) obtained from coal-tar and formaldehyde obtained by the distillation of wood.[2] The product, which was given the name of 'Bakelite' after its inventor, proved to be an excellent electrical insulator and eminently suitable for casting in moulds. Later developments led to the invention of 'laminated plastics' (such as *Formica*), which are made from sheets of paper, wood, cloth, etc., saturated and bound together with *Bakelite*.

The first of the thermoplastic materials to be produced on a commercial scale was the transparent substance which (when

[1] i.e. polymerisation processes.
[2] Formaldehyde is now made from either coal or petroleum.

produced by the English firm, Imperial Chemical Industries, Ltd) is known as *Perspex*. This is one of a group of plastics called 'acrylic resins', which includes the textile fibre *Orlon* (see p. 151).

Since 1935, when *Perspex* was first put on the market, the development of plastics (particularly thermoplastics) has proceeded at a tremendous pace, and there would be little use in attempting to list either the basic chemical materials of plastics or the trade names by which the manufactured substances are known (*Polythene, Alkathene, PVC, Buna, Terylene* and so on). It is, however, important to note that whereas originally the raw materials of the plastics industry were derived mainly from by-products of the distillation of coal, crude oil is now the chief source. For this reason the industry has tended to grow up close to refineries from which the products of 'petrochemical' cracking (methane, ethane, propane, butane, etc.) can be sold 'over the fence'—for example, the Monsanto polythene plant near Fawley and the British Hydrocarbon chemical plant near Grangemouth.

Uses of Plastics

Plastics are in general light in weight, attractive in appearance, good electrical insulators and resistant to moisture. Moreover, they lend themselves to moulding and to mass-production methods. Practically their only failing has so far been that they are incapable of resisting intense local heat. But *Polypropylin* does not suffer from this disadvantage, and is in fact used in the manufacture of electric kettles. It has even been proposed that plastics should be used for making coins. Indeed, the increasing uses for this interesting group of modern materials suggest that we may well have entered a veritable Age of Plastics.

19

HYDRO-ELECTRIC POWER

General considerations

The water power revolution
By 1850 most of the old millwheels in Europe and North America were lying idle, rusty and in disrepair. Energy produced by the new steam engines had largely superseded 'crude' water power, and industry had moved away from the river valleys to become concentrated in the coalfields. During the early years of the twentieth century, however, water power began to regain some of its former importance, as means were devised of harnessing it for the production of *hydro-electricity*,[1] which today provides one-quarter of all the world's supplies of energy. An interesting consequence of the water power revolution has been that industry is no longer fettered to the coalfields.

The essential features of a hydro-electric station
Three main developments enabled man to make more efficient use than formerly of the force of running water.
1. The perfection of the *hydraulic turbine*, a modern form of 'waterwheel' in which a controlled flow of water under pressure is directed against the blades of a wheel, so causing it to rotate.
2. The perfection of the *dynamo*, in which mechanical energy produced by the rotation of the turbine is converted into electrical energy.
3. The manufacture of improved types of *cement*, which made it possible to construct enormous concrete dams for storing the water, regulating its flow and increasing the pressure.

The dam, the turbines and the dynamos (or generators) together with large pipes called *penstocks*, which lead the water held up by the dam to the turbines below, constitute the essential features of a hydro-electric station (fig. 132).

---

[1] *Hydro* is derived from a Greek word meaning 'water'. Thermal electricity is produced by dynamos driven by steam engines.

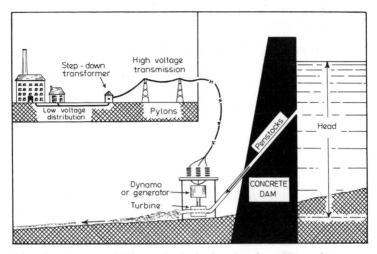

Fig. 132 The essential features of a hydro-electric power station.

Distribution and siting

Physical factors

The successful and economic operation of a station depends primarily on two conditions:

(a) *A constant and abundant flow of water.* In the long run this is dependent on precipitation in the catchment area which feeds the river, and hydroelectric stations are, therefore, most numerous in those parts of the world where rainfall is evenly distributed throughout the year. The impounding of water behind the dams to form artificial lakes to some extent obviates the difficulty caused by unevenly distributed rainfall, but regions with a 'Mediterranean', Tropical or Monsoon type of climate and regions in which the rivers freeze in winter clearly present special problems.

(b) *A sufficient head of water.* The amount of electricity generated depends not only on the volume of water flowing through the station, but also on the 'head' of water—i.e. the difference in level between the turbines and the surface of the water held up by the dam. Hence mountainous areas containing fast-flowing rivers and numerous waterfalls readily lend themselves to the generation of hydro-electricity, particularly since they are likely to include excellent natural reservoirs in the form of snowfields and glaciers. Norway, Sweden and Switzerland provide good examples, and it is understandable that such countries, lacking coal and petroleum, should have become prominent in the development of hydro-electricity. Increasing use is now, however, being made of sites in which a 'low head' is associated with a huge volume of water, as, for instance, in the Shannon scheme in Eire.

A factor of no little importance is the existence of a favourable site for the construction of a dam. The ideal site would consist of a gorge-like channel, upstream of which the valley widened out to form the basin of a potential lake, with a high waterfall on the downstream side. Local topography is very closely related to the cost of the installation (which may well amount to many millions of pounds) as well as to its eventual efficiency.

Economic factors

The most important economic factor is the existence of a market for the power produced. In the early days of hydro-electricity, when development depended to a large extent on private enterprise, the capital cost of the construction of a station and the installation of high-voltage transmission lines and transformers[1] was delicately balanced against both the expected return in the form of revenue and competition with other sources of power. Hydro-electricity, contrary to popular belief, is not always or necessarily cheaper to produce than thermal electricity. Moreover, until recently the drop in voltage over long distances made it uneconomic to transmit electricity more than 500 km (310 miles) or so. Modern large-scale undertakings are now almost always financed by governments rather than by companies or corporations, and less regard is paid to the expectation of immediatl returns than to the possibility of improving undeveloped or depressed areas. Such enterprises are usually dual- or multi-purpose projects, which involve irrigation, the control of floods, the improvement of navigation, the smelting of aluminium, etc., in addition to the supply of electricity to grid systems such as the British 'National Grid' and *Electricité de France*.

It must not be thought that hydro-electric schemes are all large-scale undertakings. They vary in size and importance, and until recently included small local installations providing only enough electricity to light, perhaps, an isolated farm in North Wales; somewhat larger stations associated with aluminium smelting plants in the Highlands of Scotland; stations which supply power and lighting to individual towns (as in New Zealand); as well as mammoth installations such as those based on the Grand Coulee and Hoover Dams in the United States (figs. 134–6).

---

[1] For reducing the voltage before the power is finally delivered to consumers.

Resources and development

During the last forty years production of hydro-electricity has increased enormously, and so many plants are now in operation or projected that it will be possible to mention only those which display special features.

North America
The most significant schemes are found in the United States and Canada, which together supply over two-fifths of the world's output.
The St Lawrence Seaway (fig. 133), which was opened to traffic in 1959, provides a good example of a dual-purpose scheme. Dams across the river near Cornwall have not only made the International Rapids section of the St Lawrence available to ocean-going vessels by impounding a lake 57 km (36 miles) long and nowhere less than 8·2 m (27 ft) deep, but have also made it possible to generate electricity at a newly constructed power-house. Electricity is also generated at a similar dam built at

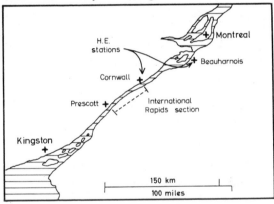

Fig. 133 Hydro-electric power stations on the St Lawrence Seaway.

Beauharnois, where the river passes round an island about 16 km (10 miles) upstream from Montreal. These two installations make the Seaway one of the world's largest producers of hydro-electricity.
The Grand Coulee Dam (figs. 134 and 135) in the state of Washington is the largest concrete structure in the world, and forms part of a plan for controlling the flood waters of the Columbia River and reclaiming arid land in the vicinity. Most of the electricity generated at the dam is used to pump water from the lake created above the dam into the Grand Coulee, a long trough, 180 m (600 ft) above the level of the river, which was carved out by the

Fig. 134 The Grand Coulee Dam.

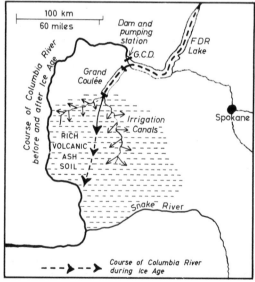

Fig. 135 The Grand Coulee project.

252   *Hydro-electric power*

Columbia when its course was temporarily diverted by a glacier in the Ice Age. From this trough, now sealed by a dam at each end, the water is fed through irrigation canals to the arid volcanic soils in the area to the south.

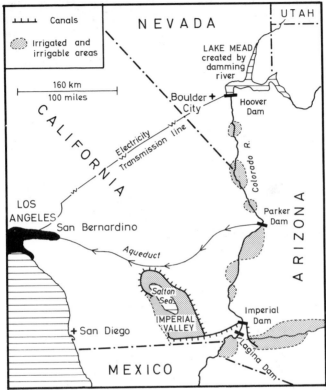

Fig. 136 The project based on the Hoover Dam.

The Hoover (or Boulder[1]) Dam (fig. 136) on the borders of Arizona and Nevada is part of a comprehensive scheme of development, which provides electricity and a municipal water supply to Los Angeles, improves navigational facilities, and controls the flow of the Colorado River, so that a regular supply of irrigation water is available to the dry lands of the Imperial Valley. With a height of 220 m (727 ft) the Hoover Dam is the second highest in the world, and electricity is transmitted to Los Angeles at 285 000 volts.

[1] The dam is close to Boulder City, and was started in 1933 during the presidency of Herbert D. Hoover. It is now officially referred to as the Hoover Dam.

The Californian Valley Project. As will be seen from fig. 137, the two main rivers of the Central Valley of California, the Sacramento and the San Joaquin, join and meet the sea in San Francisco Bay. Unfortunately the northern part of the valley is subject to periodic flooding, whereas the southern half is too dry for successful cultivation. A solution to the problem has been arrived at in the following ingenious way. A dam constructed across the Sacramento at Shasta regulates the flow of the river, while electricity generated at the dam is used to pump water in the lower part of the river into a high-level canal feeding the San Joaquin. From here the water is led by irrigation channels to the arid areas in the south.

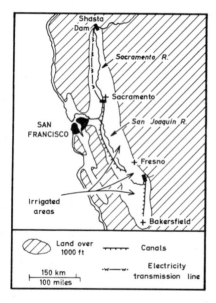

Fig. 137 The Californian Valley project.

The Kitimat Scheme (fig. 138). This undertaking in British Columbia was designed to provide abundant electricity for smelting aluminium ore imported from Jamaica. It is a particularly impressive engineering achievement in that the River Nechako (which formerly flowed eastwards to join the Fraser) has been completely blocked by a dam and its waters are now diverted westwards through a tunnel 16 km (10 miles) long. At the end of the tunnel, 788 m (2 585 ft) below the dam, a powerhouse generates electricity which is transmitted to smelters at Kitimat at the head of Douglas Channel.

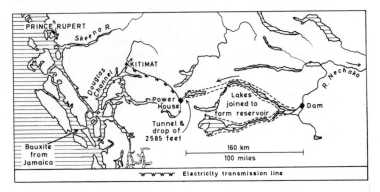

Fig. 138 The Kitimat scheme.

The Tennessee Valley Authority (TVA) Scheme was initiated by the American government in 1933 after a period of worldwide economic depression. It involved the construction of twenty dams and hydro-electric stations on the Tennessee River and its tributaries, and represents the first of the great comprehensive schemes aimed at improving and developing the resources of a region by river control.

Europe

Although Europe ranks second to North America in the development of hydro-electric power, few schemes exist which compare in size or complexity with those in the United States or Canada. Installations are, as one might expect, particularly numerous in mountainous areas which are deficient in coal, such as Norway, Sweden, Switzerland and Italy, and have in a number of cases led to industrial development which would otherwise have been impossible (the electro-metallurgical industry of Norway, for instance). Two large schemes at present under construction may be noted. The first is the *Rhône Development Plan*, ultimately involving twenty power stations, which aims to make the river Rhône navigable by 1 000-ton barges as far as Lake Geneva.[1] The second is a scheme based on loop canals which run parallel with the *Rhine* on the French side of the river from Basle to Strasbourg. This overcomes the navigational difficulties in this section and provides the opportunity for the generation of hydro-electric power. Eight power stations are at present in operation.

[1] Eight schemes (in the Génissiat, Pierre-Bènite, Bourges-Valence, Beauchastel, Baix-Logis Neuf, Montélimar, Donzère-Mondragon and Vallabrègues sections) have now been completed.

Fig. 139 Hydro-electricity generating plant near Inveruglas on the shore of Loch Lomond. Water from Loch Sloy, 5 km (3 miles) to the west, falls about 250 m (820 ft) through pipes to the power station shown in the picture. This was the first installation of its kind to be constructed after the Second World War. Surface pipelines such as those shown above are no longer tolerated; nowadays tunnels are used in an attempt to preserve the environment.

Britain has in the past given little attention to hydro-electricity, partly owing to a wealth of coal and partly owing to a lack of favourable sites. There is a number of smaller installations in North Wales and the Highlands of Scotland, but the ultimate combined output of existing and projected installations will barely equal half that of the Grand Coulee alone.

The USSR

The USSR is now the third largest producer of hydro-electricity after the USA and Canada. Her output, amounting to rather less than half that of the United States, comes from various widely distributed installations. The chief contribution formerly came from *Dnepropetrovsk*, which serves the gigantic Dnieper Combine, but new power stations at *Kuibyshev* and *Volgograd* (formerly Stalingrad), part of a large-scale project involving irrigation and the improvement of navigation on the Rivers Don and Volga, have affected a very considerable increase in production. Two huge dams are now under construction on the Angara river and another on the Yenesei.

Other Asian countries

The rest of Asia has vast potential resources, but only in Japan, the world's fourth largest producer of hydro-electricity, has any considerable development taken place, and, although little information is available there are large schemes under construction in China (e.g. at Ichang on the Yangtse).

Australia

The Snowy River Scheme, now in course of construction, is one of the few notable undertakings in the Southern Hemisphere. When complete it will double Australia's power supply of hydro-electricity and provide additional water for irrigation. The abundant waters of the southward-flowing Snowy River have been dammed and diverted through tunnels to augment the Rivers Murray and Murrumbidgee, which flow westwards across low-lying country where rainfall is too scanty to permit cultivation.

Africa

Central Africa, where rainfall is plentiful, has immense reserves of hydro-electricity, but there is at present little demand. The scheme at *Owen Falls*, completed in 1954, supplies electricity to the towns of Kampala and Tororo in Uganda, while the *Kariba Dam* project on the Zambesi is designed to provide much-needed power to Zambia and Rhodesia. The actual dam was completed in 1960, and above it the world's largest artificial lake has formed, 5 000 sq km (2 000 sq miles) in area. Probably the most important modern project is the Cabora Bassa scheme in Mozambique, due for completion in 1976. A dam on the River Zambesi about 110 km (69 miles) above Tete is designed to provide irrigation and flood control in addition to power for the exploitation of coal, iron ore and diamonds, and for the 'export' of electricity to South Africa; and a series of dams is being built on the Orange River.

South America

South America has so far made remarkably little use of hydro-electricity, except in southern Brazil, but today in almost every state in the continent at least one important undertaking is either planned or under construction.

20

ATOMIC POWER

The theory that all matter is composed of minute indivisible particles or 'atoms'[1] was first put forward by the Greek philosopher Democritus in the fourth century BC. It was later considered too absurd to be taken seriously, but was revived about 1800 and came to be generally accepted by physicists throughout the nineteenth century. Towards the end of this period the curiosity of the scientific world was aroused by the discovery that certain substances unaccountably gave off 'rays' (i.e. were *radioactive*), and the search for an explanation of the phenomenon resulted in a series of remakable achievements which revolutionised the study of physics and led not only to the explosion of the atomic bomb over Hiroshima in 1945, but also to the more recent peaceful applications of atomic energy. In view of declining reserves of coal and petroleum and the impossibility of meeting the world's demands for power solely by the production of hydro-electricity, it is indeed fortunate that a new source of energy has become available to mankind.

The scientific background

Nuclear fission

It would take far too long to trace in detail the sequence of laboratory experiments which were carried out by Rutherford, Cockroft, Chadwick and other eminent scientists in Europe and America in the course of the first forty years of the present century, and we may conveniently take up the story at the point when the practical application of their experiments first began to be realised.

By 1939 three epoch-making discoveries had been made:
1. That the atom was far more complicated in structure than Democritus had supposed. It had now been shown to consist of
(*a*) a *nucleus*, made up of particles, some of which are called *protons* and some *neutrons*; and
(*b*) a number of *electrons*, which travel round the nucleus in a

[1] The Greek word from which 'atom' is derived actually means 'indivisible'.

motion somewhat similar to that of the planets round the sun[1] (fig. 140).

2. That radioactive substances could be produced artificially. Until 1934 the only radioactive substances known were natural ones.

3. That the nucleus of an atom could be 'split' by bombarding it with a stream of neutrons.[2] Nuclear fission produced in this way is accompanied by the release of a tremendous amount of energy.

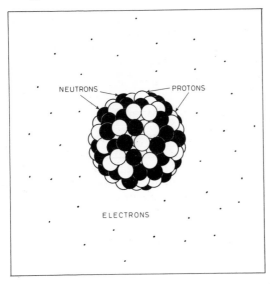

Fig. 140 The structure of a typical atom. It should be noted that the electrons move in separate planes.

The chain fission reaction

When a neutron strikes the nucleus of an atom of a 'fissionable material', it may either bounce off, be absorbed by the nucleus or cause the nucleus to split. The importance of the last of these possibilities is that further neutrons are released in the process. These may now bring about the fission of the nuclei of other atoms, which also release neutrons, so that the reaction goes on until all the atoms in the fissionable material have been similarly affected (fig. 141). Once started, a reaction of this kind may

[1] The size of an atom expressed in ordinary figures is almost incomprehensible. However, some idea may be gained from the fact that about 10 million atoms could be placed in a row across a pin's head.
[2] One way of generating a stream of neutrons is to bombard beryllium with the alpha particles emitted by radium.

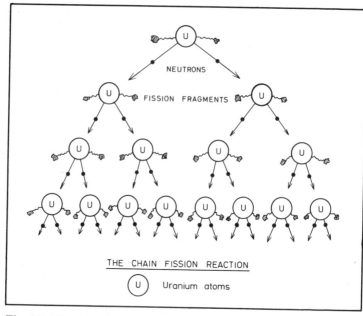

NEUTRONS

FISSION FRAGMENTS

THE CHAIN FISSION REACTION

U   Uranium atoms

Fig. 141 The chain fission reaction. Some of the neutrons emitted when the nuclei split are absorbed in reactions which do not cause fission. These are not shown in the diagram.

spread in an incredibly short space of time; a violent explosion will then take place, and 'fission fragments' will be scattered far and wide.

The nuclear reactor or atomic pile

Although the possibility of putting atomic power[1] to practical use had been envisaged in the early 1930s, very little was done until the last years of the War, when the atomic bomb was produced, in which the explosion takes the form of an uncontrolled chain reaction. After the War, efforts began to be directed also to the problem of designing a kind of 'furnace' in which the chain reaction could be controlled so as to provide a steady flow of energy instead of an explosion.

One very early type of nuclear reactor by means of which this is achieved consists of blocks of graphite built up into a cube, through which pass a number of horizontal channels (fig. 142). 'Slugs' of uranium encased in long aluminium[2] cylinders are thrust

[1] 'Atomic power' is the more popular term, but 'nuclear power' is more accurate.
[2] The aluminium casing stops the uranium from oxidising and prevents the escape of any gaseous fission products.

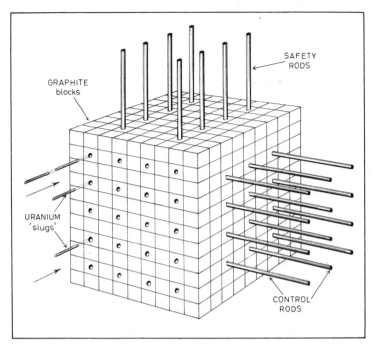

Fig. 142 A very early type of nuclear reactor or atomic pile.

into the channels, and since the structure is basically composed of alternate layers of uranium and graphite, it is often referred to as an atomic 'pile'. The function of the graphite is to act as a 'moderator'; its atoms are light, and therefore cause the neutrons to lose momentum with each collision. The speed of the reaction is governed by adjusting the position of horizontal control-rods made of steel containing cadmium or boron, which have the property of absorbing neutrons. As a safety measure, similar control rods are suspended by magnets above vertical channels in the graphite, so that in the event of the failure of any part of the mechanism they would fall under the influence of gravity and stop the reaction. The structure is surrounded first by a reflecting wall of graphite and then by a thick shield of steel and concrete, to absorb radiations which might injure bystanders.

Energy is released from the reactor in the form of heat, which is transferred to water or carbon dioxide circulating through and around the 'pile' and used to produce steam which drives a conventional steam turbine. This in turn drives a dynamo for the production of electricity.

Although the particular kind of gas-cooled reactor depicted in the diagram has now been superseded by more advanced designs (known as steam-generating heavy water reactors and fast reactors), it nevertheless serves to illustrate the basic principles involved.

Nuclear fuel

Uranium

The fuel 'burnt' in a nuclear reactor, uranium, is a heavy brassy-coloured metal, which is present in very small quantities[1] in nearly a hundred different ores. Chief among these are the

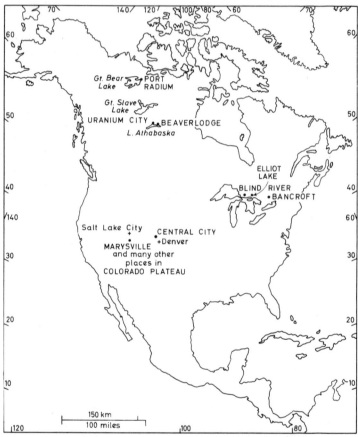

Fig. 143 Uranium-producing areas of Canada and the USA. Production at most of the Canadian mines ceased owing to reduced purchases by the USA, but in early 1968 a 'uranium-rush' began at Elliot Lake, and mining was resumed. Ore-bodies have recently been found in Labrador and northern Saskatchewan.

[1] An ore containing 1 per cent of uranium is regarded as rich. Some ores contain as little as 0·01 per cent.

yellow *carnotite* and the shiny, black *pitchblende*. Until 1930 almost the only source of uranium ores (which were at that time valued chiefly for their content of radium) was the Katanga district of the former Belgian Congo, but the discovery of nuclear fission in 1939 soon led to the search for other deposits, and today uranium and thorium (a similar heavy, radioactive metal) are mined—and in some cases quarried—in many different parts of the world. There seems no reason to suppose that all the available supplies have already been located. The search goes on, and indeed in the Colorado Plateau in the USA it has even been carried out by amateur prospectors equipped with Geiger counters[1] in circumstances reminiscent of the early gold rushes. Nor does there seem to be any likelihood of exhausting the world's supply within the foreseeable future.

Producing areas
Apart from the Communist countries, which do not publish figures of uranium production, the chief sources are now the United States, the Republic of South Africa (the Witwatersrand), Australia and Canada. The actual producing centres are usually quite small and have developed within the last twenty-five years or so out of isolated and in many cases almost inaccessible mining settlements (figs. 143 and 144).

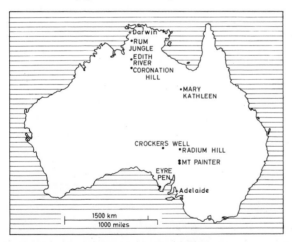

Fig. 144 Uranium-producing areas of Australia. Further deposits are known to exist in the Northern Territory and Queensland, and in the north of Western Australia.

[1] The Geiger counter is an instrument for detecting radiations. It was invented by Hans Geiger, a German who was at one time a lecturer in Manchester.

Refining

The ore is concentrated to uranium oxide at a site as near to the mine as possible, but the eventual refining to uranium metal—a long and extremely complicated process—is carried out in the purchasing country.

The development of atomic power

World requirements of power are increasing at a tremendous rate, and there are clearly ample opportunities for the use of atomic energy. Although the capital cost of installing and equipping an atomic power station is extremely high (at least £50 million), the electricity produced now costs almost exactly the same as electricity from a coal-fired station.

The United Kingdom was the first country in the world to enter into an extensive programme of development. Many coalmines were within sight of exhaustion, the rising cost of mining was reflected in the increasing cost of electricity, opportunities for the production of hydro-electric power were scanty and home-produced petroleum was then almost non-existent. The United Kingdom Atomic Energy Authority (UKAEA) was formed in 1954, and at Calder Hall in Western Cumbria the first reactor for the generation of electricity became operative in 1956 (fig. 145).

Fig. 145 Calder Hall in western Cumbria—Britain's first full-sized atomic power station.

Fig. 146 Nuclear power stations in Great Britain and other establishments under the control of the United Kingdom Atomic Energy Authority (1971). □ UKAEA establishments engaged in research; the production of uranium 235, plutonium, radioactive isotopes, etc.
● Nuclear power stations already in operation. ● Nuclear power stations under construction.

Eleven nuclear power stations are now (1974) in operation, thus completing the first nuclear programme. Britain has an installed capacity of 5 000 MW and produces about 30 per cent of the world's atomic electricity. The second nuclear programme, due for completion in 1975, has been revised and delayed, but further reactors are being added to the existing ones at Hunterston, Dungeness and Hinkley Point, and new power stations are being built at Hartlepool (formerly known as Seaton Carew) and Heysham (Fig. 146).

The *USA*, with its wealth of coal, oil and hydro-electric power, was at first reluctant to commit herself deeply, and, although a great deal of experiment was carried out, the first reactor devoted exclusively to the generation of electricity (the Shippingport reactor) was not inaugurated until 1958. The United States is now the world's second largest producer, and is planning to make extensive use of nuclear power for dual-purpose plants which will produce not only electricity, but also drinking water from sea water. The UKAEA has done a great deal of experimentation on 'desalinisation' plants of this kind, and already has one such plant in operation (at Dungeness). Britain also leads the field in the export of desalinisation equipment.

The only other comparable producers of nuclear power are, as yet, West Germany and the USSR, although output in many other countries (notably Canada) is rising rapidly.

Nuclear power and transport

The application of nuclear power to transport has aroused widespread interest, since uranium is far less bulky than other fuels, and a single charge can be made to last for years without replacement. The first nuclear-powered ship was the American submarine *Nautilus*, which was launched in 1954. The success of the *Nautilus* encouraged the United States to build numerous vessels of this type, and in 1959 the first two atomic submarines were put into service (the *George Washington* and *the Skipjack*), capable of firing ballistic missiles while submerged. She now has fifty-three. The US aircraft carrier *Enterprise* of 86 000 tons dw is now by far the largest nuclear-powered vessel afloat.

The use of nuclear power for driving locomotives is less feasible at present, since there is little to justify the extra running costs in comparison with those of other forms of propulsion; and in the case of aircraft, the weight of the protective shield surrounding the reactor is considered prohibitive, quite apart from the danger of releasing harmful radiations in the event of a crash.

Isotopes

Atoms of the same element normally contain the same number of neutrons, but about fifty years ago it was discovered that 'varieties' of elements exist whose atoms contain more or less neutrons than usual. Apart from having different atomic weights,[1] such 'varieties' or isotopes have the same chemical properties as their related elements. Isotopes of the heavier substances, such as uranium, occur in nature, and are often radioactive; but in recent years a wide range of radioactive isotopes of other elements has been made artificially by bombarding stable elements with neutrons in nuclear reactors. In referring to isotopes it is customary to place the atomic weight after the name of the element. Thus 'Iodine 126' is an isotope of natural iodine (atomic weight 127). 'Uranium 235' is an isotope of uranium, whose other naturally occurring isotope is 'Uranium 238'.

Isotopes are important in two connections:

1. Ordinary uranium metal actually consists of a combination of uranium 235 and uranium 238. It is the former of these which is used up in the atomic pile, but while the reaction is going on, the uranium 238 absorbs an extra neutron, becoming uranium 239, and is eventually removed from the pile. This now undergoes decay, and turns into a radioactive isotope of plutonium known as 'plutonium 239', which forms a 'fuel' no less suitable than uranium. Thus an atomic pile performs the amazing feat of producing further supplies of fuel out of the fuel which it has used up. Reactors in which the production of plutonium is the main consideration are called 'breeder' reactors.

2. An enormous number of radioactive isotopes is now being made by exposing more familiar elements to neutron bombardment. For these new uses are continually being found in industry (for detecting flaws in castings, measuring weights and thicknesses, etc.), in medicine (for diagnosing and treating diseases) and in agricultural science (for breeding improved varieties of plants and studying plant growth and nutrition).

---

[1] The weight of an atom is, of course, so extremely small that it is almost meaningless in ordinary figures. It is, therefore, expressed on a scale in which the weight of an atom of oxygen is 16. The mass of an electron is only $\frac{1}{1840}$ th of the mass of either a proton or a neutron, and the 'atomic weight' of an element may for all practical purposes be taken to be the arithmetical sum of the protons and neutrons contained in its atom. For example, the atomic weight of natural iodine is 127 (i.e. 53 protons + 74 neutrons).

21

TRADE

It is obvious from the preceding chapters that in the modern world we eat, drink and use an extremely wide range of commodities. Very few of them are obtained from the plants or the minerals in our own vicinity; in fact, many of them may well have come from the other side of the world and undergone complicated process manufacture. The more varied and exacting our wants become, the greater in volume and more complex in character becomes the interchange of commodities.

The nature and growth of trade

In the simple life of ancient times, each group of people was almost completely self-sufficient, and the volume of trade was insignificant. Probably only by accident did early man produce more than he required for his wife and family, but the situation must eventually have arisen when individuals or groups, either by reason of favourable environments or special aptitudes, produced surplus commodities with the intention of exchanging them with one another. Trade between nations today is essentially the same as this primitive exchange of goods; it is merely the scope and complexity of the situation which have altered. Australia, for instance, is better fitted by her environment to produce large quantities of wool than Britain; she therefore sends her wool to Britain and receives in exchange manufactured goods and machinery, in the production of which Britain has had more experience. This simple illustration could, of course, be multiplied endlessly. The countries which have commodities to spare send their surpluses abroad and import the surpluses of other countries, in order to provide themselves with the commodities they cannot produce, or do not find it convenient or profitable to produce. The increasing volume of trade throughout the ages is essentially the result of man's increasing control over his environment, of his living a fuller and richer life, in which he has found the need for a greater variety of foodstuffs and materials.

Modern overseas trade

The Industrial Revolution brought about radical changes in the pattern of world trade. Previously trade with distant lands had been largely confined to gold, silver, spices and other 'luxuries', among which were included many of the things such as sugar, tea and coffee which we now class as 'necessities'. But in the course of the nineteenth century new lands were opened up and the increasing size, speed and efficiency of ships widened the field from which a country might draw its supplies. Moreover, countries in the forefront of the Industrial Revolution ceased to produce food for themselves; it was much more profitable to concentrate on manufactured articles and to import foodstuffs and raw materials from abroad. The pattern of trade which developed out of this situation showed a general movement of *primary products*, such as grain, wool, minerals, etc., from the tropics and the southern hemisphere to the industrial lands of the northern temperate zone, with a return traffic of *secondary* (or manufactured) *products*, such as textiles or machinery. This still forms the essential pattern, although the sharp outlines have become blurred with the spread of industrialisation to the underdeveloped southern lands. A noteworthy feature of the present pattern of overseas trade is the link between western Europe and the continent of North America—a natural enough development in view of the fact that these two areas are the twin seats of western civilisation—and each has, therefore, a great deal to give to the other by way of specialised products.

The balance of trade

If a business firm spends more money than it receives, it sooner or later goes bankrupt. It is much the same with countries. No country today is completely self-sufficient; and if national bankruptcy is to be avoided, it is essential that in the long run a country should earn as much as it spends. Whether or not it is making ends meet is not always apparent from the relationship between the values of its exports and its imports—the so-called balance of trade. Many countries, in fact, perpetually show an unfavourable Balance of Trade (in which imports of goods exceed exports) without the slightest danger of economic collapse. The reason is that the Balance of Trade takes account only of visible, tangible goods. In addition to exports of this kind a wide range of *invisible exports* exists, which includes services rather than actual goods. These are not shown in trade statistics, but are included in a much more comprehensive statement of income and expenditure known as the *Balance of Payments*. Invisible exports take various forms, among which may be noted:

1. Payment for transporting the goods of foreign countries. British merchant shipping may, for instance, carry Swedish timber to Belgium or Spanish iron ore to Germany.

2. Money received as premiums for the insurance of ships or their cargoes, payment for repairing vessels and so on.

3. Interest on money which has been lent to other countries to enable them to build railways, docks, etc., and in general to develop their resources. Until the last war, when most of her overseas investments were sold, this was a valuable source of Britain's income.

4. Money spent by tourists from abroad in hotel expenses, etc. The tourist industry of Switzerland makes a considerable contribution to the national economy.

Restrictions on trade

If each country specialised in the production of those commodities which it is best fitted to produce, it might reasonably be supposed that all commodities would pass freely from one country to another. *Free trade* is not, however, always considered an advantage. The situation frequently arises when a government deems it necessary to restrict the import of certain types of goods, possibly to encourage its people to buy home-produced articles in place of similar articles made more cheaply abroad, so preventing unemployment. In this case a *tariff* may be imposed on the imported commodity—in other words, the producer is made to pay a kind of tax or 'entrance fee' on each article which will, of course, be added to the price. There is, however, always the danger that the exporting country will retaliate in the same way. The whole question thus becomes extremely complicated and involves a very precise assessment of the possible advantages and disadvantages in any particular situation. Trading agreements between countries or groups of countries which have ties of friendship or mutual interest are frequently made, abolishing existing tariffs or affording 'preferential' tariffs on goods passing between their members while 'discriminating against' the goods of countries outside their community. One such arrangement was the system of 'Commonwealth preference' which until recently operated between the United Kingdom and the Commonwealth countries.

A more topical example is the European Common Market

(officially known as the European Economic Community). This came into being in 1958, when the so-called 'Six' (Belgium, the Netherlands, Luxembourg, France, Italy and West Germany) joined in a trading alliance which aimed to abolish tariffs and other restrictions on goods passing between them and to establish a joint policy on goods entering or leaving the Market. Britain was at first reluctant to join the organisation on account of her existing commitments to the countries of the Commonwealth. Her subsequent application for membership was turned down, largely because of the opposition of Gaullist France. As a result of a further application, Britain officially joined the Common Market in January 1973, along with Denmark and Eire. The European Free Trade Association (EFTA) is a less comprehensive commercial agreement, which originally included Norway, Sweden, Denmark, Austria, Switzerland, Portugal and Britain.

The mechanism of international trade

The simplest of all forms of trade is barter—as, for example, when schoolboys 'swop' foreign stamps, penknives and the like. The question of 'money' arises when the boy who wishes to 'swop' a penknife does not want foreign stamps in exchange. The owner of the stamps may, therefore, dispose of them to a third party and accept a coin, which is useful to him only because he knows it will be acceptable to the owner of the penknife, who in turn knows that a coin of this particular value will buy, for instance, a bar of chocolate. Money thus comes to be not merely a medium of exchange, but also a standard by which to measure the comparative values of different articles.

We normally pay cash for the goods we buy by handing over coins in exchange, but in certain circumstances (as, for example, when we pay out a large sum) we write out a cheque. This is, in effect, an instruction to the bank to remove so much of the money we have deposited there and add it to the money deposited at the bank by the vendor (i.e. seller) of the goods involved in the transaction. International trade is carried out in a somewhat similar fashion, but instead of a cheque, a special type of bill, called a *bill of exchange*, is used. The bill is made out by the vendor in one country (say, Belgium) and is then signed by the purchaser in, say, Britain, to show that he 'accepts' it. The 'accepted' bill now provides authority to the vendor's bank in Belgium to credit *his* account with the agreed amount of money, and to the purchaser's bank in Britain to debit *his* account by the same amount. Many other private transactions will be taking place, involving the movement of goods from Belgium to Britain, and Britain as a country thus becomes indebted to Belgium, but at the same time reverse transactions involving the movement of goods to Belgium will also be taking place, as a result of which Belgium becomes indebted to Britain. Over a period the combined debts of each country to the other may cancel out; a certain amount of book-work is carried out in the banks, but nothing will have passed between the countries except bills of exchange and the actual goods.

Trade is, of course, rarely *bilateral*, in which case, as in the above example, only two countries are involved, exchanging goods with each other; it is usually *multilateral*, and a large number of countries are involved. But in the long run the indebtedness of any one country to the others must be equalled by the combined income from them.

Exchange rates

If the two parties to a deal are using different currencies, it is necessary for the value of the goods to be expressed in both. This in turn necessitates there being some kind of standard to which the two countries can be related. We must know, for instance, how many Belgian francs are equal in value to a pound sterling. Before 1914 most countries were 'on the Gold Standard', i.e. the units of money in each country (dollars, pounds, francs, etc.) were equal in value to a fixed weight of gold. But during the period between the wars one country after another found it impossible to guarantee its currency in this way, money became a commodity like any ordinary form of goods, and the *rate of exchange* of one currency for another fluctuated—in some cases violently and disastrously. There is not space here to describe in detail the circumstances under which these fluctuations occurred, but one typical situation may be noted. If the value of goods sold by Britain to Belgium temporarily exceeded the value of the goods sold by Belgium to Britain, the demand for the British pound became greater than the demand for the Belgian franc, and the 'price' of the pound in relation to the franc rose. In other words, you got more francs for your pound.

The inconvenience caused by varying rates of exchange proved just as great as the inconvenience of adhering to the Gold Standard, and in 1945, following a conference at Bretton Woods,[1] the International Monetary Fund was set up, whose seventy-nine[2] member nations agree to 'fix' the value of their currencies in

[1] In New Hampshire, USA.
[2] Originally only forty-four.

relation either to gold or the US dollar (which is also related to gold). Countries whose currencies have temporarily fallen in value (through an excess of imports over exports) may 'stabilise' them by borrowing from the Fund.

Towards the end of 1967 the British Government 'devalued' the pound sterling by 14 per cent. In other words, the value of the pound was fixed at a level slightly lower in terms of dollars than formerly. It was hoped that this would help to prevent the country spending abroad more than it was earning. Since the foreign customer could now buy seven cars, for example, with the number of dollars (or its equivalent in some other currency) that had previously purchased six, the volume of exports would presumably increase; conversely the foreign exchange required to cover seven tons of wheat would now bring the British buyer only six, and imports were thus expected to decrease.

22

TRANSPORT

Without transport there can be very little trade, and the two have developed side by side throughout the ages. The study of man's increasing control of his environment as shown by the evolution of transport facilities is an extremely interesting one, but it is necessary for us here to confine our attention to the chief modern forms of transport. We may, however, note that man's progress in this field has been by no means uniform, and that in a world which knows the locomotive, the motor-car and the aeroplane, merchandise is still in some regions carried on the backs of porters; such animals as llamas, elephants, camels, oxen, mules and donkeys are still used as beasts of burden; and Arab *dhows* and Chinese *junks* still play a part in the traffic of the seas.

Roads

Those of us who live in densely populated countries like England take it for granted that roads exist which will take us wherever we want to go, and that their surfaces will be reasonably adequate for the anticipated traffic. This could not have been said about England 200 years ago (or even less), and cannot be said about less highly developed parts of the world today.

Methods of construction

The earliest 'roads' were, of course, little more than tracks where the soil had been compressed by the trampling of feet along lines which formed the most convenient routes from one place to another—similar, in fact, to an ordinary 'footpath'. But such tracks were often muddy and rutted in winter and dry, dusty and uneven in summer; a great deal depended on the nature of the underlying rock. The first roads in the modern sense—i.e. tracks whose surfaces have been specially prepared by paving or some other means—were laid down by the Romans, and played an important part in the organisation of their Empire. With the decline of the Empire, Roman roads fell into disrepair, and little progress in road-construction was made until about 1810, when two Scotsmen, Thomas Telford and John Macadam, demonstrated that a sheet of broken stones two or three centimetres in diameter became consolidated with the passing of traffic into a hard, waterproof mass. The methods of the two engineers differed slightly. Telford's method involved the laying of slabs beneath the stones, but Macadam showed that this was unnecessary, and what are now described as 'macadamised' roads became standard for many years. The advent of rubber-tyred motor vehicles led to the application of a coating of 'tarmacadam'—a mixture of gravel and tar—and of late a great deal of experiment has been carried out, using concrete, rubber and other materials, in attempts to find the ideal surface under all kinds of conditions.

The importance of roads

Roads along which traffic can move smoothly and swiftly are vital to the economic life of any community. Railways and other forms of transportation play a no less important part as main arteries of commerce, but the assembling of raw materials and the distribution of finished products depend to a great extent on the existence of an adequate network of serviceable roads. Since cars and lorries can negotiate sharp bends and climb hills with gradients as steep as 1 in 3, they can reach places in difficult terrain which are inaccessible to other types of transport. The growth of the comprehensive road systems which now cover densely populated regions did not merely accompany the development of these areas; it was an integral part of it. The economic development of numerous areas in the tropics and the southern hemisphere awaits the construction of more and better roads.

Present tendencies

Although railways remain the cheapest method of transporting heavy or bulky goods overland, the increased width and improved surfaces of such modern trunk roads as the German *Autobahnen*, the Italian *autostrade* and the British Motorways (fig. 147), together with advances in the power and design of road vehicles, have made it possible to transport by road much of the heavier goods previously carried by the railways. One particular attraction of road transport is that, in the case of articles which must ultimately be delivered by load, only one operation of loading and one of unloading are required. Unfortunately the haphazard development of road patterns in former years has made the task of constructing, in densely populated countries, integrated systems in keeping with modern needs an extremely difficult one.

Fig. 147 'Spaghetti' Junction near Birmingham where the M5 meets the M6.

Railways

One of the major problems which at the beginning of the nineteenth century confronted Britain and other growing industrial nations was the transportation overland of heavy materials. It seemed at first as if canals might provide the solution, but the completion in 1825 of the first steam railway, the Stockton and Darlington, originally designed to carry coal to Teesside, ushered in a period of about a hundred years during which railways became supreme for the transport of commodities in bulk.

Patterns of development

The railway systems which evolved display patterns that are geographically interesting.

In Britain a comprehensive railway network was gradually built up out of an assortment of separate lines. These were financed by private enterprise, and so routed that they connected or passed through areas where the presence of population, industry or natural resources suggested the possibility of winning custom and earning interest on the capital invested by the shareholders. The system was essentially unplanned, and duplication resulted in a number of lines (such as the former Great Central

Railway) proving uneconomic, but few areas really suffered from lack of railway communication, and it became possible to use the resources of the country to the full.

In the open spaces of 'new' lands, such as Australia, Canada and the United States, railways proved equally valuable, but in rather a different way. Here 'population followed the railway', which served to 'open up' territories hitherto undeveloped, and the systems in these regions display a pattern consisting of long, transcontinental single-line stretches joined by occasional branch lines, which tapped areas of agricultural or mineral exploitation (fig. 148). Only where population has subsequently become dense do concentrated networks exist in any way resembling the network which covers Britain.

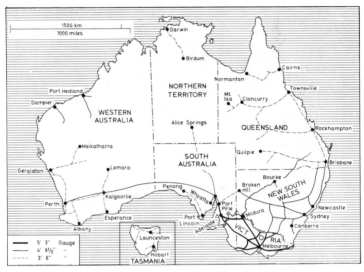

Fig. 148 The main railway lines of Australia (1971).

Physical features and railway construction

Physical features are a particularly important consideration in railway construction. Trains are normally incapable of ascending gradients steeper than about 1 in 50,[1] and in any case it is desirable that the course of a railway should be as level as possible purely on the grounds of economy of operation. Mountain barriers clearly present special problems, which in extreme cases can be solved only by means of tunnels; but even in regions of com-

[1] In the Kicking Horse Pass through the Rockies the Canadian Pacific Railway ascends a gradient of 1 in 22. The steepest main-line gradient in the British Isles (1 in 37·7) is the 3-km Lickey Incline in Warwickshire.

paratively uniform relief, local features often make it difficult to find a route which will pass through the desired areas and at the same time keep gradients to a minimum.

Railway gauges

The gauge (i.e. the distance between the rails) affects the initial cost of building a railway and the size and weight of the loads which can be transported. It also has an important bearing on the sharpness of the curves which can be negotiated. In mountainous or rugged terrain a narrow gauge is an advantage, since it allows the line to turn sharply in circumventing obstacles.

The standard gauge of 4 ft 8½ in[1]—a somewhat arbitrary figure adopted by George Stephenson for the first locomotive[2]—is used by the railways of North America, Great Britain and continental Europe (except the USSR and Spain[3]). The celebrated engineer, Isambard Kingdom Brunel, persuaded the directors of the original Great Western Railway to adopt a gauge of 7 ft, but this so-called 'broad gauge' was finally abandoned in 1892, and the Great Western Railway conformed to the gauge common to all the other railways in Britain. The railways of Southern Africa are of 3 ft 6 in gauge, but a number of countries (India and Argentina, for example) suffer considerable inconvenience from having adopted a variety of gauges. In Australia three separate gauges (3 ft 6 in, 4 ft 8½ in and 5 ft 3 in) were chosen in different parts of the continent (fig. 148), but the completion in December 1961 of a 4 ft 8½ in gauge single-track line from Wodonga (near Albury) to Melbourne has made it possible to run a through service without break of gauge from Sydney to Melbourne. This was the first stage in the 'Wentworth plan' designed to link all the mainland state capitals with standard-gauge track.

Motive power

The first locomotives were coal-fired and driven by steam, but by the early years of the present century the electric motor had been perfected, and countries like Norway, Sweden and Switzerland, which have large reserves of hydro-electric power, were quick to seize the opportunity of converting their railways to electricity. Since the new form of traction proved more capable of hauling heavy loads up long gradients, it was adopted by

[1] Since the introduction in the early 1960s of continuous welded rail the official gauge used on British railways for lengths of straight track has been 4 ft 8¾ in (1·432 m). This is due to the tendency of the rails to 'creep' on their sleepers.

[2] Stephenson is said to have adopted this figure after measuring the distance between the wheels of a coal-cart!

[3] In the USSR the gauge is 1·524 m (5 ft 0 in) and in Spain 1·676 (5 ft 6 in).

Fig. 149 *Evening Star*, the last steam locomotive to be built for British Rail.

countries such as New Zealand for those parts of their systems where mountains have to be crossed. Britain, however, at first made little use of electricity, except for suburban lines in the London area, where in view of frequent stops the capacity of the electric train for rapid acceleration is particularly valuable.

Present tendencies

Competition from other forms of transport makes it unlikely that any further railways will be built, except perhaps in the interiors of Asia and Africa, where provision for the bulk transport of raw materials is still inadequate. In Britain over the last twenty years branch lines have been robbed of so much of their traffic by buses and lorries, which afford door-to-door service, that many of them have been closed down. Moreover, steam as a motive power has now been completely superseded, and the last steam locomotive to be built for use in Britain—appropriately named *Evening Star*—was put into service at the end of 1960 (fig. 149). A considerable amount of conventional electrification (in which current is picked up from a third rail or overhead cable) is being carried out on British railways, but otherwise almost all other locomotives are now diesel-electrics, which generate electric power *en route* by burning fuel oil in diesel engines.

Rivers

The usefulness of rivers

Rivers were recognised as ready-made highways at an early stage in history; and in many parts of the equatorial and monsoon forests today they constitute almost the only practicable means of transport. Their usefulness, however, particularly for vessels of any appreciable size, depends on a number of physical considerations. Foremost among these is the extent to which they are navigable, i.e. capable of carrying traffic. The course of a river may, for instance, be interrupted by rapids (such as those at the Iron Gate on the Danube) or waterfalls (such as the Stanley Falls and others on the Congo), and shallows and shifting sandbanks may make navigation difficult or impossible. The current of many rivers (the Rhône, for example, or the rivers which flow eastwards from the Eastern Highlands of Australia) flow too fast for successful navigation, while the volume of the Orange River in South Africa and the Murray in Australia varies throughout the year, and in the period of summer drought the course of these rivers becomes little more than a series of 'water-holes'. In cold climates rivers may freeze or be obstructed by ice-floes (the St Lawrence, for instance). Such deterrents to navigation may to some extent be controlled by dredging, straightening the course of a river to accelerate the flow of water, building locks to circumvent waterfalls and maintain depths, and, as we have seen in connection with irrigation and hydro-electricity, the improvement of navigation often forms part of comprehensive schemes of river development.

Direction and other considerations

It is important that a river should flow in the required direction. Rivers such as the Ob, Yenesei and Lena in the north of Russia, and the Mackenzie in Canada, are economically useless, since they flow into seas which, apart from being frozen, lie well away from the tracks of commerce; but the Rhine and the Elbe are clearly of inestimable value to the countries through which they pass.

River transport is slow, but comparatively cheap, and is, therefore, suitable for the conveyance of bulky, non-perishable commodities like coal, iron ore, cement, bales of cotton, grain and so on. The St Lawrence, the Mississippi, the Rhine and the Seine provide good examples of rivers used in this way.

Canals

Canals represent one of man's attempts to improve on Nature. Although the Chinese thousands of years ago were skilful in the art of cutting artificial waterways to supplement the natural lines of communication provided by rivers, almost all the canals in use today (many which are now derelict) were constructed in the early days of the Industrial Revolution before the coming of the railway.

In *Britain* few of the canals built during this period now play any significant part in the economy of the country. The Grand

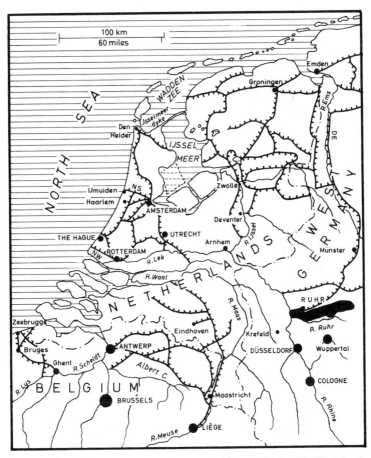

Fig. 150 The chief canals in Belgium and the Netherlands. **NS**. North Sea Canal; **NW**. New Waterway; **DE**. Dortmund-Ems Canal.

Union Canal, running from the West Midlands to the London area, and the Trent and Mersey Canal still carry an appreciable volume of traffic, while a network of canals between the Rivers Aire and Calder serves the woollen industry of West Yorkshire. The Manchester Ship Canal, which was opened in 1894, has made Manchester the eighth port (by value of its trade) in the United Kingdom.

In *Belgium* and the *Netherlands* (fig. 150) canals carry a great deal of the internal traffic, and both Rotterdam and Amsterdam are connected to the sea by ship canals (the New Waterway and the North Sea Canal respectively). The Albert Canal linking Antwerp and Liège is of vital importance.

In *Germany* an important system of canals has been built in the low-lying land between the Baltic Heights and the mountains in the southern part of the country. Ice sheets in the Quaternary period diverted the former northward-flowing rivers so that for a time they flowed westwards in more or less parallel courses. The channels cut by these Ice Age rivers and later abandoned have made it comparatively easy to join up the present rivers by canals (of which the most outstanding example is the Mittelland Canal from the Rhine to the Oder) which assist considerably in the movement of heavy goods in the North German Plain.

In *North America* the Soo Canals, which bypass the Sault-Ste Marie Rapids and join Lake Superior to Lakes Huron and Michigan, and the Welland Canal, which bypasses the Niagara Falls and connects Lake Erie to Lake Ontario, make the Great Lakes the most extensive system of inland waterways in the world. The importance of this system has been greatly enhanced by the opening of the St Lawrence Seaway.

Ocean transport

General considerations

Ocean-going vessels are far less restricted by physical considerations than any other form of transport except aircraft. In the days of sail, ships were, of course, heavily dependent on favourable winds, but the adoption of steam as motive power freed them from this limitation, and with increasing size and power they could usually afford to disregard all climatic hazards except fog and floating ice. Moreover, ocean transport is the cheapest of all forms of transport, and non-perishable commodities are often taken by sea 'the long way round' in preference to a shorter but more expensive route by land.

Developments in ocean transport

The first successful steamboat was built by an American inventor named Robert Fulton.[1] In 1807 his vessel travelled a distance of 240 km (150 miles) up the Hudson River from New York to Albany in 23 hours, but it was not until the middle of the nine-teenth century that ocean-going steamers became more numerous than sailing ships. About this same time iron was being sub-

---

[1] Steam engines had actually been used experimentally in river vessels for some years previously but Fulton is usually regarded as the 'father of the steamship'. Napoleon Bonaparte described Fulton as mad 'because he wanted to drive the fleet with boiling water!'

stituted for wood in ship construction; this in turn was replaced about twenty years later by mild steel. Motor ships (driven by diesel engines consuming crude oil) first became practicable about 1910, and now far out-number steamships. As a result of these developments, the size and speed of vessels increased, and it became customary to build special ships for different kinds of traffic.

Types of ships

Merchant ships (i.e. ships which operate on the world's trade routes) fall into five main classes.

1. *Liners* are vessels of anything up to about 70 000 gross registered tons,[1] which, although devoted principally to the transport of passengers, carry also a certain amount of cargo. Their name is derived from the fact that they keep to regular routes or 'lines'.

2. *Cargo liners*, such as banana boats or ships carrying grain, wool, meat, etc., also have room for a limited number of passengers.

3. *Tramps* are smaller cargo vessels which only rarely carry passengers. They usually have a gross tonnage of about 6 000, and may stay away from their home ports for considerable periods (sometimes years), picking up a fresh cargo from the port at which they dropped their last one, according to instructions sent to them by radio from their base.

4. *Tankers* now form the largest ships afloat. The Japanese *Nisseki Maru* is of 366 518 tons deadweight, and the *Globtik Tokyo* (completed in 1973) is of 483 664 ton dw and 377 m (nearly a quarter of a mile) long (Fig. 151).

5. *Coastal vessels*, as their name implies, are used for carrying bulky materials by sea from one part of a country to another. They are small ships so constructed as to enable them to ascend river estuaries as far as possible inland.

[1] The largest (and longest) liner afloat is the *France* (66 348 gross registered tons). The *Queen Elizabeth* (destroyed by fire in Hong Kong harbour in 1972) had a gross registered tonnage of 82 998.

It is important to understand the meaning of the word 'tonnage' in relation to shipping.

Gross registered tonnage describes the capacity of all enclosed parts of a ship between its sides and deck (including the capacity of superstructures) on the assumption that 100 cubic feet represent one ton.

Net registered tonnage (e.g. for tankers and bulk-carriers) describes the capacity only of those parts of a ship which are devoted to cargo and passengers (on the same assumption).

Deadweight tonnage is the cargo-carrying capacity (again reckoning 100 cubic feet as one ton).

But *displacement tonnage* (which is used more particularly in describing warships) is the weight of water displaced and is in effect the actual weight of the vessel and its cargo when fully laden.

Fig. 151 *Globtik Tokyo*, the world's largest oil-tanker. It has a dead-weight tonnage of 483,664, and is nearly 400 m (a quarter of a mile) long.

Bulk and container traffic

In the modern world the cost of transporting goods by sea is governed more by the cost of loading and unloading than by the length of the journey. There is, therefore, a tendency for goods to be carried whenever possible in bulk-carriers of perhaps 100 000 tons deadweight, and for large quantities of individual items to be packed by the original producers in sealed and locked containers which can be handled mechanically by fork lifts. Apart from reducing the number and cost of the operations involved at the ports, this also obviates the risk of pilferage (regrettably a major consideration with 'open' cargoes) and other risks such as damage by sea water or a shifting load. The TIR (Transport International Routiers) is the first real attempt to reach an internationally accepted code for transport, which has acquired new importance now that Britain has joined the Common Market.

Shipping routes

There is obviously little to prevent modern ocean-going vessels from visiting any part of the world's coast-lines, providing harbours exist capable of receiving them. Ships are now of such a size that a natural sheltered anchorage is no longer sufficient by itself; there must also be specially constructed docks enabling them to come alongside, and facilities for refuelling, loading

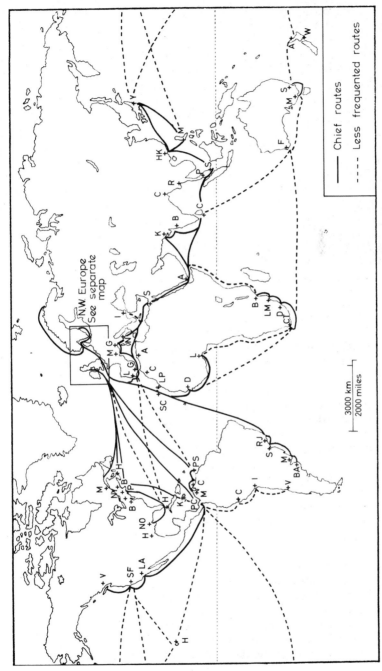

Fig. 152 The world's chief seaports and shipping routes. On this and the following map the ports, indicated by the initial letters of their names, should be identified with the help of an atlas. Note that the Suez Canal has been blocked since 1967.

Chief routes
Less frequented routes

3000 km
2000 miles

N.W. Europe
See separate
map

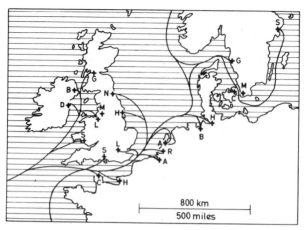

Fig. 153 The chief seaports and shipping routes of north-western Europe. The importance of ports may be assessed in various ways: by the number of ships which enter or leave them, the size of the vessels they are capable of accommodating, the weight or value of the goods they handle, or the number of passengers who pass through them. On this and the world map (fig. 145) an attempt has been made to take all these methods of assessment into consideration.

goods and embarking passengers. For this reason the largest ships are restricted to certain ports.

The world's chief ports and the principal routes between them are shown in figs. 152 and 153. The following points should be noted:

1. The most frequented route is that which joins north-western Europe and the north-eastern United States.

2. The importance of the *Suez Canal* (opened in 1869), which in normal times shortens the route from Europe to the Far East and Australia. In the course of the 'Six Days War' between Egypt and Israel in 1967 the Canal was blocked; it has not yet (1974) been re-opened, although clearing has begun.

3. The importance of the *Panama Canal* (opened in 1914), which brings the north-eastern United States into closer touch with the western side of South America and provides an alternative, westward route from Europe to Australia and the Far East.

4. The small volume of trade which passes across the Pacific compared with the Atlantic.

Air transport

In no form of transportation have such spectacular developments taken place over the last thirty years as in air transport. In 1928 a Berlin newspaper said: 'If we still see land planes over the ocean ... they must be piloted either by fools or romantic suicides.'[1] Yet now a complicated network of regular air routes covers the world, and it is possible for a business man to leave London by plane in the early morning, clinch a deal in New York in the afternoon,[2] and return in time to be at his office desk the following morning.

Modern developments in aircraft propulsion

Until almost the end of the Second World War the only practicable method of propulsion was by means of a petrol-driven reciprocating[3] engine, similar to, but much more powerful than, the engine of a car. The curved blades of propellers (or air-screws) driven by the engine cause the aircraft to move forward by pushing the air to the rear in much the same way that a swimmer advances by pushing the water behind him with his arms. There is, however, a limit to the effectiveness of air-screws; when their speed of rotation reaches a certain point, they cease to get a proper 'grip' on the air. Moreover, there is also a limit to the speed at which pistons can move backwards and forwards without disintegrating. It was, therefore, clear that any increase in the speed of aircraft would require engines of a different type, and largely owing to the impetus of war conditions, the jet engine was evolved. This drives the plane by thrusting to the rear a powerful jet of burnt gases (created by burning paraffin with an excess of air), the reaction to which causes the aircraft to move forward.[4] The basic idea of using a jet for this purpose was not new; in fact, experiments along these lines had been carried out for some time in Germany, Italy and other countries, but it was an Englishman, Sir Frank Whittle, who first succeeded in solving the many problems involved.

Modern aircraft, on the basis of their power units, may be divided into three classes:

1. *Turbo-jets,* which operate solely on the principle of jet propulsion.

[1] Quoted by Heinz Gartmann in *Science as History*, translated by Alan G. Readett (London, 1960).
[2] By London time.
[3] i.e. an engine in which a crankshaft is rotated by pistons moving back and forth.
[4] The thrust which drives the plane forward is *within the engine*. It is a popular misconception that the exhaust jet presses against the air behind the plane. A jet aircraft could fly perfectly well in a vacuum. A fireman directing a powerful jet of water from a hose provides a simple illustrative parallel. The hose (and the fireman) tend to be driven backwards by the issue of water.

2. *Turbo-props,* in which the jet of burnt gases is made also to drive an ordinary gas-turbine[1] and so rotate a supplementary air-screw. Transport planes are normally of this kind, since they can fly at slower speeds when necessary; turbo-jets cannot.

3. The traditional types of plane equipped with air-screws driven by *reciprocating* engines.

Limitations of air transport

The above developments have increased the size, speed and power of aircraft, the weight they can carry and the distance they can travel 'in one hop' (i.e. without refuelling[2]). Aircraft have thus been freed from many former limitations, such as the necessity for avoiding mountains because of complicated meteorological conditions; indeed 'stratocruisers' are capable of flying above the turbulent lower layers of the atmosphere. But the prevalence of fog, frequent thunderstorms and the risk of ice formation on the wings still to some extent limit the freedom of movement of aircraft. At the same time the increased size and complexity of the machines have made the necessity for spacious landing-grounds with adequate facilities for servicing, as well as for accommodating crews and passengers, just as vital to modern aircraft as are ports to modern ships (fig. 154).

The use of air transport

Air transport is expensive, and therefore, in spite of the carrying capacity of the aircraft of today, it is confined largely to the conveyance of passengers who wish to travel long distances in the shortest possible time and to goods of high value and small bulk (medical supplies, small intricate pieces of machinery and the like), and it is of vital importance for mail. In countries with large extent and scanty or dispersed population (such as Australia and Canada), where the construction of roads or railways would be uneconomic, air transport is invaluable. In compact countries like Britain internal air transport provides only limited competition to roads and railways, since the time occupied in travelling to and from the airports cuts down the overall saving in time,[3] which thus offers insufficient compensation for the expense of the journey. Under such conditions the use of helicopters, which, although slower than conventional aircraft, can take off and land in the heart of a populated area, provide a satisfactory alternative.

[1] Compare the hydraulic turbine used in a hydro-electric station.
[2] Refuelling while in flight is possible, but is not normal practice.
[3] An extension of the London Underground railway to connect Heathrow airport with central London is due for completion in 1975.

Fig. 154 London (Heathrow) Airport, showing the Central Area with the control tower and passenger buildings.

Air routes

The chief routes traversed by aircraft on regular scheduled flights, together with the main airports, are shown in figs. 155 and 156. The following points should be noted:

1. The map shows only those routes on which services are frequent (at least one flight per day). Many less frequent but no less significant services, which form a vital part of the system of internal communications of the southern continents in particular, cannot be shown on a map of this size.

2. Two apparently circuitous routes join London to Los Angeles, and Amsterdam to Tokyo via Anchorage in Alaska. These are approximately Great Circle[1] routes, which in each case effect a saving of about 1 500 km (940 miles) over the routes previously used avoiding high latitudes. Such developments are an in-

[1] A Great Circle is the largest circle which can be drawn on the surface of a sphere; its radius is the same as that of the sphere. The shortest distance between any two points on the surface of a sphere lies along the Great Circle which passes through them. The course taken by such a route can be found by using a school globe and stretching a piece of thin string between the two places at the ends of the route.

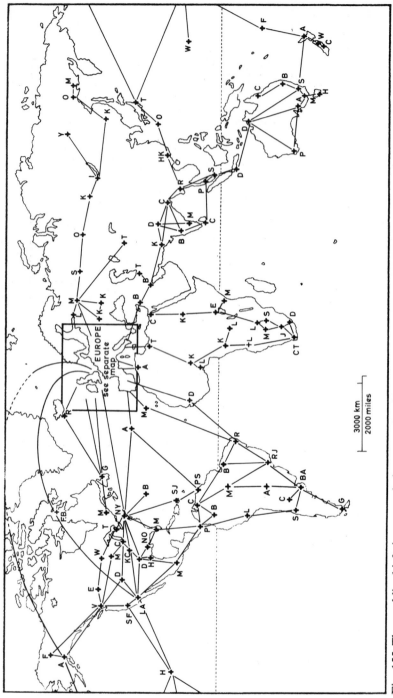

Fig. 155 The world's chief airports and air routes. On this and the following map airports are indicated by the initial letters of their names.

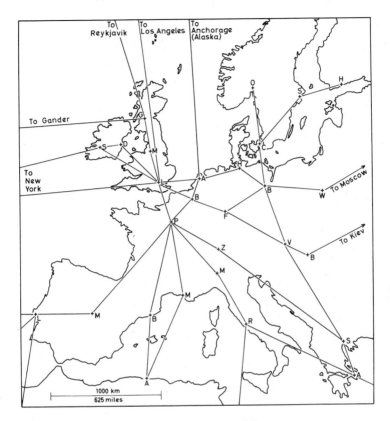

Fig. 156 The chief airports and air routes of Europe.

teresting commentary on the capabilities of modern aircraft and suggest one reason for the interest of meteorologists in weather conditions in the Arctic regions. They have an added significance in that they bring the two northern land masses 'nearer' to each other.

23

LATITUDE, LONGITUDE, TIME AND MAPS

Latitude and longitude

It is clearly essential that a method should exist by which the position of any point on the earth's surface may be accurately indicated. For this purpose we imagine the earth's surface to be covered by a network of lines known as *meridians* (or *lines of longitude*) and *parallels of latitude* (fig. 157).

Meridians

Meridians are imaginary, semicircular lines joining the North Pole to the South Pole.[1] They are numbered in degrees east and west of the *Prime Meridian* (0°), which passes through Greenwich, so that New York, for instance, is on the meridian 74° West and Melbourne on the meridian 145° East.[2] Passing through the Pacific Ocean is the meridian 180° East *or* West.

Notice (*a*) that all meridians are the same length; (*b*) that the distance between meridians decreases from the Equator to the Poles.

Parallels of latitude

These are complete circles, parallel to each other and running at right angles to the meridians. They are numbered in degrees north and south of the Equator (0°). The North and South Poles, which are, of course, points not circles, are 90° North and 90° South.

Notice (*a*) that parallels of latitude decrease in circumference from the Equator (the radius of which is the same as that of the earth) to the Poles; (*b*) that the distance between adjacent parallels is the same all over the earth.

Degrees of latitude and longitude are really degrees of arc subtended by angles at the centre of the earth (fig. 157).

By subdividing every degree of latitude and longitude into 60 minutes ('), it is possible by reference to the network of meridians and parallels to 'fix' to within two kilometres or so the position

[1] i.e. the Geographic Poles—the ends of the earth's axis of rotation.
[2] Very nearly.

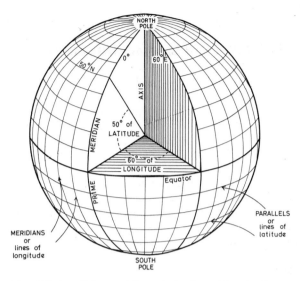

Fig. 157 Parallels, meridians, latitude and longitude.

of any place in the world. The full reference for New York is, therefore, 40° 45′ North 74° 0′ West, and for Melbourne 37° 45′ South 144° 50′ East.

How many Kilometres (miles) to a degree?

Since the distance across the earth's surface from Pole to Pole is roughly 20 000 km (12 500 miles), it is easy to calculate that one degree of latitude is approximately 110 km (20 000 ÷ 180) or 69 miles (12 500 ÷ 180). A similar calculation, 40 000 ÷ 360, (or 25 000 ÷ 360) shows that one degree of longitude *at the Equator* is also approximately 110 km (or 69 miles). At higher latitudes one degree of longitude is less than this, and close to the Poles it is very small indeed. It is useful to remember that at 60° N and 60° S one degree of longitude is about 55 km (or 35 miles).[1]

[1] The figures quoted are only approximate. The actual figures (which are complicated by the fact that the earth is really an oblate spheroid—i.e. flattened at the Poles) are as follows:

One degree of latitude near the Equator is   109·92 km (68·70 miles)
One degree of latitude near the Poles is   111·05 km (69·41 miles)
One degree of longitude near the Equator is 110·67 km (69.17 miles)

Note. One metre is officially one ten-millionth of the distance from the North Pole to the Equator along the meridian which passes through Dunkirk. This is the basic unit of the decimal measuring system devised by the French Academy of Sciences in 1791.

Determination of latitude

Until the middle of the eighteenth century, mariners had no accurate means of checking the positions of their ships on the open sea, but about this time two instruments were perfected which are still today indispensable aids to navigation. The first of these, the *sextant*, which measures the altitude[1] of a heavenly body (i.e. the angle between its direction and the sight-line to the horizon), makes possible the determination of latitude.

1. *By night* the altitude of the Pole Star[2] gives the latitude of a place without calculation (fig. 158).

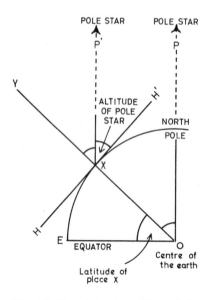

Fig. 158 Determination of latitude by night.

To determine the latitude of the place X.

Let XP' be drawn parallel to OP,
let OX be produced to Y,
and let HH' (representing the horizon sight line) be drawn through X at right-angles to OY.
The distance of the Pole Star from the earth is so great that it may be regarded as infinite, and the line XP' may, therefore, be assumed to indicate the direction of the Pole Star.
Since XP' and OP are parallel, $\angle$ YXP' $= \angle$ XOP.

[1] Or 'elevation'.
[2] In the Southern Hemisphere, the Southern Cross.

Now if two angles are equal, their complements must also be equal.

The complement of $\angle$ YXP′ is $\angle$ P′XH′, and the complement of $\angle$ XOP is $\angle$ EOX.

$\angle$ P′XH′ (the altitude of the Pole Star) $= \angle$ EOX (the latitude of the place X).

2. *By day* at the Equinoxes the latitude of a place equals 90° minus the altitude of the sun at noon (fig. 159).

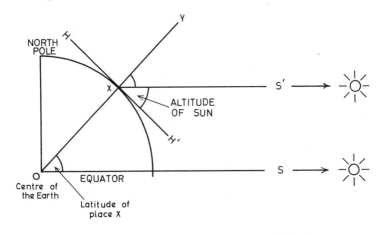

Fig. 159 Determination of latitude at 12 noon at the Equinoxes.

To determine the latitude of the place X.

Let XS′ be drawn parallel to OS,
let OX be produced to Y,
and let HH′ (representing the horizon sight-line) be drawn through X at right angles to OY.

The distance of the sun from the earth is so great that we may regard its rays as parallel, and the line XS′ may, therefore, be assumed to indicate the direction of the sun.

Since XS′ and OS are parallel, $\angle$ XOS $= \angle$ YXS′ (corresponding angles);

and since $\angle$ YXH′ is a right angle, $\angle$ XOS (the latitude of the place X) $= \angle$ YXS′ $= 90° - \angle$ S′XH′ (the altitude of the sun).

At other times of the year, when the sun is not overhead at noon on the Equator, an adjustment has to be made equal to the angle *a* (fig. 160). A further adjustment has to be made when the sun's altitude is measured at any other time of day than noon. The precise value of both these adjustments is given in the current issue of the *Nautical Almanac*.

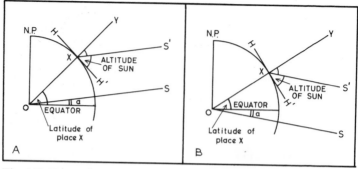

Fig. 160 Determination of latitude when the overhead sun at noon is (A) north of the Equator, and (B) south of the Equator.

Determination of longitude

Longitude is determined by comparing the difference in time between noon at Greenwich and noon at the place in question (*Local Noon*), and allowing 15 degrees of longitude for every hour separating the two noons.[1] The reasoning which underlies this and the subjects discussed in the ensuing sections is as follows:

Fig. 161 shows the situation (as seen from above the North Pole) when the sun is overhead at the Prime (or Greenwich) Meridian. At this time, at all places on the meridian[2] it is noon—i.e. the sun's altitude is greater than at any other time in the same day. Anyone near the 90°W meridian (say, in Chicago) sees the sun rising in the east, and anyone near the 90° E. meridian (say, in Calcutta) sees it sinking in the west.

Since the earth is rotating in the direction shown in the diagrams, the 90° W meridian will in due course move round so as to occupy the 'noon' position originally occupied by the Greenwich meridian, and the 90° E meridian will move to the 'midnight' position. The situation is now as shown in fig. 162.

In the course of twenty-four hours the Greenwich meridian (and, of course, all the other meridians) moves round through 360 degrees and regains its original position. In one hour, therefore, any point on the earth's surface moves through 15 degrees of arc. From this it is clear that at Greenwich noon the 15° W meridian still has 15 degrees to travel before itself reaching the noon position, and the local time on this meridian is 11 a.m.; but the 15° E meridian has gone 15 degrees past the noon position and the local time is 1 p.m.

[1] Or 4 minutes (of time) for every degree of longitude.
[2] *Meridian* is derived from Latin words meaning 'midday'.

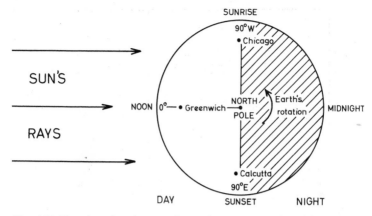

Fig. 161 The situation (as seen from above the North Pole) when the sun is overhead at the Prime (or Greenwich) Meridian.

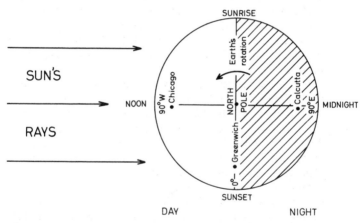

Fig. 162 The situation when the sun is overhead at 90° W.

In order to determine the longitude of a place it is obviously necessary to keep a constant record of Greenwich time (GMT).[1] The instrument which first enabled ships to do this is known as a *chronometer*, and is really an extremely accurate and reliable clock. Although now supplemented by radio, it is still an essential navigational instrument.

Two complications arise in connection with the question of time.

[1] i.e. Greenwich Mean Time. In its orbit round the sun the earth does not maintain a constant speed. Time is therefore based on the average or mean speed.

The International Date Line

We may construct a diagram (fig. 163) similar to the two preceding diagrams to show local time on selected meridians when it is noon at Greenwich on, say, Tuesday. Places on 165° W have just entered Tuesday, but for places on 165° E only one more hour of Tuesday remains; and on 180° (East or West) confusion arises as to whether it is midnight separating Monday from Tuesday or midnight separating Tuesday from Wednesday! As long as we stay on one side of the 180° line or the other, there is no difficulty; but if we move across the line, clearly some sort of adjustment must be made.

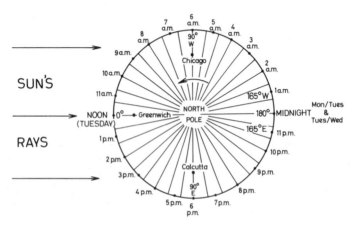

Fig. 163 Local time on selected meridians when it is noon at Greenwich on a Tuesday, and the situation at the International Date Line.

The necessary adjustment is made at the International Date Line, which for most of its length is made to coincide with the 180° meridian.

When crossing the Date Line *from west to east*, a day is repeated—for example, if the Date Line is crossed at 11 a.m. Tuesday, local time immediately becomes 11 a.m. Monday.

When crossing the Line *from east to west*, a day is omitted—for example, if the Date Line is crossed at 11 a.m. Tuesday, local time immediately becomes 11 a.m. Wednesday.

Fortunately, the 180° meridian does not pass through any large land mass, and the adjustment, therefore, needs to be made only by passengers in ships and aircraft. Where the meridian passes through groups of islands, the International Date Line is made to deviate slightly.

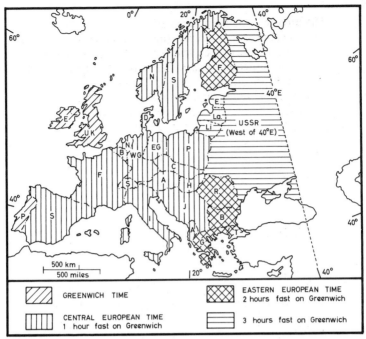

Fig. 164 Times in normal use in European countries. Notice that in France and Spain Standard Time (based on longitude) is no longer used. In 1968 Britain also adopted Central European Time, by remaining permanently on what has previously been known as British Summer Time. The experiment aroused considerable controversy and was abandoned in 1971.

Time zones

When the sun is overhead at London, it is not overhead at Bristol. In fact, Bristol noon does not occur until about 10 minutes after London noon. Similarly at Land's End it is, strictly speaking, 11.37 a.m. when it is noon at London. It would, however, lead to considerable confusion if every part of the British Isles east or west of London worked to its own local time. For this reason all parts of the British Isles agree to keep Greenwich time, which therefore becomes *Standard Time* for this particular time zone. The only inconvenience which this causes is in connection with lighting-up time for cars and cycles, which is, of course, based on the times of sunrise and sunset. Tables giving the times appropriate to each meridian are often included in diaries.

Fortunately the British Isles have only limited east–west extent; but in some countries (the USA and Australia, for example) adherence to only one standard time would lead to some strange situations. If all parts of the United States kept New York time, the clocks in San Francisco would be striking 12 o'clock noon while people were setting out for their work after breakfast! The United States (excluding Alaska) is therefore divided into four time zones separated from each other by a difference of one hour, and in travelling across the country from east to west (or vice versa) it is necessary to put one's watch 'forward' or 'back' one hour at selected points *en route*. In Australia there are three time zones separated by intervals of 1½ hours and half an hour; and three main zones in Europe also, keeping British time, Central European time (one hour fast on Greenwich) and Eastern European time (two hours fast). Standard Time in the USSR west of 40° E is three hours fast on Greenwich (fig. 164).

Direction

The mariner's compass in its modern form appears to have been invented in 1302 by an Italian named Flavio Gioja, but primitive compasses consisting of splinters of lodestone floating in bowls of water were probably used by the Chinese 2 500 years ago. The fact that a compass needle does not necessarily point to the Geographic North Pole was discovered by Cabot in 1470.

Magnetic variation

The earth is really a vast magnet, whose North Pole is at present situated in the extreme north of Canada; its South Pole is situated in Antarctica. The angle made at a point on the earth's surface by the direction of the Magnetic North Pole and the direction of the Geographic North Pole (i.e. True North—the direction along the meridian) is called Magnetic Variation,[1] and clearly differs in amount from place to place. Moreover, it may lie either east or west of True North. Lines drawn on a map through places where the Magnetic Variation is equal and to the same side of True North are known as *isogonals*.[2]

The Magnetic Poles are not stationary; they apparently oscillate within the Polar regions. The North Magnetic Pole is at present moving gradually eastwards, and it is calculated that by the year 2000 it will have interposed itself between Britain and the Geographic North Pole. The magnetic variation in Britain, which is now about 10° West, will then be 0°—but only temporarily.[3] In the margin of most Ordnance Survey maps

[1] Or Magnetic Declination.
[2] Compare isotherms, isobars, isohyets and other words beginning with 'iso'. *Isos* is Greek for 'equal'.
[3] In Cincinnati True North and Magnetic North at present virtually coincide.

the amount of the magnetic variation and its rate of change are indicated in the manner shown in fig. 165. In finding their true course it is necessary for the navigators of ships and aircraft to make constant adjustments to the readings of their magnetic compasses. These are not, however. the only adjustments which are necessary.

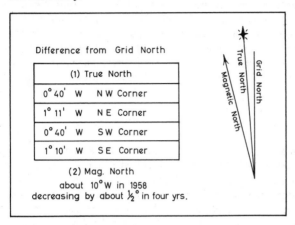

Difference from Grid North

(1) True North		
0° 40' W	N W Corner	
1° 11' W	N E Corner	
0° 40' W	S W Corner	
1° 10' W	S E Corner	

(2) Mag. North
about 10°W in 1958
decreasing by about ½° in four yrs.

Fig. 165 The manner in which magnetic variation and its annual rate of change are indicated on most Ordnance Survey maps.

Magnetic deviation

Iron contained in the structure of equipment of the craft causes the compass needle to deviate.[1] The error so caused is called Magnetic Deviation, and varies with the direction in which the ship or aircraft is pointing.

(N.B. Aircraft and ships nowadays carry *gyroscopic compasses* in addition to the more familiar mariners' (or magnetic) compasses. The readings of gyroscopic compasses are not subject to correction for variation and deviation. Moreover, a great deal of aircraft navigation is carried out by means of ingenious instruments which register a plane's course with reference to radio 'beams' transmitted specially for the purpose.)

Maps

Since Geography is the study of man's life and work in relation to his environment, it is understandable that we should frequently

[1] A similar situation arises if you try to take a compass reading while standing close to a bicycle or a wire fence.

need to make representations of the natural features of the earth's surface and the alterations and additions which man has made to them. Such representations—or maps—are of inestimable lue in geographical study.

Early maps

It is interesting that the Greek words from which 'Geography' is derived mean 'drawing pictures of the land'. The maps we find in atlases today or use in walking, cycling or motoring only remotely suggest that they are 'pictures' of the land, but the early maps—such as those sometimes seen in museums or second-hand bookshops—certainly do. Some of these show a group of buildings surrounded by a wall to represent a town, a cluster of trees to represent a forest, and so on. The coastline is often depicted as a line of cliffs and the sea decorated with boats in full sail—and there may even be fat little wind-gods on the edge of the map, puffing out their cheeks to blow the boats along! As time went by, these 'pictures' of towns, forests, etc., became simplified into *conventional symbols*, signs which do not occupy too much space on the map and which merely suggest the features they are intended to represent.

Types of maps

Maps are extremely useful to a great variety of people besides the geographer—the holiday-maker, the week-end cyclist, the civil engineer and the army general, for example; and since each requires his map to give chiefly the information suited to his particular purpose, nowadays many different kinds of maps exist. Those which show the relief (or physical features) are known as *physical* maps and those which show towns and boundaries are *political* maps. Maps are also made to show details of climate, vegetation, the use that farmers make of their land, etc., and even such things as the distribution of Roman remains.

The Ordnance Survey

Probably the most useful maps to the geographer in Britain are the 'One-inch' (to one mile)[1] Ordnance Survey maps, one sheet of which covers an area approximately the size of a small English county. These are official maps produced by a special government department, and take their name from the fact that the original survey of the country was undertaken by the Ordnance (or artillery) section of the Army. The first edition of these maps

[1] i.e. on a scale of 1:63 360. These are gradually being replaced by maps on a scale of 1:50 000. So far (1974) 102 sheets, covering the Midlands and southern England have been issued, but it will be some years before the whole of the country has been covered.

was published about 1800; the seventh edition is now being replaced by the 1:50 000 series. This type of map is described as a *topographical* map, since it shows, in addition to the physical features of the land, a wide range of features which man has added—railways, roads, churches, bridges, electric transmission lines and a multitude of other details which provide a very full picture of man's activities.

Map projections

Since the earth is a sphere, difficulties arise when we set out to make a flat representation of a large section of the earth's surface. Strictly speaking, it is impossible to make on a flat piece of paper a map of even the smallest area in which direction, distances, areas, etc., are depicted with complete accuracy; and when we seek to represent in this way the whole surface of the sphere, it is obvious that a very high degree of inaccuracy is unavoidable.

It is, however, possible to draw maps in which the accuracy of one particular set of relationships (east-west distances, north-south distances, bearings, shapes, areas, etc.) is maintained, or which strike a balance between the various types of inaccuracy. Many such methods of representation have been devised, often involving complicated mathematics.

The name 'projection' is derived from the fact that the *nets* or *graticules* (i.e. systems of meridians and parallels) which form the 'framework' of the simplest of such representations could, in fact, with suitable apparatus be 'projected' on to a screen in the manner of a film-strip projector. For example, meridians and parallels marked on a glass globe could be projected, by using a source of light at the centre of the globe, on to a flat screen touching the globe at its 'north pole'. The 'picture' on the screen would in this particular case form the graticule of a *Polar Gnomonic* projection (fig. 166), which, although generally of little use, has the property of showing Great Circle routes as straight lines.

Projections commonly used in atlases include:
1. Various types of *Conic* projection, based essentially on the principle of 'projecting' on to the inside of a cone placed over the polar regions. A particularly valuable form of conic projection is *Bonne's*, in which areas are correctly represented.
2. *Mercator's* projection.
3. *Mollweide's* projection.
4. *Sanson-Flamsteed's Sinusoidal* projection.

The last two are 'equal-area' projections, and should be carefully compared with each other and with Mercator's projection. It should further be noted that both the Mollweide and Sanson-

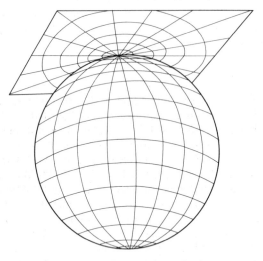

Fig. 166 The Polar Gnomonic projection.

Flamsteed projections are frequently *interrupted*—i.e. the central meridians of continents near the edges of the projections (which normally suffer considerable distortion of shape) are drawn as straight lines. The gaps created by recentring land masses in this way are made to fall in sea areas, and are not usually a serious disadvantage.

24

POPULATION AND SETTLEMENT

Throughout the greater part of this book we have been primarily concerned with discussing separately the various fields of man's activities, in showing the measure of control which he has acquired over the materials presented to him by his natural environment and in describing the methods he has adopted. We must now in conclusion examine the present distribution of population which is the result of the developments outlined in the preceding chapters.

World distribution of population

In fig. 167 the land surface of the world is broadly divided into areas of sparse, moderate and dense population. It will be noted that no attempt has been made to indicate the average number of inhabitants per square kilometre. Such figures are almost completely valueless, since they depend entirely on the size of the divisions marked out for consideration, and being averages they conceal the fact that within any one division the density may vary enormously.

At first sight of such a map one is tempted to make a number of easy generalisations which appear to explain the pattern of relative densities: that hot deserts on the tropics and cold deserts of the tundra regions are clearly a great deterrent to settlement; that dense equatorial forests like those of the Amazon Basin and high mountains such as the Andes and the Rockies are equally inhospitable; whereas the climate of cool temperate regions everywhere favours moderate settlement, and in some cases leads to great density of population. Such generalisations, of course, contain an element of truth, but a full understanding of world distribution of population 'lies rather in the history, traditions and aptitudes of the people'[1] than in any single formula based on relief, climate and vegetation.

[1] N. J. G. Pounds, *An Introduction to Economic Geography* (London, 1961, p. 119.

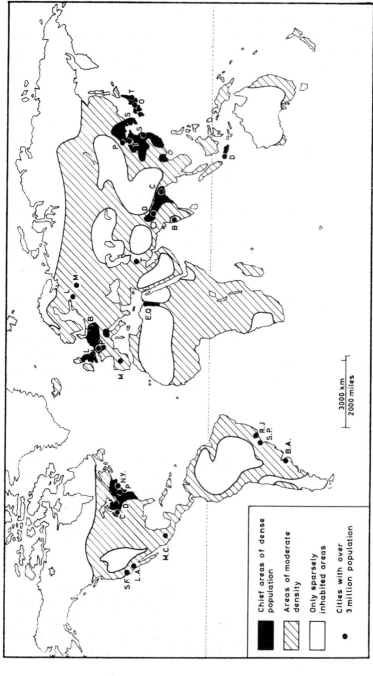

Fig. 167 World distribution of population. Cities with over 3 million inhabitants (1971) by the initial letters of their names. The figure include 'metropolitan areas.'

Chief areas of dense population

Areas of moderate density

Only sparsely inhabited areas

Cities with over 3 million population

3000 km
2000 miles

Chief areas of dense population

North-western Europe, where during the Industrial Revolution population increased rapidly. The exact reasons for this increase are not very clear, but the higher standards of living made possible by improved techniques in agriculture, and the import of food from 'new' lands, together with improvements in sanitation and medical science, resulting in a lower death-rate among babies and children, may well have been important factors.

North-eastern USA and the neighbouring areas of Canada, an industrial region similar in character to north-western Europe.

India and *Pakistan*, which by contrast contain a dense population of peasant farmers. A particularly heavy concentration occurs in the fertile alluvial lands of the lower Ganges Valley.

China, where much the same conditions prevail, with similar concentrations in the great river valleys.

Japan, which by about 1910 had achieved the remarkable feat of changing within the short space of thirty years or so from a 'medieval' state of peasant farmers into a modern industrial nation.

The lower Nile Valley, which forms a narrow ribbon of fertility through the Sahara Desert, and supports a dense population engaged in irrigation agriculture.

Java, whose high density contrasts sharply with that of other Indonesian areas. The average density of population in Java (392 per sq km, 1 438 per sq mile) is greater than in any European country except the Netherlands (555 per sq km, 1 016 per sq mile).

Units of settlement

Man is a gregarious animal, and although in certain areas (such as the Highlands of Scotland) isolated farmhouses exist, people tend to congregate in communities which nowadays vary in size from small groups of cottages or *hamlets* to vast urban concentrations like New York, Tokyo and London. Such communities form the details which together make up the generalised population pictures indicated above.

The origins of settlement

In early times when each community depended almost entirely on its own resources, the *site*—or topographical details of the immediate neighbourhood—was a paramount consideration (fig. 168). Since it was essential that the basic necessities of life should exist close at hand, a riverside site, which provided fresh water

Fig. 168 The site of Durham. The lofty spur surrounded by an incised meander of the River Wear provided an easily defensible position, later crowned by the castle and the cathedral.

for drinking and fertile alluvial soils in which food could be grown, was usually chosen in preference to any other. Another necessary consideration was defence, which caused many settlements to grow up on the insides of meanders or on low hills. Probably at a later stage, as contacts with neighbours broadened, the *location* or *situation* of a place—i.e. its position in relation to other places in the region—became an important factor, and new settlements grew up and old ones expanded where, for example, routes converged or issued from gaps in the hills, where rivers were shallow enough to be forded, where bridges could be built and so on.

It is possible to classify settlements by reference to their sites and/or location. The list which follows is by no means comprehensive, but is intended rather to provide a general indication of the various kinds of geographical advantages which led to the origin and growth of settlements. It should be noted that in many cases two or more advantages operated in conjunction.

Classification of settlements by origin

1. At the confluence of rivers (e.g. Lyons, where the Saône and Rhône meet; Koblenz, where the Rhine is joined by both the Lahn and the Moselle).
2. At a bend in a river (e.g. Sheffield).
3. At a fording point (e.g. Bedford).
4. Where a river has cut a gap through a range of hills (Lincoln and Guildford are examples of 'gap towns').
5. Where a river enters or leaves a gorge (e.g. Dresden).
6. Where a narrow river valley broadens out into a plain (e.g. Cologne).
7. Where a river enters or leaves a lake (e.g. Geneva; Kingston on Lake Ontario).
8. Where a loop in a river provides a defensible position—particularly if the loop encloses an elevated area (e.g. Durham; Shrewsbury).
9. Where an island in a river affords a defensible site or an easy crossing-place (e.g. Paris).
10. At the head of ocean navigation (e.g. Bremen) or at the head of river navigation (e.g. Basle). These, of course, depend on the size of ships, and are usually to be understood with reference to the ships of former times.
11. At the lowest bridge point (e.g. London). This also is to be understood in the light of man's former capabilities. The lowest point at which a bridge could be built was often also the head of navigation.
12. At or near the spring-line, e.g. at the foot of a scarp, where permeable and impermeable rocks meet. Numerous examples of 'spring-line villages' occur in Kent and Sussex (e.g. Westmeston; Plumpton, north of Brighton).
13. At the centre of an area of fertile lowland (e.g. Norwich).
14. Where land routes converge (Chicago is an example of such a 'nodal' town).
15. On 'islands' of permanently dry land among marshes (e.g. Ely). These are described as 'dry-point' settlements in contrast to most other types, which, since they seek water, may be described as 'wet-point' settlements.
16. Where a patch of coastal lowland occurs in a mountainous area (e.g. Trondheim).
17. On the shore of an indentation in the coastline which provides a sheltered anchorage (e.g. Falmouth).

Classification of settlements by function

Settlements may also be classified according to their functions, i.e. the parts they play in furthering the activities of the community in general. Broad differences in the 'work' performed by towns (and, indeed, villages) have always existed. Ports and inland towns, for instance, clearly differ. But the functions of various types of settlements today are as highly specialised as the work performed by most individuals. This has been particularly evident since the Industrial Revolution.

1. *Ocean ports* act as 'gateways' through which pass a country's exports and imports. It is important to notice that every port is intimately associated with a *hinterland*—an area 'behind' the port which feeds it with exports and absorbs its imports. The industrial district of Lancashire, for example, is the hinterland of Liverpool. If the hinterland declines in importance, or if the approach to the port proves too shallow for navigation, the port decays (e.g. Boston in Lincolnshire; King's Lynn). Ports may be subdivided into *commercial ports*, dealing principally with goods (e.g. Glasgow; Hull), and *passenger ports* (e.g. Cherbourg; Southampton, though this is less true now than formerly).

2. *Outports* are comparatively new deep-water substitutes for old ports in which the water is too shallow to accommodate modern ships (e.g. St. Nazaire is the outport of Nantes; Avonmouth is the outport of Bristol).

3. *Entrepôts* are ports which receive goods for distribution to other countries than their own (e.g. Rotterdam; Singapore).

4. *Naval ports* are ports on which warships are based, and are chosen for strategic considerations. An adequate anchorage is essential, but a hinterland is unnecessary (e.g. Portsmouth; Toulon).

5. *Packet-stations* are ports which at one time were almost exclusively concerned with the transport of mails and passengers across narrow seas (e.g. Calais; Harwich; Newhaven).

6. *Inland ports* are those which, although situated a considerable distance from the sea, can be reached by certain types of ocean-going vessels (e.g. Duisburg-Ruhrort).

7. *Fishing ports* (e.g. Grimsby; Aberdeen; Stavanger).

8. *Seaside resorts* have grown up where the natural features of the coastline or the surrounding district are attractive to the holiday-maker (e.g. Bournemouth; Warnemünde; Nice; Palm Beach, Florida).

9. *Market towns* are settlements larger than villages which grew up as convenient meeting-places at which the people of the region could buy and sell (e.g. Market Harborough in Leicestershire).

10. *Industrial towns* are principally concerned with the manufacture of commodities in factories (e.g. Huddersfield; Detroit).

11. *Mining towns* are those whose origin is essentially due to the presence of local mineral wealth (e.g. Merthyr Tydfil in Wales;

Fig. 169 Peterlee, a 'new town' on low ground 16 km (10 miles) to the east of Durham. This photograph should be carefully compared with the one showing Durham (Fig. 168). In the case of Peterlee so-called 'geographical factors' have clearly been of little consequence; *location* is here more important than *site*.

Johannesburg; Uranium City).

12. *Inland resorts* are inland towns which cater for visitors who come to admire the scenery or engage in local sports (e.g. Davos in Switzerland; Banff in Canada). Resorts at which invalids 'take the waters' (i.e. medicinal waters) are known as *spas* (e.g. Bath; Droitwich; Buxton).

13. *Capital cities* are, of course, the seats of government, and are normally occupied more by administration and organisation than industry. Many cities and towns may be described as 'local capitals' if they undertake on a smaller scale similar functions to those of national capitals (e.g. Manchester). 'Old' capitals (e.g. London; Rome) provide interesting comparisons with 'new' ones (e.g. Canberra; Brasília).

14. *'New towns'* (fig. 169) have been deliberately created as a result of governmental planning, to relieve the pressure of population in urban areas or to provide more agreeable sur-roundings for workers (e.g. Harlow in Essex; Crawley in Sussex; Cwmbran in South Wales).

15. *Dormitory towns* are towns in which people who travel a considerable distance to their work sleep and spend their leisure hours. Such towns (e.g. Hayward's Heath) are numerous around London.

Modern trends

During the present century, and particularly in the last thirty years, a pronounced tendency has existed in more advanced countries for population to become concentrated in urban centres. In many ways this is a natural result of the Industrial Revolution, but quite apart from the necessary movement of population from the field to the factory, a number of what may be described as 'human factors' operate, as people, tiring of the comparative isolation of country life, become attracted by the fuller amenities of the towns and cities.

There are very good reasons for regarding these tendencies, especially in combination, as undesirable, and the distribution of settlement and industry nowadays comes within the sphere of government supervision. In Britain, for example, all projected developments must be approved by the Department of the Environment before permission is granted for houses to be built, new industries to be set up or old ones to be expanded. In this way it is hoped to ensure that the amenities of town and country are preserved, and that no group of towns is forced to rely on the pursuit of one chief occupation or the production of one particular type of commodity. Moreover, an attempt is made to ensure that a 'Green Belt' is incorporated in metropolitan areas.

Site and location cannot, of course, even in modern times, be completely disregarded, but they are no longer overriding considerations.

*   *   *   *   *

It is fitting that this book should end on the theme of People and Places, for these are the two basic elements of geographical study. Never before have Places on the earth's surface been brought so close together, and never before have People known so much about each other's lives and problems. It is to be hoped that greater knowledge will lead to greater understanding and goodwill.

Examination Questions

The following examination questions have been selected from a careful analysis of the papers set for the General Certificate of Education examinations at Ordinary Level by the various Examining Boards, who have kindly given permission to reproduce them. The Boards are indicated as follows: The Associated Examining Board (**A.**); the Cambridge Local Examinations Syndicate (**C.**); the University of London (**L.**); the Northern Universities Joint Matriculation Board (**N.**) the Northern Ireland General Certificate of Education Examining Board (**N.I.**); the University of Oxford Schools Examining Delegacy (**O.**); the Scottish Certificate of Education Examining Board (**Sc.**); the Southern Universities' Joint Board (**So.**); the Welsh Joint Education Committee (**W.**).

The questions are arranged more or less in the order of the chapters; a strict division would be impossible, as many questions include more than one topic. Questions in which any reference is made to topics outside the scope of this book, or which are based on photographs, maps or charts supplied to the candidate, have been excluded. This has necessarily involved the omission of a number of useful questions, but avoids the inconvenience to the teacher of finding that further equipment is required before certain of the questions can be set as an exercise.

The necessity for diagrams and sketch-maps in answering the questions cannot be over-emphasised. Artistic ability is not required; it is sufficient that illustrative sketches should be reasonably large, clear and bold in outline, and should avoid irrelevant detail. Printed lettering should be used on the diagrams, not ordinary writing. With a little practice, it is not really difficult to cultivate a clear, even style. Citation of actual examples is no less important.

One final point, though obvious, is often overlooked. The pupil should familiarise himself with the precise meaning of words and phrases commonly used in examination questions, e.g. 'factor', 'development', 'location', 'significance'.

1   Give an account of the world distribution and most favourable conditions for growth of wheat *or* rice *or* maize and describe steps being taken in any *one* continent to increase production of the grain you choose.   (**So.**)

2   Select *one* area important for *each* of the following: maize, coffee. For each commodity:
(a) draw a sketch map to show the precise location of the area;
(b) describe the geographical conditions favouring its production in that area.   (**A.**)

3   Choose *one* of the following cereals: wheat, maize, rice.
(a) Describe the geographical conditions which favour its cultivation.   .
(b) Name the chief producing countries and briefly describe the international trade in the commodity.   (**A.**)

4   Choose *one* of the following and *name* and *locate* an area where it is an important activity. With the aid of diagrams write a descriptive account of the activity you select explaining how it is influenced by geographical factors.
(a) Natural rubber production,
(b) coffee cultivation,
(c) hydro-electric power production,
(d) wheat growing,
(e) wool production.   (**N.I.**)

5   Choose *one* of the following—rice, rubber, sugar cane.
(a) Describe the conditions which favour its production.
(b) Name the chief producing countries and briefly describe the international trade in the commodity.   (**A.**)

6   Choose *two* of the following crops: coffee, cocoa, sugar cane.
(a) For *each* of your two chosen crops, describe the geographical conditions which favour its cultivation.
(b) For *one* of your chosen crops, name the chief producing countries and briefly describe the international trade in the commodity.   (**A.**)

7   (a) Explain what you understand by *each* of the following terms: monoculture, shifting cultivation, stock rearing, transhumance;
(b) Choose *one* of the above terms and by detailed reference to an area in which it is practised describe the conditions which make it suitable at the present time.   (**A.**)

8   The following table lists the total population and the number

of cattle in the six leading cattle-producing countries for a recent year:

	No of cattle (000's)	Total population (000's)
India	188,800	511,115
U.S.A.	108,862	199,319
U.S.S.R.	93,028	235,543
Brazil	90,505	85,655
China	62,800	716,000
Argentine	47,000	23,031

Choose *four* of these leading cattle-producing countries and for the four you have chosen show how physical and human factors have contributed to the contrasts between them in the number of cattle per head of the population. (**N.**)

9 Choose *one* of the following and *name* and *locate* an area where it is an important commercial activity. Write a descriptive account of the activity you select explaining how it is influenced by geographical factors:
   (a) tea cultivation,
   (b) rice production,
   (c) sea fishing,
   (d) jute growing. (**N.I.**)

10 Choose *one* of the following and *name* and *locate* an area where it is an important activity. Write a descriptive account of the activity you select explaining how it is influenced by geographical factors, and illustrate your answer where possible by sketch maps and diagrams:
   (a) iron ore mining,
   (b) wheat growing,
   (c) rubber cultivation,
   (d) cattle ranching. (**N.I.**)

11 (a) Choose *one* area of temperate grassland and give an explanatory account of the farming.
   (b) Describe (i) the similarities and (ii) the differences between this chosen area and an area of tropical grassland. (**So.**)

12 Select any *one* country outside the British Isles and give an account of *either* its iron and steel *or* its textile industry. Mention the factors which have favoured the development of the industry in that country. (**A.**)

13 (a) Give *two* basic differences between taiga and selva forests.
   (b) Describe briefly the climatic conditions (i.e. seasonal

temperatures and precipitation) associated with each forest area.

(c) Write a short account of world trade in timber and the reasons for the increase in the use of this basic raw material. **(Sc.)**

14 Select *three* of the following activities: Lumbering; Commercial fishing; Large-scale grain farming; Tropical Plantation farming; Rice growing. For each of the *three* selected, choose an area from outside the British Isles where it is practised, and (i) name and locate the area on a sketch map; (ii) describe how the activity is conducted; (iii) give the geographical factors which have aided its development. **(W.)**

15 (a) Explain what is meant by the terms "co-operative farming" and "tropical subsistence farming".

(b) For each type of farming, name a locality where it is of importance and give *two* reasons why it is practised there.

(c) Write an account of the methods used and the products produced in *each* of the localities you have chosen. **(N.)**

16 Write explanatory accounts of *two* of the following:
  (a) land reclamation,
  (b) soil erosion,
  (c) water problems,
  (d) plantation agriculture,
  (e) shifting cultivation.
Illustrate your answer with specific examples. **(A.)**

17 (a) Explain clearly the conditions that make irrigation necessary.

(b) Illustrating your answer with specific examples, describe the problems that may result from irrigation.

(c) With reference to *one* area show the influence of irrigation on farming. **(So.)**

18 Farmers, scientists and engineers are increasing the world's food supply by tackling the problems of soil erosion, insect pests and lack of rainfall.
  Choose *two* of these problems and for *each*:
  (a) Explain the nature of the problem.
  (b) Describe the steps which man is taking to overcome it.
  (c) Locate on a sketch map a major area where it occurs.
  (C.)

19 (a) Explain briefly what is understood by the term "soil erosion".

(b) Name *two* areas where the problem of soil erosion is serious.

(c) Suggest ways in which soil erosion is being prevented and controlled. Illustrate your answer by reference to specific cases. **(A.)**

20 Write an informative paragraph about each of *four* of the following. Give examples where possible.

Hinterland	Siting of airports
Pipelines	Shifting cultivation
Soil erosion	Primary producers **(Sc.)**

21 Choose one product which is manufactured in *two* areas in different continents (*excluding* the British Isles).

(a) Show how, in *each* of the two areas, the supply of raw materials, markets and power has influenced the location of the manufacturing industry.

(b) State briefly the physical or climatic conditions which control the supply of raw materials. **(O.)**

22 Choose *two* of the following commodities:
  (i) Copper in tropical Africa.
  (ii) Iron ore in *either* Scandinavia *or* Australia.
  (iii) Tin in South-east Asia.
  (iv) Bauxite in The West Indies.
  (v) Nitrates in South America.

(a) By means of separate sketch maps, locate the main producing areas for *both* of the commodities chosen.

(b) For *one* of your chosen commodities, describe the difficulties in extracting and exporting the commodity. To which markets is the commodity exported? **(A.)**

23 *Either*
(a) What are the main sources of energy used in modern industry? How have the world distribution and usage of these resources led to the current energy crisis?

Or
(b) With reference to the North Atlantic:
  (i) List the principal varieties of fish caught.
  (ii) Show by means of a map where the chief fishing grounds lie.
  (iii) What efforts are being made to conserve resources?
  (N.I.)

24 What geographical factors may influence the siting of *either* a major heavy chemicals plant *or* a major oil refinery? Illustrate your answer by reference to specific examples. **(A.)**

25   (a) Choose an area *outside* North America, Europe and the U.S.S.R. where large quantities of oil are produced.
(i) Draw a sketch map to locate the area.
(ii) Describe the markets for the oil and how it is transported to them.
(b) What conditions determine the location of oil wells and refineries? (**O.**)

26   With reference to particular examples give the geographical conditions which influence the location and development of *two* of the following:
(a) the chemical industry,
(b) motor vehicle production,
(c) pulp and paper production,
(d) pipelines. (**So.**)

27   The world demand for fuel and power is approximately doubling every twenty-five years.
(a) Explain why this is so.
(b) For any *one* country, outline the changes that have taken place during the present century, pointing out the different sources and locations of the fuel and power used. (**A.**)

28   Explain with the aid of maps and/or diagrams *two* of the following terms:
(a) the International Date Line,
(b) conurbations,
(c) extensive agriculture,
(d) nomadism. (**L.**)

29   What geographical factors influence the siting of a hydro-electric scheme? Illustrate your answer by reference to specific examples. (**A.**)

30   Select *one* of the following:
(a) Discuss the geographical factors which influence the pattern of world airways.
(b) Choose any national capital city and discuss the geographical factors which have influenced its growth during the last quarter century.
(c) Show how migration within the last three or four decades has affected the development of any country of your choice. (**N.I.**)

31   The factors which are commonly cited to explain the location of individual industries are: raw materials, power resources, labour supply, transport facilities, and markets. Select any *one* industry you have studied in any country, outside the

British Isles, and show how these factors have affected that industry. (**A.**)

32 Explain how relief and other factors influence the pattern of the railway network, and the routes taken in
(a) France and (b) Australia. (**So.**)

33 *Either* Write a geographical account explaining the factors which influence major air routes and the siting of international airports.
Or Describe the shipping routes passing and the cargoes carried around the Cape of Good Hope. (**L.**)

34 Select *four* contrasting examples from different parts of the world to show how the environment can influence *either* house construction *or* the means of transport. (**L.**)

35 (a) Select *one* southern continent and name in it *one* area with a well-developed communications network, and *one* area where communications are poor.
(b) Write an account of the advantages and disadvantages which have influenced the development of transport and communications in these areas. (**L.**)

36 Choose *three* of the following terms: conurbation, 'new town', 'million city', outport, federal capital.
In *each case*:
(a) describe precisely the meaning of the term;
(b) name an example; and
(c) give the reasons for its development. (**A.**)

37 (a) Describe *briefly two* of the following:
(i) bulk cargo ships,
(ii) container ships,
(iii) drifters.
(b) With reference to particular examples explain why the location and size of ports have changed considerably during the last few centuries. (**So.**)

38 Write geographical accounts illustrated by specific examples from the British Isles of *three* of the following:
(a) container ports,
(b) motorways,
(c) nuclear power stations,
(d) natural gas,
(e) new towns and 'overspill' towns,
(f) air and water pollution. (**L.**)

39 (a) On a fully labelled sketch map show the distribution of population in *one* Southern Continent.

(b) Show how the distribution is influenced by (i) relief, (ii) climate, (iii) minerals.

(c) Suggest reasons for the tendency of people to concentrate in large cities. (**N.**)

40 With reference to a map of population in your atlas, explain why some parts of *either* South America *or* Australia have high concentrations of population while others are almost uninhabited. (**So.**)

41 Choose separate examples from the Southern Hemisphere of (a) an industrial town, (b) a port, and (c) a route centre.

With the aid of a sketch map, describe the geographical factors which have contributed to the importance of each town selected. (**So.**)

42 (a) Name *four* cities which have a population in excess of one million located in different continents.

(b) Suggest reasons why there are relatively few 'million cities' in the southern hemisphere.

(c) Choose *two* of the 'million cities' you have named and explain why each has grown to its great size. (**A.**)

43 Select *one major* city.

(i) Show by means of suitable illustrations how it has grown in recent years. (Say, since the end of World War II.)

(ii) What geographical and other factors have influenced its growth? (**N.I.**)

44 From outside the British Isles choose *three* important towns, each with a different function. Show how the function of *each* town has been influenced by its situation and by other factors. (**N.**)

45 (i) Explain, with the aid of diagrams, what is meant by latitude and longitude.

(ii) Calculate the time at Greenwich when it is 10.00 p.m. in Buenos Aires (Longitude 60°W).

(iii) Explain why at the Poles the sun does not set for many weeks on end at certain times of the years. (**W.**)

46 Showing your working, calculate the local times at San Francisco (38°N 122°W), San Antonio, Texas (29°N 98°W) and Portland, Maine (44°N 70°W) when it is midday at Washington D.C. (39°N 77°W), and:

(a) explain, briefly, the differences in time you find;

(b) explain how latitude will affect the number of daylight hours in winter at San Antonio and Portland. (**So.**)

Index

Abaca, 147
Aborigines (Australian), 5–6
Acetate process, 149–50
'Acid' (silica) bricks, 184
Acrilan, 150
Adits, 219
Afrormosia, 114
Afsluitdijk, 165
Age-hardening, 204
Air routes, 289–91
Air transport, 286–91
Airports, 289–91
Albe (*Alpen*), 158
Alfalfa, 40
Alkathene, 247
Alloys, 175, 182, 209
Allspice, 96
Alluvial (mineral) deposits, 177
Alpaca, 134
Aluminium, 178, 203–5
Anadromous fish, 56
Angora goat, 134
Angora rabbit, 134
Aniseed, 96
Anodising, 203
Anthracite, 221, 223
Anthrax, 41
Antimony, 211
Apples, 87
Apricots, 89
Ardil, 150
Arkwright's Water-frame, 141
Artificial silk, 149
Asbestos, 212
Ash (tree), 117
Asphalt, 243
Aswan, 161–3
Atom, structure of, 259

Atomic pile, 260–1
Atomic power, 258–67
Auls, 9
Autobahnen, 275
Autostrade, 275
Avocado pears, 86

Babbitt metal, 201
Bacon, 52
Bakelite, 246
Bakewell, Robert, 37
Balance of Payments, 270
Balance of Trade, 269
Balsa, 111
Bananas, 89–91
Barley, 14, 16, 24–5
Basic Bessemer process, 183–4
'Basic' bricks, 184
Basic Oxygen Steel-making, 186
Basin irrigation, 159–60
Bass, 148
Bauxite, 204–5
Bedford Level, 167
Beech, 117
Beer, 78–9
Belem, 122
Beryllium, 211, 259
Bessemer converter, 182–3
Bilateral trade, 272
Bill of Exchange, 271–2
Birch, 117
Bismuth, 212
Bituminous coal, 221–2
Bituminous shales, 238, 244
Blackband ironstone, 187, 191
Black bread, 26
Blackcurrants, 88
Black earth, 18

Nitrates, 168
Nitre, 168
Nodal towns, 309
Nomads, nomadic, 8–10, 154
Non-ferrous metals, 176
Norfolk Rotation, 169–70
Nuclear fission, 258–60
Nuclear power stations in Great Britain, 264–6
Nuclear reactor, 260–2
Nutmegs, 96
Nuts, 92
Nylon, 150

Oak, 117
Oats, 14, 16, 25–6
Obechi, 111
Ocean transport, 282–7
Oil palms, 101
Oils, types of, 97
Olives, 89, 99
Opencast mining, 219
Open-hearth process, 184–5
Oranges, 88
Ordnance Survey, 302–3
Ore (definition of), 174
Oriental agriculture, 154, 156
Orlon, 151, 247
Osmium, 208
Outports, 310
Overfishing, 61, 65
Overgrazing, 171
Overstocking, 171
Owen Falls, 162, 257

Packet-stations, 310
Paddy, 27–8
Palm oil, 102–4, 201
Palm-kernel oil, 104
Panama Canal, 286
Panning, 177, 206
Paprika, 95
Pará (city), 122
Pará rubber, 122
Paraffin, 236–7
Parallels of Latitude, 292–5
Parsnips, 32
Pasteurisation, 42
Pastoral farming, 154

Pastoralists, 8–10
Peaches, 89
Pearl oysters, 64
Pears, 85
Peat, 221–2
Pelagic fish, 56, 58
Penstocks, 248–9
Pepper, 95
Perbunan, 126
Perennial irrigation, 160
Peri, 87
Perlon, 150
Perspex, 247
Petro-chemicals, 247
Petrol, 236–7
Petroleum, 231–47; definition of, 266; producing areas, 241–5; refineries (British), 245; refining, 234–7; transport of, 238–9
Pewter, 200
Phormium tenax, 148
Phosphates, 168
Phosphor-bronze, 195
Phylloxera, 89
Pig iron, 179
Pigs, 50–2
Pimento, 96
Pine, 117
Pineapples, 91
Pipelines, 239, 242
Pitch Lake, 243
Pitchblende, 263
Pitchpine, 115
Placer deposits, 177, 206
Plankton, 54–5
Plantation agriculture, 154
Plastics, 150, 246–7
Platinum, 208–9
Plums, 87
Plush, 145
Polders, 44, 164
Polenta, 23
Polymerisation, 126, 150, 237–8, 246
Polypropylin, 247
Polythene, 247
Polyvinyl chloride (PVC), 199, 247